Everyday Mathematics®

The University of Chicago School Mathematics Project

Assessment Handbook

Grade **5**

McGraw Hill **Education**

Chicago, IL • Columbus, OH • New York, NY

The University of Chicago School Mathematics Project (UCSMP)

Max Bell, Director, UCSMP Elementary Materials Component; Director, *Everyday Mathematics* First Edition; James McBride, Director, *Everyday Mathematics* Second Edition; Andy Isaacs, Director, *Everyday Mathematics* Third Edition; Amy Dillard, Associate Director, *Everyday Mathematics* Third Edition; Rachel Malpass McCall, Associate Director, *Everyday Mathematics* Common Core State Standards Edition

Authors
Jean Bell, William M. Carroll, Amy Dillard, Kathleen Pitvorec

Common Core State Standards Edition
Sarah R. Burns, Mary Ellen Dairyko, Rachel Malpass McCall, Cheryl G. Moran, Lila K. Schwartz

Technical Art
Diana Barrie

Teacher in Residence
Soundarya Radhakrishnan

Contributors
Nancy Baranowski, Martha Di Lorenzo, Roma Rdzanek, Marlene Stanley, Sharon Draznin, Nancy Hanvey, Laurie Leff, Denise Porter, Herb Price, Joyce Timmons, Lisa Winters

Acknowledgements
We gratefully acknowledge the work of the following classroom teachers who provided input and suggestions as we designed this handbook: Huong Banh, Fran Moore, Jenny Waters, and Lana Winnet.

Photo Credits
Cover (l)Steven Hunt/Stone/Getty Images, (c)Martin Mistretta/Stone/Getty Images, (r)Digital Stock/CORBIS, (bkgd)PIER/Stone/Getty Images; **Back Cover Spine** Martin Mistretta/Stone/Getty Images.

Permissions
The quotes on pages 4, 5, 8, and 35 are reprinted with permission from *Knowing What Students Know: The Science and Design of Educational Assessment* © 2001 by the National Academy of Sciences, courtesy of the National Academies Press, Washington, D.C.

This material is based upon work supported by the National Science Foundation under Grant No. ESI-9252984. Any opinions, findings, conclusions, or recommendations expressed in this material are those of the authors and do not necessarily reflect the views of the National Science Foundation.

everyday**math**.com

Send all inquiries to:
McGraw-Hill Education
STEM Learning Solutions Center
P.O. Box 812960
Chicago, IL 60681

ISBN: 978-0-07-657703-3
MHID: 0-07-657703-1

Printed in the United States of America.

3 4 5 6 7 8 9 QDB 17 16 15 14 13 12

McGraw-Hill is committed to providing instructional materials in Science, Technology, Engineering, and Mathematics (STEM) that give all students a solid foundation, one that prepares them for college and careers in the 21st century.

*The **McGraw·Hill** Companies*

Contents

**Philosophy of Assessment
in *Everyday Mathematics* 1**

Introduction 1
Balanced Assessment 2
What Are the Purposes of
Assessment? 2
What Are the Contexts for
Assessment? 3
What Are the Sources of Evidence
for Assessment? 4
What Content Is Assessed? 5
Creating a Balanced Assessment Plan 7
Ongoing Assessment 8
Ongoing Assessment—Informing
Instruction. 9
Ongoing Assessment—Recognizing
Student Achievement 10
Writing/Reasoning Prompts for
Math Boxes 15
Portfolios 16
Periodic Assessment 18
Progress Check Written Assessments. . 19
Oral and Slate Assessment. 20
Student Self Assessment. 21
Open Response Tasks 21
Beginning-of-Year, Mid-Year, and
End-of-Year Assessments 23
External Assessment 24
Record Keeping 25
Class Checklists and Individual
Profiles of Progress 25
Options for Recording Data on
Checklists. 27

Assessment Management
Spreadsheets 28
Introduction 28
Frequently Asked Questions 31
Recommended Reading 36
***Everyday Mathematics* Goals**. 37

Assessment Overvivews 51

Beginning-of-Year Assessment Goals   51A
Unit 1. 52
Unit 2. 60
Unit 3. 68
Unit 4. 76
Unit 5. 84
Unit 6. 92
Mid-Year Assessment Goals. 100
Unit 7. 102
Unit 8. 110
Unit 9. 118
Unit 10. 126
Unit 11. 134
Unit 12. 142
End-of-Year Assessment Goals 150

Assessment Masters 153

Glossary 313

Index 315

Philosophy of Assessment in *Everyday Mathematics*®

Introduction

Too often, school assessment tends to provide only scattered snapshots of student achievement rather than continuous records of growth. In *Everyday Mathematics*, assessment is like a motion picture, revealing the development of each student's mathematical understanding over time while also giving the teacher useful feedback about the instructional needs of individual students and the class.

For assessment to be useful to teachers, students, parents, and others, the *Everyday Mathematics* authors believe that ...

◆ Teachers need to have a variety of assessment tools and techniques to choose from so students can demonstrate what they know in a variety of ways and teachers can have reliable information from multiple sources.

◆ Students should be included in the assessment process. Self assessment and reflection are skills students will develop over time if they are encouraged.

◆ Assessment and instruction should be closely aligned. Assessment should assist teachers in making instructional decisions concerning individual students and the class.

◆ Assessment should focus on all important outcomes, not only on outcomes that are easy to measure.

◆ A good assessment program makes instruction easier.

◆ The best assessment plans are developed by teachers working collaboratively within schools and districts.

Everyday Mathematics offers many opportunities for assessing students' knowledge and skills. This handbook describes the *Everyday Mathematics* assessment resources and serves as a guide for navigating through those resources and helping you design and implement a balanced classroom assessment plan.

Balanced Assessment

When planning a balanced assessment, begin by asking several basic questions:

- *What are the purposes of assessment?*
- *What are the contexts for assessment?*
- *What are the sources of evidence for assessment?*
- *What content is assessed?*

What Are the Purposes of Assessment?

The purposes of assessment serve three main functions: to support learning, to measure achievement, and to evaluate programs. Each purpose is integral to achieving a balanced assessment plan.

Formative assessment supports learning by providing information about students' current knowledge and abilities so you can plan future instruction more effectively. Formative assessment encourages students to identify their areas of weakness or strength so they can focus their efforts more precisely.

Summative assessment measures student growth and achievement. A summative assessment might be designed, for example, to determine whether students have learned certain material by the end of a fixed period of study.

Program evaluation means judging how well a program is working. A school district, for example, may want to identify schools with especially strong mathematics programs so their successes can be replicated in other schools with weaker programs. Program evaluation makes this possible.

Assessment tools and techniques often serve more than one purpose. Assessments built into a curriculum might give teachers information they can use to plan future instruction more effectively or prepare progress reports. District administrators might use this information to allocate professional development resources.

Purposes of Assessment

Formative Assessment	Summative Assessment	Program Evaluation
◆ Used to plan instruction ◆ Helps students to reflect on their progress	◆ Used to measure student growth and achievement ◆ Helps determine if students have learned content	◆ Used to evaluate overall success of the math program

What Are the Contexts for Assessment?

Assessment occurs in a variety of contexts.

♦ **Ongoing assessment** involves gathering information from students' everyday work. These assessments can take place at the same time as regular classroom instruction.

♦ **Periodic assessment** consists of formal assessments that are built in to a curriculum, such as an end-of-unit Progress Check.

♦ **External assessment** is independent of the curriculum. An example of an external assessment is a standardized test.

Everyday Mathematics supports all three contexts for assessment, and it provides tools and materials for ongoing and periodic assessments that you can use to create a balanced assessment plan.

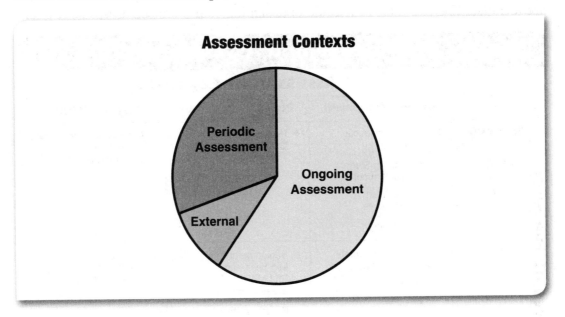

The sizes of the sections of the circle in the figure above are meant to be suggestive, but the exact proportions of ongoing, periodic, and external assessments will vary depending on your grade level, the time of year, state and district mandates, and many other factors.

For all *Everyday Mathematics* assessments, provide students with tools that may be helpful in completing the assessment. Such tools include, but are not limited to, number lines, number grids, scratch paper, base-10 blocks, coins and bills, counters, blank situation diagrams, Pattern Blocks, and Geometry Templates.

What Are the Sources of Evidence for Assessment?

Assessment is a process of reasoning from evidence.

(Pellegrino, Chudowsky, and Glaser 2001, 36)

The evidence for assessing what students know is indirect because we cannot know exactly what they are thinking. Evidence about students' knowledge and capabilities comes from observing students while they are actively engaged and from analyzing the products of their work. Whatever conclusions we may make about students' thinking must be based on **observations** or **products.**

The table below shows the different contexts for assessment and the sources of evidence used for each context. Specific assessment tasks in *Everyday Mathematics* are included. Use this table as a guide in designing your balanced assessment plan.

Sources of Evidence and Assessment Contexts

		Assessment Contexts		
		Ongoing Assessment	**Periodic Assessment**	**External Assessment**
Sources of Evidence	**Observation**	◆ Informing Instruction notes ◆ Recognizing Student Achievement notes for • Mental Math and Reflexes ◆ "Kid watching"	◆ Progress Check Oral/Slate Assessments	◆ Classroom observations by resource teachers or other outside experts
	Product	◆ Recognizing Student Achievement notes for • Journal pages • Exit Slips • Games record sheets • Math Boxes ◆ Writing/Reasoning prompts ◆ Portfolio opportunities	◆ Beginning-of-Year, Mid-Year, and End-of-Year assessments ◆ Progress Check Written Assessments ◆ Student Self Assessments ◆ Open Response problems	◆ Standardized tests mandated by the school district or the state

Each context for assessment (ongoing, periodic, or external) can yield evidence through observations or products.

- ◆ Observing students as they are doing their daily work can provide a great deal of information about their understandings, skills, and dispositions; this kind of ongoing observational assessment may be considered "kid watching."
- ◆ A written assessment that is included as part of a curriculum is an example of a periodic product assessment.
- ◆ A classroom visit by an outside expert who will observe particular students is an example of an external assessment using observational evidence.

What Content Is Assessed?

> *Assessment does not exist in isolation, but must be closely aligned with the goals of curriculum and instruction.*
>
> (Pellegrino, Chudowsky, and Glaser 2001, 36)

In recent years, national organizations and most states have issued detailed sets of learning goals and standards, which provide useful guidance about what content is important to learn and, therefore, important to assess. Aligning assessment, curriculum, and instruction with standards and goals increases coherence in the system and produces better outcomes. To help teachers understand the structure of *Everyday Mathematics* and therefore better understand what to assess, the authors developed Program Goals, which are organized by content strand and carefully articulated across the grades. Below are the six content strands and their related Program Goals:

Everyday Mathematics Program Goals

Number and Numeration
- Understand the meanings, uses, and representations of numbers
- Understand equivalent names for numbers
- Understand common numerical relations

Operations and Computation
- Compute accurately
- Make reasonable estimates
- Understand meanings of operations

Data and Chance
- Select and create appropriate graphical representations of collected or given data
- Analyze and interpret data
- Understand and apply basic concepts of probability

Measurement and Reference Frames
- Understand the systems and processes of measurement; use appropriate techniques, tools, units, and formulas in making measurements
- Use and understand reference frames

Geometry
- Investigate characteristics and properties of two- and three-dimensional geometric shapes
- Apply transformations and symmetry in geometric situations

Patterns, Functions, and Algebra
- Understand patterns and functions
- Use algebraic notation to represent and analyze situations and structures

Program Goals are threads that weave the curriculum together across grades. "Compute accurately," for example, is a Program Goal. Students in *Everyday Mathematics* are expected to compute accurately. The expectations for a student achieving this goal in Grade 2 are obviously different from what is expected from a student in Grade 6. For this reason, the Program Goals are further refined through Grade-Level Goals.

Grade-Level Goals are guideposts along trajectories of learning that span multiple years. They are the big ideas at each grade level; they do not capture all of the content covered. The Grade-Level Goals describe how *Everyday Mathematics* builds mastery over time—first through informal exposure, later through more formal instruction, and finally through application. Because the Grade-Level Goals are cumulative, it is essential for students to experience the complete curriculum at each grade level. The example below shows the development of Grade-Level Goals for models for the operations.

Grade K	Identify join and take-away situations.
Grade 1	Identify change-to-more, change-to-less, comparison, and parts-and-total situations.
Grade 2	Identify and describe change, comparison, and parts-and-total situations; use repeated addition, arrays, and skip counting to model multiplication; use equal sharing and equal grouping to model division.
Grade 3	Recognize and describe change, comparison, and parts-and-total situations; use repeated addition, arrays, and skip counting to model multiplication; use equal sharing and equal grouping to model division.
Grade 4	Use repeated addition, skip counting, arrays, area, and scaling to model multiplication and division.
Grade 5	Use repeated addition, arrays, area, and scaling to model multiplication and division; use ratios expressed as words, fractions, percents, and with colons; solve problems involving ratios of parts of a set to the whole set.
Grade 6	Use ratios and scaling to model size changes and to solve size-change problems; represent ratios as fractions, percents, and decimals, and using a colon; model and solve problems involving part-to-whole and part-to-part ratios; model rate and ratio number stories with proportions; use and explain cross multiplication and other strategies to solve proportions.

All assessment opportunities in *Everyday Mathematics* are linked to specific Grade-Level Goals. The curriculum is designed so that the vast majority of students will reach the Grade-Level Goals for a given grade upon completion of that grade and as a result will be well prepared to succeed in higher levels of mathematics. The complete list of Program Goals and Grade-Level Goals begins on page 37 of this handbook.

Creating a Balanced Assessment Plan

In *Everyday Mathematics,* assessment is primarily designed to help you

◆ learn about students' current knowledge and abilities so you can plan future instruction more effectively—formative assessment; and

◆ measure students' progress toward and achievement of Grade-Level Goals—summative assessment.

Although there is no one right assessment plan for all classrooms, all assessment plans should provide a balance of assessment sources from different contexts. See the chart on page 4 of this handbook for specific assessment tasks in *Everyday Mathematics* that support the different sources and contexts.

Planning Tips

Do not try to use all the assessment resources at once. Instead, devise a manageable, balanced plan. Choose those tools and techniques that best match your teaching style and your students' needs.

Consider the following guidelines:

◆ Start small.
◆ Incorporate assessment into your daily class routine.
◆ Set up an easy and efficient record-keeping system.
◆ Personalize and adapt the plan as the year progresses.

Your assessment plan should be designed to answer these questions:

◆ How is the class doing?
◆ How are individual students doing?
◆ How do I need to adjust instruction to meet students' needs?
◆ How can I communicate to students, parents, and others about the progress being made?

The following sections of this handbook provide further details about the tools and techniques you can use to develop a balanced assessment plan. Using these tools, you can support student learning, improve your instruction, measure student growth and achievement, and make the most of your experience with *Everyday Mathematics.*

Ongoing Assessment

> *No single test score can be considered a definitive measure of a student's competence. Multiple measures enhance the validity and fairness of the inferences drawn by giving students various ways and opportunities to demonstrate their competence.*
>
> (Pellegrino, Chudowsky, and Glaser 2001, 253)

An integral part of a balanced assessment plan involves gathering information from student's everyday work. Opportunities for collecting ongoing assessment in the form of observations and products are highlighted in *Everyday Mathematics* through Informing Instruction and Recognizing Student Achievement notes.

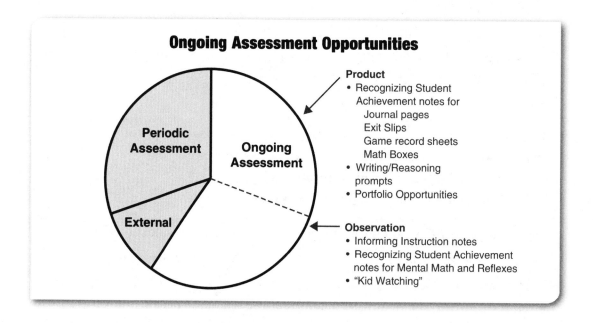

Ongoing Assessment— Informing Instruction

Informing Instruction notes are designed to help you anticipate and recognize common errors and misconceptions in students' thinking and alert you to multiple solution strategies or unique insights that students may offer. These notes suggest how to use observations of student's work to effectively adapt instruction.

 **Sample 1** **Informing Instruction**

 Ongoing Assessment: Informing Instruction

Watch for students who have difficulty reading the leaves as separate numbers in the stem-and-leaf plots. Have them list the numbers from the plot, use the list to help them answer the questions, and verify their selection of the median.

 **Sample 2** **Informing Instruction**

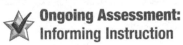 **Ongoing Assessment:** Informing Instruction

Watch for students who are having difficulty organizing their work with mixed numbers. Ask them to circle the fraction portion of each mixed number, copy the part of the number that is not circled (the whole-number part) into the answer blank, and then perform the division on the circled fraction portion.

Ongoing Assessment—
Recognizing Student Achievement

Each lesson in *Everyday Mathematics* contains a Recognizing Student Achievement note. These notes highlight specific tasks that teachers can use for assessment to monitor students' progress toward Grade-Level Goals.

These tasks include:

◆ *Journal* pages (written problems—sometimes including explanations)
◆ Mental Math and Reflexes (oral or slate)
◆ Exit Slips (explanations of strategies and understanding)
◆ *Everyday Mathematics* games (record sheets or follow-up sheets)
◆ Math Boxes (written practice problems)

Each Recognizing Student Achievement note identifies the task to gather information from, the concept or skill to be assessed, and the expectations for a child who is *making adequate progress* toward meeting the specific Grade-Level Goal.

 **Sample 1** **Recognizing Student Achievement**
Math Journal 1

 **Ongoing Assessment:**
Recognizing Student Achievement

Journal page 176
Problems
5 and 6

Use **journal page 176, Problems 5 and 6** to assess students' facility with interpreting data displayed in line plots. Students are making adequate progress if their writing demonstrates an understanding of the data's meanings in relation to data descriptions. Some students may refer to data landmarks in their explanations.

[Data and Chance Goal 2]

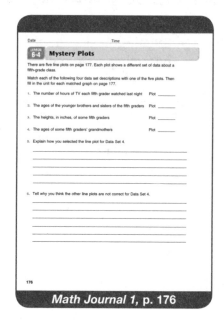

Math Journal 1, p. 176

Sample 2 Recognizing Student Achievement
Mental Math and Reflexes

Ongoing Assessment: Recognizing Student Achievement

Mental Math and Reflexes ★

Use the **Mental Math and Reflexes problem sets** to assess students' ability to solve extended multiplication facts mentally. Students are making adequate progress if they correctly respond to the multiplication problems. Some students may also be successful with the division problems.

[Operations and Computation Goal 1]

Mental Math and Reflexes ★

Use slate procedures and write all problems on the board or Class Data Pad so students can visually recognize the patterns.

●○○ 7 * 8 56	●●○ 42 ÷ 7 6	●●● 560 ÷ 70 8
70 * 8 560	420 ÷ 7 60	5,600 ÷ 700 8
70 * 80 5,600	4,200 ÷ 7 600	56,000 ÷ 7,000 8
700 * 80 56,000	42,000 ÷ 7 6,000	

Sample 3 Recognizing Student Achievement
Exit Slip

Ongoing Assessment: Recognizing Student Achievement

Exit Slip ★

Ask students to respond to the following question on an **Exit Slip** (*Math Masters*, page 414) or half-sheet of paper. *Which is easier to use—the full-circle protractor or the half-circle protractor? Why?* Students are making adequate progress if their answers demonstrate an understanding of how to use both protractor types.

[Measurement and Reference Frames Goal 1]

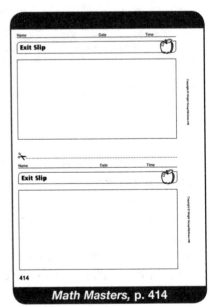

Math Masters, p. 414

Sample 4 **Recognizing Student Achievement**
Game Record Sheet

 Ongoing Assessment:
Recognizing Student Achievement

Math Masters
Page 474

Use the *Frac-Tac-Toe* gameboard (**Math Masters, page 474**) to assess students' facility with naming fraction-decimal equivalents. Have students record their fractions on the gameboard instead of using removable counters. Students are making adequate progress if they have correctly identified equivalencies.

[Number and Numeration Goal 5]

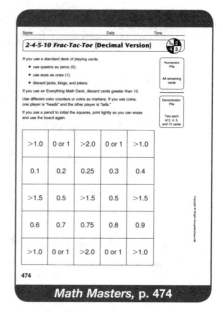

Math Masters, p. 474

 Sample 5 **Recognizing Student Achievement**
Math Boxes

 Ongoing Assessment:
Recognizing Student Achievement

Math Boxes
Problem 3 ★

Use **Math Boxes, Problem 3** to assess students' ability to compare decimals. Students are making adequate progress if they correctly identify the first three problems. Some students may correctly identify the last two problems.

[Number and Numeration Goal 4]

3. Write < or >.

0.17 _____ 1.71

0.03 _____ 0.12

1.9 _____ 1.89

5.4 _____ 5.04

2.24 _____ 2.2

The Recognizing Student Achievement tasks were chosen with the expectation that the majority of students will be successful with them. Students who are *making adequate progress* as defined by a Recognizing Student Achievement task are on a trajectory to meet the corresponding Grade-Level Goal. Based on student progress toward Grade-Level Goals, you may choose to use Readiness activities or Enrichment activities to modify your instructional plan to meet an individual student's needs. See the chart on the next page for how to understand and use the results of the Recognizing Student Achievement tasks.

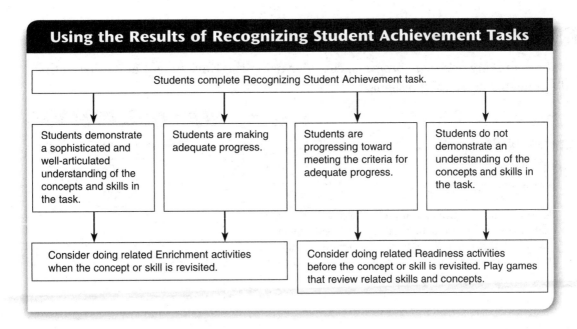

Using the Results of Recognizing Student Achievement Tasks

Students complete Recognizing Student Achievement task.

Students demonstrate a sophisticated and well-articulated understanding of the concepts and skills in the task.

Students are making adequate progress.

Students are progressing toward meeting the criteria for adequate progress.

Students do not demonstrate an understanding of the concepts and skills in the task.

Consider doing related Enrichment activities when the concept or skill is revisited.

Consider doing related Readiness activities before the concept or skill is revisited. Play games that review related skills and concepts.

 Sample **Recognizing Student Achievement**

The following example illustrates how to implement further Enrichment or Readiness for a given Recognizing Student Achievement task.

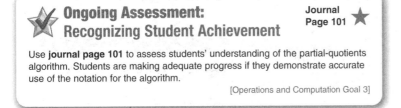

Ongoing Assessment: Recognizing Student Achievement

Journal Page 101

Use **journal page 101** to assess students' understanding of the partial-quotients algorithm. Students are making adequate progress if they demonstrate accurate use of the notation for the algorithm.

[Operations and Computation Goal 3]

Math Journal 1, p. 101

Sample **Enrichment**

If students are *making adequate progress,* consider using the Enrichment activities in this lesson, if applicable, or related lessons.

ENRICHMENT

▶ **Exploring Divisibility by the Digits**

(*Math Masters,* p. 105)

PARTNER ACTIVITY

5–15 Min

To apply students' understanding of factors, have them explore divisibility from another perspective. Students examine 3-digit numbers that meet certain divisibility criteria. Then they use the same criteria to identify larger numbers.

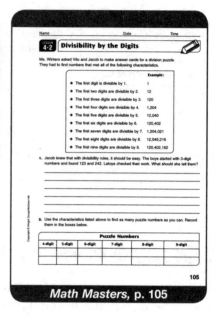

Math Masters, p. 105

Sample **Readiness**

If students are *not making adequate progress,* consider using the Readiness activities before teaching related lessons.

READINESS

▶ **Modeling Division with Base-10 Blocks**

(*Math Masters,* p. 114)

SMALL-GROUP ACTIVITY

15–30 Min

To provide experience with division using a concrete model, have students explore a long division algorithm using base-10 blocks. Pose the problem 4)623. Have students model the dividend (623) with base-10 blocks. Ask a volunteer to explain what it means to divide 623 blocks by 4. It means that the 623 blocks are to be grouped into 4 equal piles. Have each small group of students take four pieces of paper and distribute the blocks equally on each of the four pieces of paper.

They will need to make trades. For example, each of the four groups of blocks gets 1 flat, and there will be 2 flats left over. Students trade these 2 flats for 20 longs. Then they distribute the 22 longs among the 4 groups of blocks. Each of the four groups gets 5 longs, and 2 longs are left over. Students trade these 2 longs for 20 cubes. They distribute 20 of the 23 cubes evenly among the four groups. There are 3 cubes left over.

Have a volunteer interpret the model. Each group has 155 cubes. There are 3 left over. So 623 divided by 4 is 155 with a remainder of 3.

Students work alone or with a partner to complete *Math Masters,* page 114. They represent base-10 blocks with the symbols, □, l, and ▪.

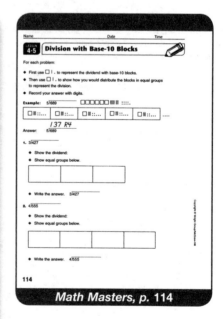

Math Masters, p. 114

Writing/Reasoning Prompts for Math Boxes

Every unit contains suggestions for prompts to use with Math Boxes problems. Use these prompts in a number of ways: (1) Collect student responses to these prompts on Exit Slips. (2) Request that students keep a math notebook where they record their answers to Math Message problems, Exit Slip prompts, and Writing/Reasoning prompts for Math Boxes problems. (3) Have students record responses on Math Log or Exit Slip masters and then add them to their portfolio collections.

 Sample 1 Writing/Reasoning Prompt

Writing/Reasoning Have students write a response to the following: *Explain how you converted the fractions to mixed numbers in Problem 2.* Sample answer: For the whole number part, I found how many groups of the denominator were in the numerator. The fraction part was what was left.

2. Write each fraction as a whole number or a mixed number.

   a. $\frac{17}{4}$ = _____

   b. $\frac{24}{3}$ = _____

   c. $\frac{5}{2}$ = _____

   d. $\frac{9}{8}$ = _____

   e. $\frac{32}{5}$ = _____

 Sample 2 Writing/Reasoning Prompt

Writing/Reasoning Have students write a response to the following: *Explain your answer to the question in Problem 3 and how you chose the values for the data set.* Because the average cannot be greater than the maximum in the data set, 53 inches cannot be Esther's average since 50 is the maximum number. I chose 5 numbers for the data set that could be added together and divided by 5 so that the average would equal 53.

3. Esther did 5 standing jumps. Her longest jump was 50 in. Could her average jump be 53 in.?

   _____

   Create a data set for Esther's jumps that could have this average.

   _____

Portfolios

Portfolios are a versatile tool for student assessment. They help students reflect on their mathematical growth and help you understand and document that growth. Portfolios are part of a balanced assessment plan in that they:

◆ emphasize progress over time;
◆ involve students more directly in the assessment process as they participate in selecting work and explaining what the work demonstrates; and
◆ document strengths and weaknesses in a student's mathematical development.

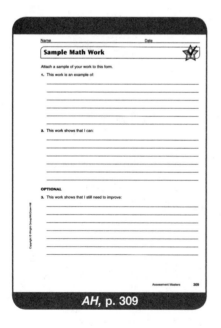 is the symbol used to indicate opportunities to collect students' work for portfolios. Several portfolio opportunities are highlighted in each unit, but in addition to highlighted opportunities, you and your students can choose from the variety of work in daily lessons to add to students' portfolios.

Consider asking students to write about their selected works. Two optional masters, Sample Math Work and Discussion of My Math Work, are provided for this.

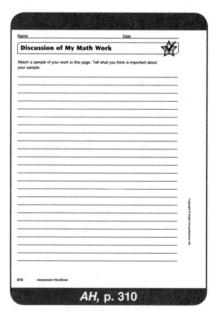

AH, p. 309

AH, p. 310

See pages 304–311 in this book for additional masters that you might ask students to complete periodically and incorporate into their portfolios. *For example:*

◆ Evaluating My Math Class   ◆ Weekly Math Log
◆ My Math Class   ◆ Number-Story Math Log

You may also ask parents to complete a Parent Reflections page (*Assessment Handbook*, page 312) for inclusion in student portfolios.

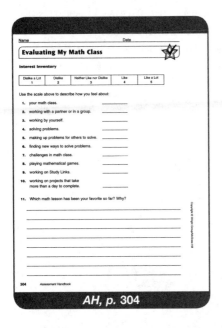

AH, p. 304

AH, p. 305

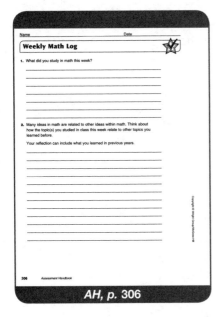

AH, p. 306

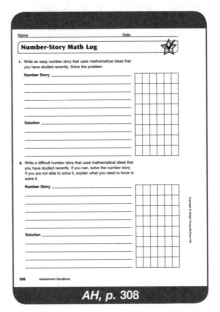

AH, p. 308

Periodic Assessment

Periodic assessments are another key component of a balanced assessment plan. Progress Check lessons and Beginning-of-Year, Mid-Year, and End-of-Year assessments require students to complete a variety of tasks, including short answer questions, open response problems, and reflection questions. These tasks provide you and your students with the opportunity to regularly review and reflect upon their progress—in areas that were recently introduced as well as in areas that involve long-term retention and mastery.

The figure below lists the various periodic assessment tasks provided in *Everyday Mathematics*.

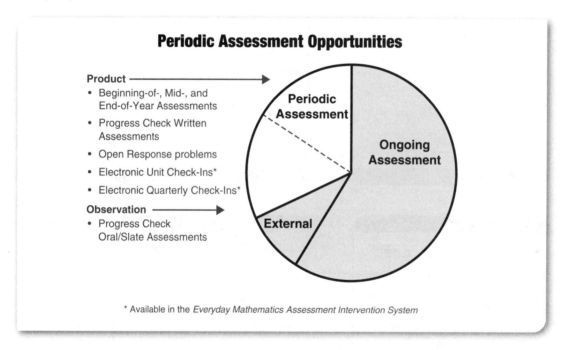

Progress Check Written Assessments

Each Progress Check lesson includes a Written Assessment incorporating tasks that address content from lessons in the current and previous units. The Grade-Level Goals addressed in the Written Assessment are listed at the beginning of the lesson. These assessments provide information for evaluating student progress and planning for future instruction.

Written Assessments are one way students demonstrate what they know. Maximize opportunities for students to show the breadth of their knowledge on these assessments by adapting questions as appropriate. Beginning on page 51 in the unit-specific section of this handbook, there are suggested modifications for the Written Assessments that will allow you to tailor questions and get a more accurate picture of what students know.

Experts in assessment distinguish between summative and formative purposes of assessment. Summative assessment measures student growth and achievement so you can determine whether students have learned certain material. Formative assessment provides information about students' current knowledge and abilities so you can plan future instruction more effectively.

Accordingly, all *Everyday Mathematics* Progress Check written assessments include two parts:

◆ Part A is designed for summative purposes. The questions provide teachers with information on how students are progressing toward Grade-Level Goals. The questions can be used in the same way as Recognizing Student Achievement notes. Students *making adequate progress* toward Grade-Level Goals should do fairly well on this section.

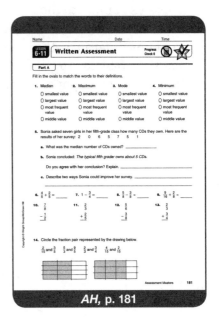

AH, p. 181

◆ Part B is designed for formative purposes. The questions can be used to establish baselines for documenting student growth over time. The questions also assist teachers in their long-term planning in the same way as Informing Instruction notes help teachers in planning lessons.

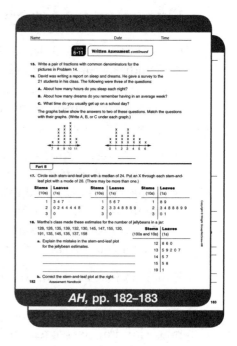

AH, pp. 182–183

Oral and Slate Assessment

Each Progress Check lesson features an Oral and Slate Assessment that includes problems similar to those in Mental Math and Reflexes, which appears in each lesson. You may choose to manage the collection of information from these problems differently than you do with the daily practice. For example, you may give the problems to small groups of students at a time or have students record their answers on paper rather than on slates.

Student Self Assessment

Each Progress Check lesson includes a Self Assessment master that students complete. These Self Assessments are part of a balanced assessment plan as they allow:

◆ students to reflect on their progress, strengths, and weaknesses;
◆ teachers to gain insights into how students perceive their progress; and
◆ teachers and students to plan how to address weaknesses.

The Self Assessment engages students in evaluating their competency with the concepts and skills addressed in the unit. For each skill or concept, students check a box to indicate one of the following:

◆ I can do this on my own and explain how to do it.
◆ I can do this on my own.
◆ I can do this if I get help or look at an example.

If students feel as though they need help or do not understand, consider talking with them about how they may learn more about the concept or skill. Look to related Readiness activities in Part 3 of lessons and to games for ideas about further developing students' understanding.

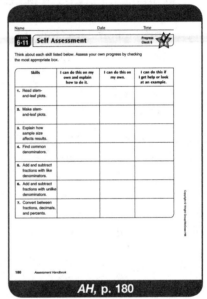

AH, p. 180

Open Response Tasks

Each Progress Check lesson includes an Open Response task linked to one or more Grade-Level Goals emphasized in the unit. These Open Response assessment tasks can provide additional balance in an assessment plan as they allow students to:

◆ become more aware of their problem-solving processes as they communicate their understanding, for example, through words, pictures, or diagrams;
◆ apply a variety of strategies to solve the longer tasks;
◆ further demonstrate their knowledge and understanding through application of skills and concepts in meaningful contexts; and
◆ be successful on a variety of levels.

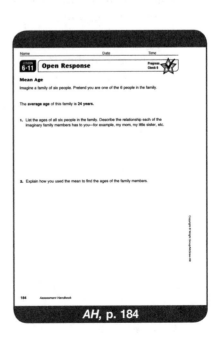

AH, p. 184

The Open Response tasks have been selected with the following points in mind:

◆ The problem context makes sense to students.

◆ The skill level of the problem is appropriate for students.

◆ The problem involves mathematics in which students have a foundation.

◆ The mathematics of the problem is important to the grade level. The problem addresses one or more Grade-Level Goals for the grade.

◆ The problem has connections to the real world that students have experience with.

◆ The problem may not be a multistep problem, but the solution strategy involves several steps.

◆ The problem may have more than one correct solution.

In the unit-specific section of this handbook that begins on page 51, each Open Response task has suggested implementation strategies, a sample task-specific rubric, and annotated student samples demonstrating the expectations described in the rubric. The unit-specific section also includes suggestions for adapting the Open Response task to meet the needs of a diverse group of students.

The sample rubrics are on a 4-point scale. The top two scores (4 points and 3 points) are designated for student work that demonstrates success with the task. The bottom two scores (2 points and 1 point) are designated for student work that does not demonstrate success with the task; 0 points are reserved for situations where students have made no effort to understand or solve the problem.

In general, the sample rubrics focus on assessing the following items:

◆ whether the mathematics students use is correct;

◆ whether the solution strategy makes sense, is reasonable, addresses the problem, and may lead to a successful solution;

◆ whether the explanation of the strategy is clear and easy to follow; and

◆ whether the solution is correct (or correct except for minor errors).

Mean Age Rubric

4	Lists six ages totaling 144, including self. The age of each family member is reasonable. Clearly explains the role of the mean in solving the problem. Refers to either using the mean of 24 or the total of the ages based on the mean in the solution strategy.
3	Lists six ages totaling 144, including self. The age of most of the family members is reasonable. Explains how the problem was solved using the mean, but the explanation might refer only to adding or dividing.
2	Lists six ages. Might include self in the list. The explanation includes some reference to using the mean to solve the problem, but there might be steps missing or incorrect. The process for solving the problem is not clear.
1	Might list six ages. There is little evidence of an understanding of mean or how to apply the concept of mean to solving the problem.
0	Does not attempt to solve the problem.

You may want to work with other teachers from your grade level to apply the *Everyday Mathematics* rubric to your students' work or to create rubrics for scoring these tasks. Consider the expectations of standardized tests in your area when creating or applying a rubric and modify this sample rubric as appropriate. For more student involvement, consider having students participate in developing a list of expectations for a Level-4 paper.

Beginning-of-Year, Mid-Year, and End-of-Year Assessments

To provide a snapshot of how students are progressing toward a broader range of Grade-Level Goals, the program includes three assessments at each grade level—Beginning-of-Year, Mid-Year, and End-of-Year. These assessments cover important concepts and skills presented throughout the year. The Beginning-of-Year, Mid-Year, and End-of-Year assessments provide additional information that you may wish to include in developing your balanced assessment plan.

External Assessment

Outside tests, which are one example of external assessment, are generally tests given at the school, district, or state level, or are nationally standardized tests. Most teachers are familiar with the standardized tests that have multiple-choice responses. The frustrating aspect of this type of test is that it analyzes a narrow range of mathematical thinking and does not assess the depth and breadth of the mathematical knowledge that should be attained in a well-implemented *Everyday Mathematics* classroom.

Everyday Mathematics can help your students function more effectively in testing environments. For example, some Math Boxes problems have been tailored to help prepare students for the formats of an outside test. Even without such preparation, *Everyday Mathematics* students generally do just as well on the computation sections of standardized tests. However, they do much better on concepts and problem-solving sections than students in traditional programs.

More recently, some district and state tests have included performance assessments or open-ended components. *Everyday Mathematics* presents varied mathematics tasks that prepare students for these testing situations: problems requiring students to explain their thinking, writing prompts designed to help students explore content more deeply, and richer Open Response tasks that may require an entire class period for students to solve. If you have a choice in your district, encourage the use of these performance-based or open-ended assessments. They better depict the depth of your students' understandings, as well as their abilities to communicate mathematically, solve problems, and reason.

Performance-based assessments developed at the school or district level probably provide the best opportunities to gather information about student achievement in local classrooms. Teams of teachers and administrators can develop assessments and rubrics that enhance the learning process rather than focus on narrow thinking used only in a small portion of mathematical activities. At some grade levels, these assessments can be used exclusively. When standardized testing is mandatory at a certain grade level, performance-based assessments can provide a better picture of the mathematical education occurring in the classroom than other types of standardized tests.

Record Keeping

If you teach *Everyday Mathematics* as intended and use the techniques described in this book, you will soon have a vast amount of information about students' mathematical skills and understanding. This section of the handbook offers several tools to help you organize and record this information.

Class Checklists and Individual Profiles of Progress

Each lesson in *Everyday Mathematics* identifies a suggested ongoing assessment opportunity in the form of a Recognizing Student Achievement note. These notes highlight specific tasks from which teachers can collect student performance data to monitor and document students' progress toward meeting specific Grade-Level Goals. Each unit in *Everyday Mathematics* contains a Progress Check lesson with suggested periodic assessment tasks. A wealth of assessment information can be collected from these and other sources.

To help you keep track of students' progress in areas that are important to your school and district, checklists for individuals and for the class are provided beginning on page 246 of this handbook. There are Class Checklists for each unit and for each quarter. There are Individual Profiles of Progress for each unit. These checklists provide an organizational system for recording the information you collect to assess student progress on Grade-Level Goals.

The unit checklists include places to record information gathered from the Recognizing Student Achievement notes and from the Progress Check lesson in the unit. The checklists identify the related Grade-Level Goal for each Recognizing Student Achievement task. There is an additional column in which you can add your comments or other notes. To simplify data entry, these checklists are organized according to lesson number.

The quarterly checklists include places to record information gathered throughout the quarter from the Recognizing Student Achievement tasks. To simplify the process of aggregating data in meaningful ways, these checklists are organized according to mathematical strand.

You may prefer using the Class Checklists (on the right) to gather and organize information, transferring selected information to the Individual Profiles of Progress sheet for each student's portfolio or for use during parent conferences.

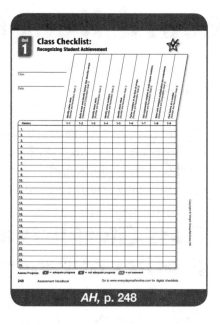

AH, p. 248

Checklist Flow Chart

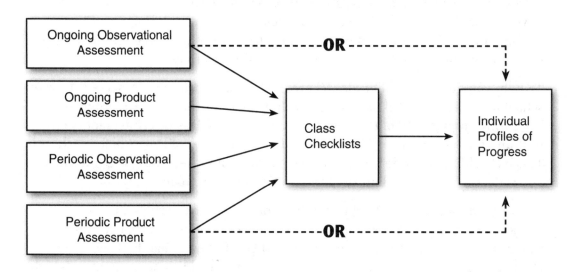

The Individual Profiles of Progress, Class Checklists, and Quarterly Checklists can be found in the Assessment Masters beginning on page 246 of this handbook. Blank checklists have been provided as well. Assessment checklists are also available online at www.everydaymathonline.com.

Options for Recording Data on Checklists

There are several different record-keeping schemes for checklists. Two such schemes are described below.

Option 1

Because Recognizing Student Achievement suggestions include descriptions of the expectations for *making adequate progress,* consider recording this information on a checklist using the following:

A	Student is making adequate progress toward Grade-Level Goal.
N	Student is not making adequate progress toward Grade-Level Goal.

or

✓	Student is making adequate progress toward Grade-Level Goal.
–	Student is not making adequate progress toward Grade-Level Goal.

Option 2

As the teacher, you can decide how you define what is *making adequate progress* and what is not. For example, if you use a 4-point rubric like the sample below, you may decide to define 3 or 4 points as *making adequate progress* and 1 or 2 points as *not making adequate progress.*

4 points	Student is making adequate progress. Student solves the problem correctly and demonstrates a sophisticated and well-articulated understanding of the concept or skill being assessed.
3 points	Student is making adequate progress. Student solves the problem correctly with only minor errors and demonstrates a developmentally appropriate understanding of the concept or skill being assessed.
2 points	Student is not making adequate progress. Student appears to understand some components of the problem and attempts to solve the problem. Student demonstrates an understanding of the concept or skill being assessed that is marginally short of what is expected.
1 point	Student is not making adequate progress. Student appears to not understand the problem but makes some attempt to solve it. Student demonstrates an understanding of the concept or skill being assessed that is significantly short of what is expected.
0 points	Student does not attempt to solve the problem.

Assessment Management Spreadsheets

Introduction

The digital *Everyday Mathematics Assessment Management Spreadsheets* are designed to help you track and record information about student progress towards the *Everyday Mathematics* Grade-Level Goals and the Common Core State Standards. This application contains digital versions of all of the Class Checklists and Individual Profiles of Progress located at the back of this book and can be found at www.everydaymathonline.com.

Everyday Mathematics: Common Core State Standards Edition was designed so the vast majority of students will be successful in mastering the Common Core State Standards and the *Everyday Mathematics* Grade-Level Goals for a given grade upon completion of that grade. Each assessment task provides a snapshot of a student's progress toward the corresponding Grade-Level Goal(s). Taken together, these snapshots form a moving picture that can help you assess whether a student is on a trajectory, or path, to meet the Grade-Level Goal.

Record Keeping

You can use the digital *Everyday Mathematics Assessment Management Spreadsheets* to enter student performance information for the following assessment types:

◆ Ongoing Assessment: Recognizing Student Achievement
◆ Progress Check: Oral and Slate
◆ Progress Check: Written Assessment Parts A and B
◆ Progress Check: Open Response
◆ Beginning-of-Year Assessment
◆ Mid-Year Assessment
◆ End-of-Year Assessment

You can also easily complement the assessments provided in *Everyday Mathematics* by adding student performance data from tasks you design or from the many other tasks in the *Everyday Mathematics* curriculum.

Grading Assistance

While grading is not the primary goal of the *Everyday Mathematics Assessment Management Spreadsheets,* the tool can assist you in assigning grades and creating report cards. You can use it to record student progress on many types of assessment tasks, including those that you create, so your evidence for assessment is based on multiple sources. These records of student performance, combined with the careful observations you make about your students' work, will help you assign fair and accurate grades.

Using the Digital *Assessment Management Spreadsheets*

The digital *Assessment Management Spreadsheets* include many features for supporting your balanced assessment plan. *For example:*

◆ All the suggested *Everyday Mathematics* assessment tasks are built into the system. Selecting a unit number will bring you to a screen that mirrors the Class Checklist masters, which list all the assessment tasks in a given unit.

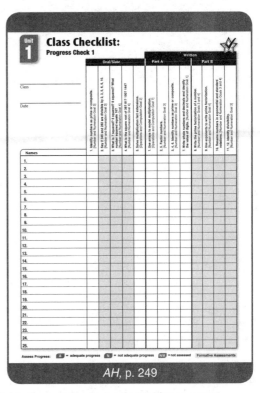

Digital versions of these checklists for all units are available through the Assessment Management Spreadsheets, *found at www.everydaymathonline.com.*

◆ A digital version of the Individual Profile of Progress can be automatically generated from the digital class checklists. You can add text comments for individual students on the digital Individual Profile of Progress.

◆ Teacher-created tasks can be added to the digital spreadsheets.

◆ In addition to classifying students' performance as "making adequate progress" or "not making adequate progress," there is a 0- to 4-point (detailed) scoring option. The detailed scoring option can be used for all assessments or just for open-response items. You can determine the level of specificity that best suits your assessment needs.

For assistance with the *Assessment Management Spreadsheets* and specific feature instructions, click the Help link at the top of any screen within the tool.

Frequently Asked Questions

1. **Do the Grade-Level Goals summarize all the concepts and skills that are covered each year?**

   No; Although the Grade-Level Goals reflect the core of the curriculum at each grade level, they are not comprehensive. They do not capture all the content that is addressed each year. Nor are they a list of activities that are completed each year. Some grade-level content supports future Grade-Level Goals that are not articulated at the given grade level.

2. **With all these Grade-Level Goals, how will I know when I'm simply exposing students to a concept or skill?**

   The *Everyday Mathematics* curriculum aims for student proficiency with concepts and skills through repeated exposures over several years. The *Teacher's Lesson Guide* alerts teachers to content that is being introduced for the first time through Links to the Future notes. These notes provide specific references to future Grade-Level Goals and help teachers understand introductory activities at their grade level in the context of the entire K–6 curriculum.

   All the content in *Everyday Mathematics* is important, whether it's being experienced for the first or the fifth time. The *Everyday Mathematics* curriculum is similar to an intricately woven rug, with many threads that appear and reappear to form complex patterns. Different students will progress at different rates, so multiple exposures to important content are critical for accommodating individual differences. The program was created so it is consistent with how students learn mathematics. It builds understanding over a period of time, first through informal exposure and later through more formal and directed instruction. For students to succeed, they need the opportunity to experience all that the curriculum has to offer in every grade.

3. **There are a lot of lessons in my grade-level materials. Do I have to finish all of them? For example, I teach second grade. Automaticity with multiplication facts is not a Grade-Level Goal until third grade. Can't I just skip all of the second-grade lessons that cover multiplication facts?**

Everyday Mathematics was created to be consistent with how students actually learn mathematics, building understanding over time, first through informal exposure and later through more formal instruction. Because the Grade-Level Goals are cumulative, it is essential for students to experience the complete curriculum at each grade level. Children in *Second Grade Everyday Mathematics,* for example, participate in many hands-on activities designed to develop an understanding of multiplication. This makes it possible for students to achieve multiplication goals in third grade.

4. **Do I need to keep track of progress on Program Goals?**

Program Goals are the threads that weave the content together across grade levels and form the skeleton of the curriculum. The Program Goals are further refined through the Grade-Level Goals. *Everyday Mathematics* provides a variety of tools you can use to assess student progress on the Grade-Level Goals throughout the year. Because every Grade-Level Goal is related to a Program Goal, you are gathering information at this less-specific level as well. This allows great flexibility in reporting to parents. Depending on how your district requires you to aggregate data, you can look broadly at content strands, more closely at Program Goals, or specifically at Grade-Level Goals using the suggested assessments in *Everyday Mathematics*.

5. **What do the authors mean by "adequate progress"?**

Students who are making adequate progress as defined by a Recognizing Student Achievement note are on a trajectory to meet the Grade-Level Goal. Such students have successfully accomplished what is expected up to that point in the curriculum. If students continue to progress as expected, then they will demonstrate proficiency with the Grade-Level Goal upon completion of the year.

The performance expectations described in the Recognizing Student Achievement notes for any given Grade-Level Goal progress developmentally throughout the year. The level of performance that is expected in October is not the same as what is expected in April. The term *adequate progress* describes the level of competency that the majority of students can be expected to have at a particular time. The authors of *Everyday Mathematics* chose the Recognizing Student Achievement tasks with the expectation that the majority of students would be successful with them, which is in line with the expectation that the vast majority of students will successfully reach the Grade-Level Goals for their grade level.

6. **Do students have to complete all of the Recognizing Student Achievement tasks before I can know whether they are making adequate progress?**

Each lesson in *Everyday Mathematics* contains a Recognizing Student Achievement note. These notes highlight specific tasks from which teachers can collect student performance data to monitor and document students' progress toward meeting specific Grade-Level Goals. Each Recognizing Student Achievement note addresses part of a Grade-Level Goal. The suggested assessment tasks build a complete picture over time for each Grade-Level Goal. If students perform well on one or two Recognizing Student Achievement tasks for a goal, that may not provide enough information about the goal in its entirety. Teachers are the experts in their classrooms. If you choose to not do some of the Recognizing Student Achievement tasks, consider collecting similar information from tasks you designate to assemble a complete picture for each Grade-Level Goal.

7. **Can I use only Math Boxes to collect assessment information? They seem to have all the skills in them.**

Everyday Mathematics includes a variety of assessment tasks to ensure that all students have sufficient opportunities to demonstrate what they know. Some students best demonstrate their knowledge through pencil-and-paper tasks, some through performance tasks, and some through explanations and demonstrations. The assessment tasks in the program have been chosen to accommodate a range of learners. Using only one tool might limit what you are able to learn about your students.

8. **I understand that *Everyday Mathematics* provides a Recognizing Student Achievement task for every lesson. May I choose my own instead of or in addition to the ones designated by the curriculum? If I don't think the results of a particular Recognizing Student Achievement task accurately reflect what a student knows, what should I do?**

The Recognizing Student Achievement tasks and Progress Check questions occur at carefully chosen points, based on the opportunities for distributed practice that occur throughout the program. Assessment tasks were also designed to vary the ways in which students are assessed for each Grade-Level Goal.

The *Everyday Mathematics* authors respect teachers as professionals and expect that teachers will use their professional judgment when assessing students. If a particular Recognizing Student Achievement task does not adequately assess student achievement, the teacher may choose to disregard it. The *Everyday Mathematics* authors also anticipate that students' performances on tasks that are not identified in Recognizing Student Achievement notes will often provide useful information regarding their progress toward a particular Grade-Level Goal. Teachers should feel free to link such tasks to appropriate Grade-Level Goals and include them in their assessment stories.

9. **I understand the different record-keeping options that were presented in this handbook. My district, however, evaluates students by assigning traditional letter grades. How should I evaluate student performance?**

Because local assessment systems are based on local norms and values, it would be impossible to design a system that would apply universally. But the authors of *Everyday Mathematics* recognize that many teachers are required by their districts to give traditional grades. And although it is impossible to design a single grading system that will work for everyone, there are some broad principles to follow:

◆ Grades should be fair and based on evidence that can be documented.
◆ Evidence for grading should come from multiple sources.
◆ Grades should be based on content that is important. They should not be based only on the content that is most easily assessed.
◆ The grading system should be aligned with both state and local standards and with the curriculum.

10. **Suppose a student makes adequate progress on the majority of Recognizing Student Achievement tasks and Progress Check questions for a given Grade-Level Goal throughout the year. At the end of the year how likely is it that the student will have achieved the Grade-Level Goal?**

The Recognizing Student Achievement and Progress Check tasks supply a great deal of data on which teachers can base inferences about students' achievement of Grade-Level Goals. In the case of a consistent pattern of adequate progress on assessment tasks for a given Grade-Level Goal, one can reasonably conclude that the student has in fact achieved the given goal. As with any assessment, however, inferences based on positive performance are more straightforward than those based on negative performance. That is, if a student performs well, the most straightforward conclusion is that the student has probably mastered the material; whereas if a student performs poorly, there are many possible explanations, only one of which is a lack of mastery.

Teachers should also recognize that inferences about what students know should always be considered provisional, because the inferences are fallible, based as they are on incomplete information, and because students are constantly growing and changing.

According to *Knowing What Students Know*:

> *. . . by its very nature, assessment is imprecise to some degree. Assessment results are estimates, based on samples of knowledge and performance drawn from the much larger universe of everything a person knows and can do. . . . Assessment is a process of reasoning from evidence. Because one cannot directly perceive students' mental processes, one must rely on less direct methods to make judgments about what they know*
>
> (Pellegrino, Chudowsky, and Glaser 2001, 36)
>
> *An assessment is a tool designed to observe students' behavior and produce data that can be used to draw reasonable inferences about what students know.*
>
> (Pellegrino, Chudowsky, and Glaser 2001, 42)

11. What about a student who normally performs well in class but does poorly on the electronic Quarterly Check-Ins?

Electronic Quarterly Check-Ins are just one piece of the *Everyday Mathematics* assessment story; they are not meant to stand alone and do not provide a complete picture of student progress toward any one goal. Because they can be administered and scored electronically, they provide teachers with some relatively easy data collection. However, because the electronic Quarterly Check-Ins were written in multiple-choice format, they are limited in the information they can provide about what a student knows.

The pencil-and-paper Mid-Year and End-of-Year Assessments are the "best" assessments we offer in *Everyday Mathematics*. They are more comprehensive in their coverage of what students should be responsible for knowing at the time they are given. Students are able to show what they know in a variety of ways, and teachers can gather more information about a student by reviewing the work produced during one of these assessments.

We recommend that teachers administer both the Quarterly Check-Ins and the Mid- and End-of-Year Assessments. However, teachers worried about over-testing may choose to skip the review portion of the Quarter 2 Check-In, as the questions related to those goals are assessed in a more comprehensive manner on the Mid-Year Assessment.

Recommended Reading

Black, Paul, and Dylan Wiliam. "Assessment and Classroom Learning." *Assessment in Education* (March, 1998): 7–74.

———. "Inside the Black Box: Raising Standards Through Classroom Assessment." *Phi Delta Kappan* 80, no. 2 (October, 1998): 139–149.

Bryant, Brian R., and Teddy Maddox. "Using Alternative Assessment Techniques to Plan and Evaluate Mathematics." *LD Forum 21,* no. 2 (winter, 1996): 24–33.

Eisner, Elliot W. "The Uses and Limits of Performance Assessment." *Phi Delta Kappan* 80, no. 9 (May, 1999): 658–661.

Kulm, Gerald. *Mathematics Assessment: What Works in the Classroom.* San Francisco: Jossey-Bass Publishers, 1994.

National Council of Teachers of Mathematics (NCTM). *Curriculum and Evaluation Standards for School Mathematics.* Reston, Va.: NCTM, 1989.

———. *Assessment Standards for School Mathematics.* Reston, Va.: NCTM, 1995.

———. *Principles and Standards for School Mathematics.* Reston, Va.: NCTM, 2000.

National Research Council. Committee on the Foundations of Assessment. Pellegrino, James W., Naomi Chudowsky, and Robert Glaser, eds. *Knowing What Students Know: The Science and Design of Educational Assessment.* Washington, D.C.: National Academy Press, 2001.

National Research Council, Mathematical Sciences Education Board. *Measuring What Counts: A Conceptual Guide for Mathematics Assessment.* Washington, D.C.: National Academy Press, 1993.

Pearson, Bethyl, and Cathy Berghoff. "London Bridge Is Not Falling Down: It's Supporting Alternative Assessment." *TESOL Journal* 5, no. 4 (summer, 1996): 28–31.

Shepard, Lorrie A. "Using Assessment to Improve Learning." *Educational Leadership* 52, no. 5 (February, 1995): 38–43.

Stenmark, Jean Kerr, ed. *Mathematics Assessment: Myths, Models, Good Questions, and Practical Suggestions.* Reston, Va.: National Council of Teachers of Mathematics, 1991.

Stiggens, Richard J. *Student-Centered Classroom Assessment.* Englewood Cliffs, N.J.: Prentice-Hall, 1997.

Webb, N. L., and A. F. Coxford, eds. *Assessment in the Mathematics Classroom: 1993 Yearbook.* Reston, Va.: National Council of Teachers of Mathematics, 1993.

http://everydaymath.uchicago.edu/

Everyday Mathematics GOALS

The following tables list the Grade-Level Goals organized by Content Strand and Program Goal.

Everyday Mathematics®

Content Strand: NUMBER AND NUMERATION

Program Goal: Understand the Meanings, Uses, and Representations of Numbers

Content	Kindergarten	First Grade	Second Grade	Third Grade	Fourth Grade	Fifth Grade	Sixth Grade
Rote counting	**Goal 1.** Count on by 1s to 100; count on by 2s, 5s, and 10s and count back by 1s with number grids, number lines, and calculators.	**Goal 1.** Count on by 1s, 2s, 5s, and 10s past 100 and back by 1s from any number less than 100 with and without number grids, number lines, and calculators.	**Goal 1.** Count on by 1s, 2s, 5s, 10s, 25s, and 100s past 1,000 and back by 1s, 10s, and 100s from any number less than 1,000 with and without number grids, number lines, and calculators.				
Rational counting	**Goal 2.** Count 20 or more objects; estimate the number of objects in a collection.	**Goal 2.** Count collections of objects accurately and reliably; estimate the number of objects in a collection.					
Place value and notation	**Goal 3.** Model numbers with manipulatives; use manipulatives to exchange 1s for 10s and 10s for 100s; recognize that digits can be used and combined to read and write numbers; read numbers up to 30.	**Goal 3.** Read, write, and model with manipulatives whole numbers up to 1,000; identify places in such numbers and the values of the digits in those places.	**Goal 2.** Read, write, and model with manipulatives whole numbers up to 10,000; identify places in such numbers and the values of the digits in those places; read and write money amounts in dollars-and-cents notation.	**Goal 1.** Read and write whole numbers up to 1,000,000; read, write, and model with manipulatives decimals through hundredths; identify places in such numbers and the values of the digits in those places; translate between whole numbers and decimals represented in words, in base-10 notation, and with manipulatives.	**Goal 1.** Read and write whole numbers up to 1,000,000,000 and decimals through thousandths; identify places in such numbers and the values of the digits in those places; translate between whole numbers and decimals represented in words and in base-10 notation.	**Goal 1.** Read and write whole numbers and decimals; identify places in such numbers and the values of the digits in those places; use expanded notation to represent whole numbers and decimals.	**Goal 1.** Read and write whole numbers and decimals; identify places in such numbers and the values of the digits in those places; use expanded notation, number-and-word notation, exponential notation, and scientific notation to represent whole numbers and decimals.

Everyday Mathematics

Content Strand: NUMBER AND NUMERATION *cont.*

Program Goal: Understand the Meanings, Uses, and Representations of Numbers *cont.*

Content	Kindergarten	First Grade	Second Grade	Third Grade	Fourth Grade	Fifth Grade	Sixth Grade
Meanings and uses of fractions	**Goal 4.** Use manipulatives to model half of a region or a collection; describe the model.	**Goal 4.** Use manipulatives and drawings to model halves, thirds, and fourths as equal parts of a region or a collection; describe the model.	**Goal 3.** Use manipulatives and drawings to model fractions as equal parts of a region or a collection; describe the models and name the fractions.	**Goal 2.** Read, write, and model fractions; solve problems involving fractional parts of a region or a collection; describe strategies used.	**Goal 2.** Read, write, and model fractions; solve problems involving fractional parts of a region or a collection; describe and explain strategies used; given a fractional part of a region or a collection, identify the unit whole.	**Goal 2.** Solve problems involving percents and discounts; describe and explain strategies used; identify the unit whole in situations involving fractions.	**Goal 2.** Solve problems involving percents and discounts; explain strategies used; identify the unit whole in situations involving fractions, decimals, and percents.
Number theory		**Goal 5.** Use manipulatives to identify and model odd and even numbers.	**Goal 4.** Recognize numbers as odd or even.	**Goal 3.** Find multiples of 2, 5, and 10.	**Goal 3.** Find multiples of whole numbers less than 10; identify prime and composite numbers; find whole-number factors of numbers.	**Goal 3.** Identify prime and composite numbers; factor numbers; find prime factorizations.	**Goal 3.** Use GCFs, LCMs, and divisibility rules to manipulate fractions.

Program Goal: Understand Equivalent Names for Numbers

Content	Kindergarten	First Grade	Second Grade	Third Grade	Fourth Grade	Fifth Grade	Sixth Grade
Equivalent names for whole numbers	**Goal 5.** Use manipulatives, drawings, and numerical expressions involving addition and subtraction of 1-digit numbers to give equivalent names for whole numbers up to 20.	**Goal 6.** Use manipulatives, drawings, tally marks, and numerical expressions involving addition and subtraction of 1- or 2-digit numbers to give equivalent names for whole numbers up to 100.	**Goal 5.** Use tally marks, arrays, and numerical expressions involving addition and subtraction to give equivalent names for whole numbers.	**Goal 4.** Use numerical expressions involving one or more of the basic four arithmetic operations to give equivalent names for whole numbers.	**Goal 4.** Use numerical expressions involving one or more of the basic four arithmetic operations and grouping symbols to give equivalent names for whole numbers.	**Goal 4.** Use numerical expressions involving one or more of the basic four arithmetic operations, grouping symbols, and exponents to give equivalent names for whole numbers; convert between base-10, exponential, and repeated-factor notations.	**Goal 4.** Apply the order of operations to numerical expressions to give equivalent names for rational numbers.

Everyday Mathematics

Content Strand: NUMBER AND NUMERATION *cont.*

Program Goal: Understand Equivalent Names for Numbers *cont.*

Content	Kindergarten	First Grade	Second Grade	Third Grade	Fourth Grade	Fifth Grade	Sixth Grade
Equivalent names for fractions, decimals, and percents			**Goal 6.** Use manipulatives and drawings to model equivalent names for $\frac{1}{2}$.	**Goal 5.** Use manipulatives and drawings to find and represent equivalent names for fractions; use manipulatives to generate equivalent fractions.	**Goal 5.** Use numerical expressions to find and represent equivalent names for fractions and decimals; use and explain a multiplication rule to find equivalent fractions; rename fourths, fifths, tenths, and hundredths as decimals and percents.	**Goal 5.** Use numerical expressions to find and represent equivalent names for fractions, decimals, and percents; use and explain multiplication and division rules to find equivalent fractions and fractions in simplest form; convert between fractions and mixed numbers; convert between fractions, decimals, and percents.	**Goal 5.** Find equivalent fractions and fractions in simplest form by applying multiplication and division rules and concepts from number theory; convert between fractions, mixed numbers, decimals, and percents.

Program Goal: Understand Common Numerical Relations

Content	Kindergarten	First Grade	Second Grade	Third Grade	Fourth Grade	Fifth Grade	Sixth Grade
Comparing and ordering numbers	**Goal 6.** Compare and order whole numbers up to 20.	**Goal 7.** Compare and order whole numbers up to 1,000.	**Goal 7.** Compare and order whole numbers up to 10,000; use area models to compare fractions.	**Goal 6.** Compare and order whole numbers up to 1,000,000; use manipulatives to order decimals through hundredths; use area models and benchmark fractions to compare and order fractions.	**Goal 6.** Compare and order whole numbers up to 1,000,000,000 and decimals through thousandths; compare and order integers between −100 and 0; use area models, benchmark fractions, and analyses of numerators and denominators to compare and order fractions.	**Goal 6.** Compare and order rational numbers; use area models, benchmark fractions, and analyses of numerators and denominators to compare and order fractions and mixed numbers; describe strategies used to compare fractions and mixed numbers.	**Goal 6.** Choose and apply strategies for comparing and ordering rational numbers; explain those choices and strategies.

Everyday Mathematics

Content Strand: OPERATIONS AND COMPUTATION

Program Goal: Compute Accurately

Content	Kindergarten	First Grade	Second Grade	Third Grade	Fourth Grade	Fifth Grade	Sixth Grade
Addition and subtraction facts	Goal 1. Use manipulatives, number lines, and mental arithmetic to solve problems involving the addition and subtraction of single-digit whole numbers; demonstrate appropriate fluency with addition and subtraction facts within 5.	Goal 1. Demonstrate appropriate fluency with addition and subtraction facts through 10 + 10.	Goal 1. Demonstrate automaticity with all addition facts through 10 + 10 and fluency with the related subtraction facts.	Goal 1. Demonstrate automaticity with all addition and subtraction facts through 10 + 10; use basic facts to compute fact extensions such as 80 + 70.	Goal 1. Demonstrate automaticity with addition and subtraction fact extensions.		
Addition and subtraction procedures		Goal 2. Use manipulatives, number grids, tally marks, mental arithmetic, and calculators to solve problems involving the addition and subtraction of 1-digit whole numbers with 2-digit whole numbers; calculate and compare the values of combinations of coins.	Goal 2. Use manipulatives, number grids, tally marks, mental arithmetic, paper & pencil, and calculators to solve problems involving the addition and subtraction of multidigit whole numbers; describe the strategies used; calculate and compare values of coin and bill combinations.	Goal 2. Use manipulatives, mental arithmetic, paper-and-pencil algorithms and models, and calculators to solve problems involving the addition and subtraction of whole numbers and decimals in a money context; describe the strategies used and explain how they work.	Goal 2. Use manipulatives, mental arithmetic, paper-and-pencil algorithms and models, and calculators to solve problems involving the addition and subtraction of whole numbers and decimals through hundredths; describe the strategies used and explain how they work.	Goal 1. Use manipulatives, mental arithmetic, paper-and-pencil algorithms and models, and calculators to solve problems involving the addition and subtraction of whole numbers, decimals, and signed numbers; describe the strategies used and explain how they work.	Goal 1. Use mental arithmetic, paper-and-pencil algorithms and models, and calculators to solve problems involving the addition and subtraction of whole numbers, decimals, and signed numbers; describe the strategies used and explain how they work.

Everyday Mathematics

Content Strand: OPERATIONS AND COMPUTATION *cont.*

Program Goal: Compute Accurately *cont.*

Content	Kindergarten	First Grade	Second Grade	Third Grade	Fourth Grade	Fifth Grade	Sixth Grade
Multiplication and division facts				**Goal 3.** Demonstrate automaticity with multiplication facts through 10 × 10.	**Goal 3.** Demonstrate automaticity with multiplication facts through 10 * 10 and proficiency with related division facts; use basic facts to compute fact extensions such as 30 * 60.	**Goal 2.** Demonstrate automaticity with multiplication and division fact extensions.	
Multiplication and division procedures				**Goal 4.** Use arrays, mental arithmetic, paper-and-pencil algorithms and models, and calculators to solve problems involving the multiplication of 2- and 3-digit whole numbers by 1-digit whole numbers; describe the strategies used.	**Goal 4.** Use manipulatives, mental arithmetic, paper-and-pencil algorithms and models, and calculators to solve problems involving the multiplication of multidigit whole numbers by 2-digit whole numbers and the division of multidigit whole numbers by 1-digit whole numbers; describe the strategies used and explain how they work.	**Goal 3.** Use manipulatives, mental arithmetic, paper-and-pencil algorithms and models, and calculators to solve problems involving the multiplication of whole numbers and decimals and the division of multidigit whole numbers and decimals by whole numbers; express remainders as whole numbers or fractions as appropriate; describe the strategies used and explain how they work.	**Goal 2.** Use mental arithmetic, paper-and-pencil algorithms and models, and calculators to solve problems involving the multiplication and division of whole numbers, decimals, and signed numbers; describe the strategies used and explain how they work.

Everyday Mathematics

Content Strand: OPERATIONS AND COMPUTATION *cont.*

Program Goal: Compute Accurately *cont.*

Content	Kindergarten	First Grade	Second Grade	Third Grade	Fourth Grade	Fifth Grade	Sixth Grade
Procedures for addition and subtraction of fractions					**Goal 5.** Use manipulatives, mental arithmetic, and calculators to solve problems involving the addition and subtraction of fractions and mixed numbers; describe the strategies used.	**Goal 4.** Use mental arithmetic, paper-and-pencil algorithms and models, and calculators to solve problems involving the addition and subtraction of fractions and mixed numbers; describe the strategies used and explain how they work.	**Goal 3.** Use mental arithmetic, paper-and-pencil algorithms and models, and calculators to solve problems involving the addition and subtraction of fractions and mixed numbers; describe the strategies used and explain how they work.
Procedures for multiplication and division of fractions						**Goal 5.** Use area models, mental arithmetic, paper-and-pencil algorithms and models, and calculators to solve problems involving the multiplication of fractions and mixed numbers; use visual models, paper-and-pencil methods, and calculators to solve problems involving the division of fractions; describe the strategies used.	**Goal 4.** Use mental arithmetic, paper-and-pencil algorithms and models, and calculators to solve problems involving the multiplication and division of fractions and mixed numbers; describe the strategies used and explain how they work.

Everyday Mathematics

Content Strand: OPERATIONS AND COMPUTATION *cont.*

Program Goal: Make Reasonable Estimates

Content	Kindergarten	First Grade	Second Grade	Third Grade	Fourth Grade	Fifth Grade	Sixth Grade
Computational estimation		**Goal 3.** Estimate reasonableness of answers to basic fact problems (e.g., Will 7 + 8 be more or less than 10?).	**Goal 3.** Make reasonable estimates for whole number addition and subtraction problems; explain how the estimates were obtained.	**Goal 5.** Make reasonable estimates for whole number addition, subtraction, multiplication, and division problems; explain how the estimates were obtained.	**Goal 6.** Make reasonable estimates for whole number and decimal addition and subtraction problems and whole number multiplication and division problems; explain how the estimates were obtained.	**Goal 6.** Make reasonable estimates for whole number and decimal addition, subtraction, multiplication, and division problems and fraction and mixed number addition and subtraction problems; explain how the estimates were obtained.	**Goal 5.** Make reasonable estimates for whole number, decimal, fraction, and mixed number addition, subtraction, multiplication, and division problems; explain how the estimates were obtained.

Program Goal: Understand Meanings of Operations

Content	Kindergarten	First Grade	Second Grade	Third Grade	Fourth Grade	Fifth Grade	Sixth Grade
Models for the operations	**Goal 2.** Identify join and take-away situations.	**Goal 4.** Identify change to more, change-to-less, comparison, and parts-and-total situations.	**Goal 4.** Identify and describe change, comparison, and parts-and-total situations; use repeated addition, arrays, and skip counting to model multiplication; use equal sharing and equal grouping to model division.	**Goal 6.** Recognize and describe change, comparison, and parts-and-total situations; use repeated addition, arrays, and skip counting to model multiplication; use equal sharing and equal grouping to model division.	**Goal 7.** Use repeated addition, skip counting, arrays, area, and scaling to model multiplication and division.	**Goal 7.** Use repeated addition, arrays, area, and scaling to model multiplication and division; use ratios expressed as words, fractions, percents, and with colons; solve problems involving ratios of parts of a set to the whole set.	**Goal 6.** Use ratios and scaling to model size changes and to solve size-change problems; represent ratios as fractions, percents, and decimals, and using a colon; model and solve problems involving part-to-whole and part-to-part ratios; model rate and ratio number stories with proportions; use and explain cross multiplication and other strategies to solve proportions.

Everyday Mathematics

Content Strand: DATA AND CHANCE

Program Goal: Select and Create Appropriate Graphical Representations of Collected or Given Data

Content	Kindergarten	First Grade	Second Grade	Third Grade	Fourth Grade	Fifth Grade	Sixth Grade
Data collection and representation	**Goal 1.** Collect and organize data to create class-constructed tally charts, tables, and bar graphs.	**Goal 1.** Collect and organize data to create tally charts, tables, bar graphs, and line plots.	**Goal 1.** Collect and organize data or use given data to create tally charts, tables, graphs, and line plots.	**Goal 1.** Collect and organize data or use given data to create charts, tables, graphs, and line plots.	**Goal 1.** Collect and organize data or use given data to create charts, tables, graphs, and line plots.	**Goal 1.** Collect and organize data or use given data to create graphic displays with reasonable titles, labels, keys, and intervals.	**Goal 1.** Collect and organize data or use given data to create graphic displays with reasonable titles, labels, keys, and intervals.

Program Goal: Analyze and Interpret Data

Content	Kindergarten	First Grade	Second Grade	Third Grade	Fourth Grade	Fifth Grade	Sixth Grade
Data analysis	**Goal 2.** Use graphs to answer simple questions.	**Goal 2.** Use graphs to answer simple questions and draw conclusions; find the maximum and minimum of a data set.	**Goal 2.** Use graphs to ask and answer simple questions and draw conclusions; find the maximum, minimum, mode, and median of a data set.	**Goal 2.** Use graphs to ask and answer simple questions and draw conclusions; find the maximum, minimum, range, mode, and median of a data set.	**Goal 2.** Use the maximum, minimum, range, median, mode, and graphs to ask and answer questions, draw conclusions, and make predictions.	**Goal 2.** Use the maximum, minimum, range, median, mode, and mean and graphs to ask and answer questions, draw conclusions, and make predictions.	**Goal 2.** Use data landmarks, measures of spread, and graphs to ask and answer questions, draw conclusions, and make predictions; compare and contrast the median and mean of a data set.

Program Goal: Understand and Apply Basic Concepts of Probability

Content	Kindergarten	First Grade	Second Grade	Third Grade	Fourth Grade	Fifth Grade	Sixth Grade
Qualitative probability	**Goal 3.** Describe events using *certain, possible, impossible,* and other basic probability terms.	**Goal 3.** Describe events using *certain, likely, unlikely, impossible,* and other basic probability terms.	**Goal 3.** Describe events using *certain, likely, unlikely, impossible,* and other basic probability terms; explain the choice of language.	**Goal 3.** Describe events using *certain, very likely, likely, unlikely, very unlikely, impossible,* and other basic probability terms; explain the choice of language.	**Goal 3.** Describe events using *certain, very likely, likely, unlikely, very unlikely, impossible,* and other basic probability terms; *use more likely, equally likely, same chance, 50–50, less likely,* and other basic probability terms to compare events; explain the choice of language.	**Goal 3.** Describe events using *certain, very likely, likely, unlikely, very unlikely, impossible,* and other basic probability terms; *use more likely, equally likely, same chance, 50–50, less likely,* and other basic probability terms to compare events; explain the choice of language.	

Everyday Mathematics

Content Strand: DATA AND CHANCE *cont.*

Program Goal: Understand and Apply Basic Concepts of Probability *cont.*

Content	Kindergarten	First Grade	Second Grade	Third Grade	Fourth Grade	Fifth Grade	Sixth Grade
Quantitative probability				**Goal 4.** Predict the outcomes of simple experiments and test the predictions using manipulatives; express the probability of an event by using "___ out of ___" language.	**Goal 4.** Predict the outcomes of experiments and test the predictions using manipulatives; summarize the results and use them to predict future events; express the probability of an event as a fraction.	**Goal 4.** Predict the outcomes of experiments, test the predictions using manipulatives, and summarize the results; compare predictions based on theoretical probability with experimental results; use summaries and comparisons to predict future events; express the probability of an event as a fraction, decimal, or percent.	**Goal 3.** Use the Multiplication Counting Principle, tree diagrams, and other counting strategies to identify all possible outcomes for a situation; predict results of experiments, test the predictions using manipulatives, and summarize the findings; compare predictions based on theoretical probability with experimental results; calculate probabilities and express them as fractions, decimals, and percents; explain how sample size affects results; use the results to predict future events.

Everyday Mathematics

Content Strand: MEASUREMENT AND REFERENCE FRAMES

Program Goal: Understand the Systems and Processes of Measurement; Use Appropriate Techniques, Tools, Units, and Formulas in Making Measurements

Content	Kindergarten	First Grade	Second Grade	Third Grade	Fourth Grade	Fifth Grade	Sixth Grade
Length, weight, and angles	**Goal 1.** Use nonstandard tools and techniques to estimate and compare weight and length; identify standard measuring tools.	**Goal 1.** Use nonstandard tools and techniques to estimate and compare weight and length; measure length with standard measuring tools.	**Goal 1.** Estimate length with and without tools; measure length to the nearest inch and centimeter; use standard and nonstandard tools to measure and estimate weight.	**Goal 1.** Estimate length with and without tools; measure length to the nearest $\frac{1}{2}$ inch and $\frac{1}{2}$ centimeter; draw and describe angles as records of rotations.	**Goal 1.** Estimate length with and without tools; measure length to the nearest $\frac{1}{4}$ inch and $\frac{1}{2}$ centimeter; use tools to measure and draw angles; estimate the size of angles without tools.	**Goal 1.** Estimate length with and without tools; measure length with tools to the nearest $\frac{1}{8}$ inch and millimeter; estimate the measure of angles with and without tools; use tools to draw angles with given measures.	**Goal 1.** Estimate length with and without tools; measure length with tools to the nearest $\frac{1}{16}$ inch and millimeter; estimate the measure of angles with and without tools; use tools to draw angles with given measures.
Area, perimeter, volume, and capacity			**Goal 2.** Partition rectangles into unit squares and count unit squares to find areas.	**Goal 2.** Describe and use strategies to measure the perimeter of polygons; find the areas of rectangles.	**Goal 2.** Describe and use strategies to measure the perimeter and area of polygons, to estimate the area of irregular shapes, and to find the volume of rectangular prisms.	**Goal 2.** Describe and use strategies to find the perimeter of polygons and the area of circles; choose and use appropriate methods, including formulas, to find the areas of rectangles, parallelograms, and triangles, and the volume of a prism; define *pi* as the ratio of a circle's circumference to its diameter.	**Goal 2.** Choose and use appropriate formulas to calculate the circumference of circles and to solve area, perimeter, and volume problems.
Units and systems of measurement			**Goal 3.** Describe relationships between days in a week and hours in a day.	**Goal 3.** Describe relationships among inches, feet, and yards; describe relationships between minutes in an hour, hours in a day, days in a week.	**Goal 3.** Describe relationships among U.S. customary units of measure and among metric units of measure.	**Goal 3.** Describe relationships among U.S. customary units of measure and among metric units of measure.	

Everyday Mathematics

Program Goal: Understand the Systems and Processes of Measurement; Use Appropriate Techniques, Tools, Units, and Formulas in Making Measurements *cont.*

Content	Kindergarten	First Grade	Second Grade	Third Grade	Fourth Grade	Fifth Grade	Sixth Grade
Money	**Goal 2.** Identify pennies, nickels, dimes, quarters, and dollar bills.	**Goal 2.** Know and compare the value of pennies, nickels, dimes, quarters, and dollar bills; make exchanges between coins.	**Goal 4.** Make exchanges between coins and bills.				

Program Goal: Use and Understand Reference Frames

Content	Kindergarten	First Grade	Second Grade	Third Grade	Fourth Grade	Fifth Grade	Sixth Grade
Temperature	**Goal 3.** Describe temperature using appropriate vocabulary, such as *hot, warm,* and *cold;* identify a thermometer as a tool for measuring temperature.	**Goal 3.** Identify a thermometer as a tool for measuring temperature; read temperatures on Fahrenheit and Celsius thermometers to the nearest 10°.	**Goal 5.** Read temperature on both the Fahrenheit and Celsius scales.				
Time	**Goal 4.** Describe and use measures of time periods relative to a day and week; identify tools that measure time.	**Goal 4.** Use a calendar to identify days, weeks, months, and dates; tell and show time to the nearest half and quarter hour on an analog clock.	**Goal 6.** Tell and show time to the nearest five minutes on an analog clock; tell and write time in digital notation.	**Goal 4.** Tell and show time to the nearest minute on an analog clock; tell and write time in digital notation.			
Coordinate systems					**Goal 4.** Use ordered pairs of numbers to name, locate, and plot points in the first quadrant of a coordinate grid.	**Goal 4.** Use ordered pairs of numbers to name, locate, and plot points in all four quadrants of a coordinate grid.	**Goal 3.** Use ordered pairs of numbers to name, locate, and plot points in all four quadrants of a coordinate grid.

Everyday Mathematics

Content Strand: GEOMETRY

Program Goal: Investigate Characteristics and Properties of Two- and Three-Dimensional Geometric Shapes

Content	Kindergarten	First Grade	Second Grade	Third Grade	Fourth Grade	Fifth Grade	Sixth Grade
Lines and angles			**Goal 1.** Draw line segments and identify parallel line segments.	**Goal 1.** Identify and draw points, intersecting and parallel line segments and lines, rays, and right angles.	**Goal 1.** Identify, draw, and describe points, intersecting and parallel line segments and lines, rays, and right, acute, and obtuse angles.	**Goal 1.** Identify, describe, compare, name, and draw right, acute, obtuse, straight, and reflex angles; determine angle measures in vertical and supplementary angles and by applying properties of sums of angle measures in triangles and quadrangles.	**Goal 1.** Identify, describe, classify, name, and draw angles; determine angle measures by applying properties of orientations of angles and of sums of angle measures in triangles and quadrangles.
Plane and solid figures	**Goal 1.** Identify and describe plane and solid figures including circles, squares, triangles, rectangles, spheres, and cubes.	**Goal 1.** Identify and describe plane and solid figures including circles, triangles, squares, rectangles, spheres, cylinders, rectangular prisms, pyramids, cones, and cubes.	**Goal 2.** Identify, describe, and model plane and solid figures including circles, triangles, squares, rectangles, hexagons, trapezoids, rhombuses, spheres, cylinders, rectangular prisms, pyramids, cones, and cubes.	**Goal 2.** Identify, describe, model, and compare plane and solid figures including circles, polygons, spheres, cylinders, rectangular prisms, pyramids, cones, and cubes using appropriate geometric terms including the terms *face, edge, vertex,* and *base.*	**Goal 2.** Describe, compare, and classify plane and solid figures, including polygons, circles, spheres, cylinders, rectangular prisms, cones, cubes, and pyramids, using appropriate geometric terms including *vertex, base, face, edge,* and *congruent.*	**Goal 2.** Describe, compare, and classify plane and solid figures using appropriate geometric terms; identify congruent figures and describe their properties.	**Goal 2.** Identify and describe similar and congruent figures and describe their properties; construct a figure that is congruent to another figure using a compass and straightedge.

Program Goal: Apply Transformations and Symmetry in Geometric Situations

Content	Kindergarten	First Grade	Second Grade	Third Grade	Fourth Grade	Fifth Grade	Sixth Grade
Transformations and symmetry	**Goal 2.** Identify shapes having line symmetry.	**Goal 2.** Identify shapes having line symmetry; complete line-symmetric shapes or designs.	**Goal 3.** Create and complete two-dimensional symmetric shapes or designs.	**Goal 3.** Create and complete two-dimensional symmetric shapes or designs; locate multiple lines of symmetry in a two-dimensional shape.	**Goal 3.** Identify, describe, and sketch examples of reflections; identify and describe examples of translations and rotations.	**Goal 3.** Identify, describe, and sketch examples of reflections, translations, and rotations.	**Goal 3.** Identify, describe, and sketch (including plotting on the coordinate plane) instances of reflections, translations, and rotations.

Everyday Mathematics

Content Strand: PATTERNS, FUNCTIONS, AND ALGEBRA

Program Goal: Understand Patterns and Functions

Content	Kindergarten	First Grade	Second Grade	Third Grade	Fourth Grade	Fifth Grade	Sixth Grade
Patterns and functions	**Goal 1.** Extend, describe, and create visual, rhythmic, and movement patterns; use rules, which will lead to functions, to sort, make patterns, and play "What's My Rule?" and other games.	**Goal 1.** Extend, describe, and create numeric, visual, and concrete patterns; solve problems involving function machines, "What's My Rule?" tables, and Frames-and-Arrows diagrams.	**Goal 1.** Extend, describe, and create numeric, visual, and concrete patterns; describe rules for patterns and use them to solve problems; use words and symbols to describe and write rules for functions involving addition and subtraction and use those rules to solve problems.	**Goal 1.** Extend, describe, and create numeric patterns; describe rules for patterns and use them to solve problems; use words and symbols to describe and write rules for functions involving addition, subtraction, and multiplication and use those rules to solve problems.	**Goal 1.** Extend, describe, and create numeric patterns; describe rules for patterns and use them to solve problems; use words and symbols to describe and write rules for functions that involve the four basic arithmetic operations and use those rules to solve problems.	**Goal 1.** Extend, describe, and create numeric patterns; describe rules for patterns and use them to solve problems; write rules for functions involving the four basic arithmetic operations; represent functions using words, symbols, tables, and graphs and use those representations to solve problems.	**Goal 1.** Extend, describe, and create numeric patterns; describe rules for patterns and use them to solve problems; represent patterns and rules using algebraic notation; represent functions using words, algebraic notation, tables, and graphs; translate from one representation to another and use representations to solve problems involving functions.

Program Goal: Use Algebraic Notation to Represent and Analyze Situations and Structures

Content	Kindergarten	First Grade	Second Grade	Third Grade	Fourth Grade	Fifth Grade	Sixth Grade
Algebraic notation and solving number sentences	**Goal 2.** Read and write expressions and number sentences using the symbols $+$, $-$, and $=$.	**Goal 2.** Read, write, and explain expressions and number sentences using the symbols $+$, $-$, and $=$ and the symbols $>$ and $<$ with cues; solve equations involving addition and subtraction.	**Goal 2.** Read, write, and explain expressions and number sentences using the symbols $+$, $-$, $=$, $>$, and $<$; solve number sentences involving addition and subtraction; write expressions and number sentences to model number stories.	**Goal 2.** Read, write, and explain number sentences using the symbols $+$, $-$, $\times$, $\div$, $=$, $>$, and $<$; solve number sentences; write expressions and number sentences to model number stories.	**Goal 2.** Use conventional notation to write expressions and number sentences using the four basic arithmetic operations; determine whether number sentences are true or false; solve open sentences and explain the solutions; write expressions and number sentences to model number stories.	**Goal 2.** Determine whether number sentences are true or false; solve open number sentences and explain the solutions; use a letter variable to write an open sentence to model a number story; use a pan-balance model to solve linear equations in one unknown.	**Goal 2.** Determine whether equalities and inequalities are true or false; solve open number sentences and explain the solutions; use a pan-balance model to solve linear equations in one or two unknowns; use trial-and-error and equivalent equations strategies to solve linear equations in one unknown.

Everyday Mathematics

Content Strand: PATTERNS, FUNCTIONS, AND ALGEBRA *cont.*

Program Goal: Use Algebraic Notation to Represent and Analyze Situations and Structures *cont.*

Content	Kindergarten	First Grade	Second Grade	Third Grade	Fourth Grade	Fifth Grade	Sixth Grade
Order of operations				**Goal 3.** Recognize that numeric expressions can have different values depending on the order in which operations are carried out; understand that grouping symbols can be used to affect the order in which operations are carried out.	**Goal 3.** Evaluate numeric expressions containing grouping symbols; insert grouping symbols to make number sentences true.	**Goal 3.** Evaluate numeric expressions containing grouping symbols and nested grouping symbols; insert grouping symbols and nested grouping symbols to make number sentences true; describe and use the precedence of multiplication and division over addition and subtraction.	**Goal 3.** Describe and apply the conventional order of operations.
Properties of the arithmetic operations		**Goal 3.** Apply the Commutative and Associative Properties of Addition and the Additive Identity to basic addition fact problems.	**Goal 3.** Describe the Commutative and Associative Properties of Addition and the Additive Identity and apply them to mental arithmetic problems.	**Goal 4.** Describe and apply the Commutative and Associative Properties of Addition and Multiplication and the Multiplicative Identity; apply the Distributive Property of Multiplication over Addition.	**Goal 4.** Describe and apply the Distributive Property of Multiplication over Addition.	**Goal 4.** Describe and apply properties of arithmetic.	**Goal 4.** Describe and apply properties of arithmetic and multiplicative and additive inverses.

Assessment Overviews

This section summarizes the assessment opportunities in each unit. Ongoing assessments, such as the Informing Instruction and Recognizing Student Achievement notes, are listed by lesson. Portfolio opportunities, paired or linked Math Boxes, and Writing/Reasoning prompts are also highlighted. You will find information on periodic assessments as well. Modifications for each unit's Progress Check Written Assessment, tips for implementing Open Response tasks (including rubrics for each task), and sample student responses for each rubric level are provided.

Contents

Beginning-of-Year Assessment Goals 51A
Unit 1   Number Theory 52
Unit 2   Estimation and Computation 60
Unit 3   Geometry Explorations and the American Tour 68
Unit 4   Division 76
Unit 5   Fractions, Decimals, and Percents 84
Unit 6   Using Data; Addition and Subtraction of Fractions 92
Mid-Year Assessment Goals 100
Unit 7   Exponents and Negative Numbers 102
Unit 8   Fractions and Ratios 110
Unit 9   Coordinates, Area, Volume, and Capacity 118
Unit 10 Using Data; Algebra Concepts and Skills 126
Unit 11 Volume 134
Unit 12 Probability, Ratios, and Rates 142
End-of-Year Assessment Goals 150

Beginning-of-Year Assessment Goals

The Beginning-of-Year Assessment (pages 227A–D) can be used to gauge students' readiness for the content they will encounter early in fifth grade. This allows you to plan your instruction accordingly. The following table provides the goals for all the problems in the Beginning-of-Year Assessment.

Problem(s)	Grade-Level Goal
1	**Data and Chance Goal 2:** Use the maximum, minimum, range, median, mode, and mean and graphs to ask and answer questions, draw conclusions, and make predictions.
2	**Operations and Computation Goal 1:** Use manipulatives, mental arithmetic, paper-and-pencil algorithms and models, and calculators to solve problems involving the addition and subtraction of whole numbers, decimals, and signed numbers; describe the strategies used and explain how they work.
3a, 4a	**Geometry Goal 1:** Identify, describe, compare, name, and draw right, acute, obtuse, straight, and reflex angles; determine angle measures in vertical and supplementary angles and by applying properties of sums of angle measures in triangles and quadrangles.
3b, 4b	**Measurement and Reference Frames Goal 1:** Estimate length with and without tools; measure length with tools to the nearest $\frac{1}{8}$ inch and millimeter; estimate the measure of angles with and without tools; use tools to draw angles with given measures.
5	**Operations and Computation Goal 3:** Use manipulatives, mental arithmetic, paper-and-pencil algorithms and models, and calculators to solve problems involving the multiplication of whole numbers and decimals and the division of multidigit whole numbers and decimals by whole numbers; express remainders as whole numbers or fractions as appropriate; describe the strategies used and explain how they work.
6	**Geometry Goal 2:** Describe, compare, and classify plane and solid figures using appropriate geometric terms; identify congruent figures and describe their properties.
7	**Operations and Computation Goal 3:** Use manipulatives, mental arithmetic, paper-and-pencil algorithms and models, and calculators to solve problems involving the multiplication of whole numbers and decimals and the division of multidigit whole numbers and decimals by whole numbers; express remainders as whole numbers or fractions as appropriate; describe the strategies used and explain how they work.
8	**Data and Chance Goal 4:** Predict the outcomes of experiments, test the predictions using manipulatives, and summarize the results; compare predictions based on theoretical probability with experimental results; use summaries and comparisons to predict future events; express the probability of an event as a fraction, decimal, or percent.
9, 10	**Operations and Computation Goal 6:** Make reasonable estimates for whole number and decimal addition, subtraction, multiplication, and division problems and fraction and mixed number addition and subtraction problems; explain how the estimates were obtained.
11	**Measurement and Reference Frames Goal 1:** Estimate length with and without tools; measure length with tools to the nearest $\frac{1}{8}$ inch and millimeter; estimate the measure of angles with and without tools; use tools to draw angles with given measures.
12	**Data and Chance Goal 2:** Use the maximum, minimum, range, median, mode, and mean and graphs to ask and answer questions, draw conclusions, and make predictions.

Assessment Overview

In this unit, students explore finding factors and products, and are introduced to prime and composite numbers. Use the information in this section to develop your assessment plan for Unit 1.

Ongoing Assessment

Opportunities for using and collecting ongoing assessment information are highlighted in Informing Instruction and Recognizing Student Achievement notes. Student products, along with observations and suggested writing prompts, provide a range of useful assessment information.

Informing Instruction

The Informing Instruction notes highlight students' thinking and point out common misconceptions. Informing Instruction in Unit 1: Lessons 1-6, 1-7, and 1-9.

Recognizing Student Achievement

The Recognizing Student Achievement notes highlight specific tasks from which teachers can collect assessment data to monitor and document student progress toward meeting Grade-Level Goals.

Lesson	Content Assessed	Where to Find It
1♦1	**Identify place value.** [Number and Numeration Goal 1]	*TLG*, p. 19
1♦2	**Build arrays and identify factors that describe arrays.** [Operations and Computation Goal 7]	*TLG*, p. 24
1♦3	**Identify factor pairs.** [Number and Numeration Goal 3]	*TLG*, p. 30
1♦4	**Identify prime numbers.** [Number and Numeration Goal 3]	*TLG*, p. 35
1♦5	**Identify place value.** [Number and Numeration Goal 1]	*TLG*, p. 40
1♦6	**Factor numbers in the form of arrays.** [Number and Numeration Goal 3]	*TLG*, p. 43
1♦7	**Use exponential notation to write square numbers.** [Number and Numeration Goal 4]	*TLG*, p. 50
1♦8	**Solve and compare multiplication fact extensions.** [Operations and Computation Goal 2]	*TLG*, p. 55
1♦9	**Find factors of a number.** [Number and Numeration Goal 3]	*TLG*, p. 60

Math Boxes

Math Boxes, one of several types of tasks highlighted in the Recognizing Student Achievement notes, have an additional useful feature. Math Boxes in most lessons are paired or linked with Math Boxes in one or two other lessons that have similar problems. Paired or linked Math Boxes in Unit 1: 1-1 and 1-3; 1-2 and 1-4; 1-5, 1-7, and 1-9; and 1-6 and 1-8.

Writing/Reasoning Prompts

In Unit 1, a variety of writing prompts encourage students to explain their strategies and thinking, to reflect on their learning, and to make connections to other mathematics or life experiences. Here are some of the Unit 1 suggestions:

Lesson	Writing/Reasoning Prompts	Where To Find It
1♦1	You can say that 14 is 7 times as great as 2. You can also say that 14 is 2 times as great as 7. Write similar statements for the equation 8 * 6 = 48.	*TLG*, p. 19
1♦3	30 is 5 times as great as 6 and 30 is 6 times as great as 5. Write similar statements for the equation 7 * 6 = 42.	*TLG*, p. 30
1♦5	Explain your multiplication strategy.	*TLG*, p. 40
1♦6	Explain how you know your answer is correct for the elapsed time problem.	*TLG*, p. 46
1♦8	Was Jason correct when he said that 64 is a prime number? Explain your answer.	*TLG*, p. 56

Portfolio Opportunities

Portfolios are a versatile tool for assessment. They help students reflect on their mathematical growth and help teachers understand and document that growth. Each unit identifies several student products that can be selected and stored in a portfolio. Here are some of the Unit 1 suggestions:

Lesson	Portfolio Opportunities	Where to Find It
1♦2	Students solve magic square and heterosquare array problems.	*TLG*, p. 26
1♦3	Students compare the size of the product to the size of one factor based on the size of the other factor.	*TLG*, p. 30
1♦5	Students use place-value concepts to explore divisibility.	*TLG*, p. 41
1♦6	Students apply their understanding of elapsed time to explain their solution strategy.	*TLG*, p. 46
1♦10	Students solve a problem using factors and rules of divisibility and describe their strategies.	*TLG*, p. 65

Periodic Assessment

Every Progress Check lesson includes opportunities to observe student progress and to collect student products in a variety of ways—Self Assessment, Oral and Slate Assessment, Written Assessment, and an Open Response task. For more details, see the first page of Progress Check 1, Lesson 1-10 on page 62, of the *Teacher's Lesson Guide*.

Progress Check Modifications

Written Assessments are one way students demonstrate what they know. The table below shows modifications for the Written Assessment in this unit. Use these to maximize opportunities for students to demonstrate what they know. Modifications can be given individually or written on the board for the class.

Problem(s)	Modifications for Written Assessment
1	For Problem 1, use counters to model the arrays before drawing them.
6	For Problem 6, first translate each statement into its positive form. Then cross out all the numbers that do not fit the statement.
7	For Problem 7, place each digit in a place-value chart before recording your final number.
12	For Problem 12, make a list of hints you could give someone to help them solve this problem.

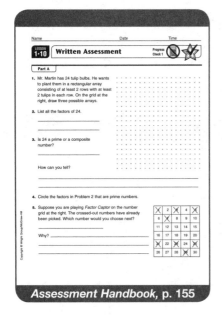

Assessment Handbook, p. 155

The Written Assessment for the Unit 1 Progress Check is on pages 155–156.

Open Response, *Divisibility*

Description

For this task, students use factor patterns to solve a puzzle with divisibility and remainders.

Focus

◆ **Factor numbers.**
  [Number and Numeration Goal 3]

◆ **Use rules of divisibility.**
  [Operations and Computation Goal 3]

◆ **Use arrays to model multiplication and division.**
  [Operations and Computation Goal 7]

Assessment Handbook, p. 157

Implementation Tips

◆ Have students restate the problem in their own words.

◆ Remind students that they must check their answers for every case listed, not just for one that works for one parameter of the problem.

Modifications for Meeting Diverse Needs

◆ Have students use counters to solve the problem. Have them take away one counter at a time until each hint is true. Consider reading *A Remainder of One* or *One Hundred Hungry Ants* by Elinor J. Pinczes before solving the problem.

◆ Have students find an answer for the problem if there are at least 100 students in the fifth grade. Have them explain a rule for how they can find multiple answers to the problem. *(Sample answer: 85—I know it has to be an odd multiple of 5 and one less than the number has to be a multiple of 2, 3, and 4.)*

Improving Open Response Skills

Before students begin the task, have them look over the problem and generate a list of vocabulary words that they might use in the explanation—for example, *arrays, rows, left over,* and *divide by.*

Note: The wording and formatting of the text on the student samples that follow may vary slightly from the actual task your children will complete. These minor discrepancies will not affect the implementation of the task.

Rubric

This rubric is designed to help you assess levels of mathematical performance on this task. It emphasizes mathematical understanding with only a mention of clarity of explanation. Consider the expectations of standardized tests in your area when applying a rubric. Modify this sample rubric as appropriate.

4
Determines that there are 25 dancers. Clearly explains or illustrates how the concepts of multiples, divisibility, remainders, or factors are used. Justifies the solution including all of the problem parameters. Uses mathematical vocabulary in the explanation, for example, *multiples*, *divide*, *remainder*, *arrays*, *rows*, and so on.

3
Determines that there are 25 dancers. Explains or illustrates how the concepts of multiples, divisibility, remainders, or factors are used. Justifies the solution including some of the problem parameters. Might use mathematical vocabulary in the explanation, for example, *multiples*, *divide*, *remainder*, *arrays*, *rows*, and so on.

2
Might determine that there are 25 dancers. Attempts to explain or illustrate how the concepts of multiples, divisibility, remainders, or factors are used. The explanation might be incomplete or confusing, but it makes sense in the context of the problem.

1
Attempts to solve the problem and explain or illustrate the strategy used. There is little evidence of understanding the problem.

0
Does not attempt to solve the problem.

Sample Student Responses

This Level 4 paper illustrates the following features: A trial-and-error method is described for finding the solution of 25. The illustration clearly shows that arrays with remainders are used to check the answer for all of the hints. The explanation uses the terms *take away* and *rows*.

This Level 4 paper illustrates the following features: The explanation describes using counters to build arrays for odd multiples of 5 and then checking for divisibility. The explanation clearly describes how all the hints were checked. The explanation uses the terms *take away*, *multiple*, *even*, *divisible*, and *arrays*.

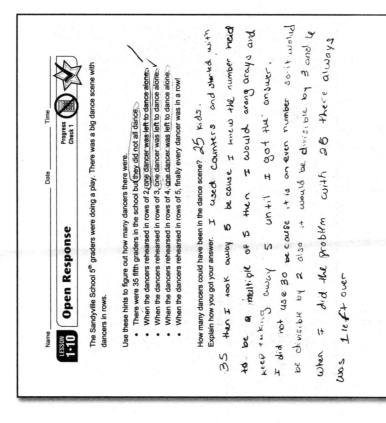

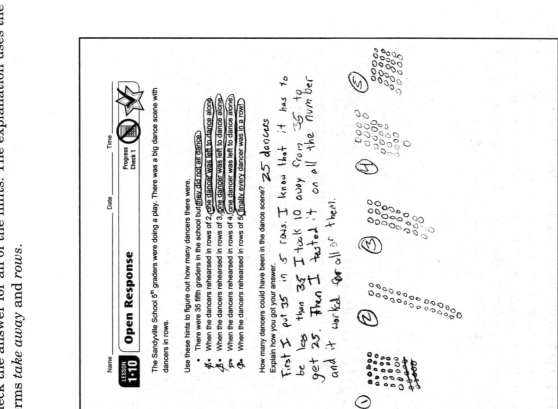

This Level 3 paper illustrates the following features: A trial-and-error strategy with counters is used to find the solution. The explanation describes starting at 33 and checking the odd numbers of counters for divisibility by 2, 3, and 4 until finding that 25 worked. The explanation uses the terms *remainder* and *odd numbers*.

This Level 3 paper illustrates the following features: A trial-and-error strategy beginning with numbers less than 35 is used to find the solution. The explanation describes some steps of how the hints were checked, but it is not clear or complete. The explanation uses the terms *rows* and *columns*.

This Level 1 paper illustrates the following features: There is some evidence of understanding of the problem. A 5-by-5 array is described with a mention of taking away 6 to get the answer. There is no reference to divisibility by 2, 3, or 4. The explanation is incomplete.

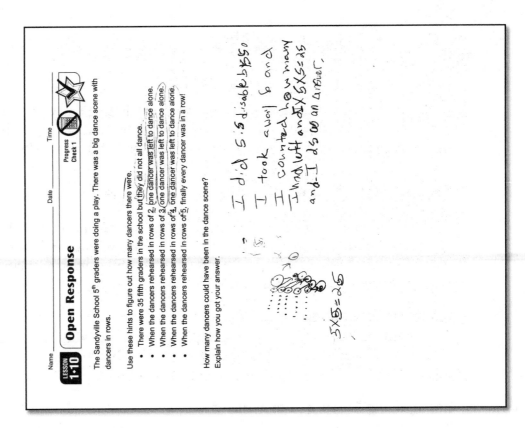

This Level 2 paper illustrates the following features: The explanation describes starting with an array of 35 counters and removing columns of 5 until reaching 25 counters. Some steps are missing from the explanation, and there is no mention of remainders.

Assessment Overview

In this unit, students extend their work with estimating answers to computation problems, pencil-and-paper computation algorithms, and data collection. Use the information in this section to develop your assessment plan for Unit 2.

Ongoing Assessment

Opportunities for using and collecting ongoing assessment information are highlighted in Informing Instruction and Recognizing Student Achievement notes. Student products, along with observations and suggested writing prompts, provide a range of useful assessment information.

Informing Instruction

The Informing Instruction notes highlight students' thinking and point out common misconceptions. Informing Instruction in Unit 2: Lessons 2-6, 2-7, 2-8, 2-9, and 2-10.

Recognizing Student Achievement

The Recognizing Student Achievement notes highlight specific tasks from which teachers can collect assessment data to monitor and document student progress toward meeting Grade-Level Goals.

Lesson	Content Assessed	Where to Find It
2◆1	**Solve extended facts problems mentally.** [Operations and Computation Goal 2]	*TLG*, p. 81
2◆2	**Solve multidigit addition problems.** [Operations and Computation Goal 1]	*TLG*, p. 88
2◆3	**Use the trade-first method with multidigit subtraction problems.** [Operations and Computation Goal 1]	*TLG*, p. 95
2◆4	**Write open number sentences to model given situations.** [Patterns, Functions, and Algebra Goal 2]	*TLG*, p. 101
2◆5	**Compare decimals.** [Number and Numeration Goal 6]	*TLG*, p. 104
2◆6	**Explain why the Probability Meter is labeled with fractions, decimals, and percents.** [Number and Numeration Goal 5]	*TLG*, p. 113
2◆7	**Add and subtract whole numbers.** [Operations and Computation Goal 1]	*TLG*, p. 119
2◆8	**Make reasonable magnitude estimates for multiplication problems based on number sentences.** [Operations and Computation Goal 6]	*TLG*, p. 124
2◆9	**Explain how to solve multiplication problems.** [Operations and Computation Goal 3]	*TLG*, p. 130
2◆10	**Know place value and compare large numbers.** [Number and Numeration Goals 1 and 6]	*TLG*, p. 136

Math Boxes

Math Boxes, one of several types of tasks highlighted in the Recognizing Student Achievement notes, have an additional useful feature. Math Boxes in most lessons are paired or linked with Math Boxes in one or two other lessons that have similar problems. Paired or linked Math Boxes in Unit 2: 2-1 and 2-3; 2-2 and 2-4; 2-5 and 2-7; 2-6 and 2-9; and 2-8 and 2-10.

Writing/Reasoning Prompts

In Unit 2, a variety of writing prompts encourage students to explain their strategies and thinking, to reflect on their learning, and to make connections to other mathematics or life experiences. Here are some of the Unit 2 suggestions:

Lesson	Writing/Reasoning Prompts	Where to Find It
2•2	Leroy rounded 56.199 to 60. Rosina said he was incorrect. Do you agree or disagree with Rosina?	*TLG*, p. 89
2•3	Explain how you know the angle is an obtuse angle without measuring it.	*TLG*, p. 96
2•4	Explain how 60 * 4 can help you solve 240 ÷ 60.	*TLG*, p. 101
2•5	Explain how you solved Problem 5a.	*TLG*, p. 108
2•6	Write a number story for $3 + n = 17$.	*TLG*, p. 114
2•7	Explain how you solved Problem 5b.	*TLG*, p. 118

Portfolio Opportunities

Portfolios are a versatile tool for assessment. They help students reflect on their mathematical growth and help teachers understand and document that growth. Each unit identifies several student products that can be selected and stored in a portfolio. Here are some of the Unit 2 suggestions:

Lesson	Portfolio Opportunities	Where to Find It
2•2	Students explain rounding.	*TLG*, p. 89
2•3	Students identify an obtuse angle without measuring it.	*TLG*, p. 96
2•5	Students explain their solution strategies for decimal subtraction.	*TLG*, p. 108
2•6	Students order fractions, decimals, and percents.	*TLG*, p. 114
2•9	Students explain how to use the lattice multiplication method.	*TLG*, p. 130
2•9	Students explore and analyze an ancient Egyptian method of multiplying.	*TLG*, p. 131
2•11	Students explain and describe strategies used for multidigit multiplication and division problems.	*TLG*, p. 141

Periodic Assessment

Every Progress Check lesson includes opportunities to observe student progress and to collect student products in a variety of ways—Self Assessment, Oral and Slate Assessment, Written Assessment, and an Open Response task. For more details, see the first page of Progress Check 2, Lesson 2-11 on page 138, of the *Teacher's Lesson Guide*.

Progress Check Modifications

Written Assessments are one way students demonstrate what they know. The table below shows modifications for the Written Assessment in this unit. Use these to maximize opportunities for students to demonstrate what they know. Modifications can be given individually or written on the board for the class.

Problem(s)	Modifications for Written Assessment
1–6	For Problems 1–6, build the numbers with base-10 blocks and model the problems with the blocks.
8	For Problem 8, use the standard-measure conversion chart in the Reference Section in your journal to fill in the blanks.
16, 17	For Problems 16 and 17, find the sum for the numbers. Describe at least two advantages and two disadvantages of writing numbers in expanded notation before adding them.
18	For Problem 18, write each number from the data set on a stick-on note and arrange the stick-on notes to find the landmarks.

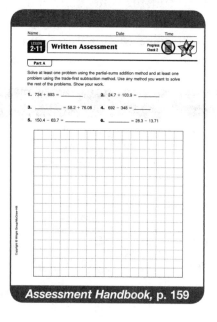

Assessment Handbook, p. 159

The Written Assessment for the Unit 2 Progress Check is on pages 159–162.

Open Response, *Fund Raising*

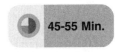

Description

For this task, students calculate the amount of money raised and donated by two classes, based on clues that involve doubling and halving.

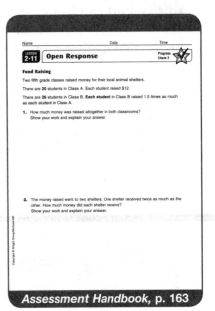

Focus

◆ **Describe and explain strategies used for multidigit multiplication and division problems.** [Operations and Computation Goal 3]

◆ **Multiply whole numbers and decimals.** [Operations and Computation Goal 3]

◆ **Use scaling to model multiplication and division.** [Operations and Computation Goal 7]

Implementation Tips

◆ Review the meaning of *1.5 times* and *double*.

Assessment Handbook, p. 163

Modifications for Meeting Diverse Needs

◆ Have students separate Problem 1 into two simpler problems. Label one sheet of paper Class A—20 Students and a second piece of paper Class B—26 Students. Have them write how much each student earns on each sheet and compute the separate totals before computing the grand total.

◆ Have students compute the fraction of the grand total each class earned and the fraction of the grand total each shelter received. Have them write an explanation for how they figured out their answers.

Improving Open Response Skills

Before students begin the task, have them read the problem individually, and think about and record what information they know, and what questions they have to answer in order to solve the problem. Have students share in small groups and make a list of the information and the questions they can refer back to during the task.

Note: The wording and formatting of the text on the student samples that follow may vary slightly from the actual task your children will complete. These minor discrepancies will not affect the implementation of the task.

Rubric

This rubric is designed to help you assess levels of mathematical performance on this task. It emphasizes mathematical understanding with only a mention of clarity of explanation. Consider the expectations of standardized tests in your area when applying a rubric. Modify this sample rubric as appropriate.

4 — Uses the correct number of students and multipliers of $12 and $18 (1.5 ∗ $12) for each class. Recognizes that one shelter receives twice as much as the other. Clearly states all answers with units, and calculates the total correctly. Clearly and completely describes the steps of the solution strategy for each part of the problem.

3 — Uses the correct number of students and multipliers of $12 and $18 (1.5 ∗ $12) for each class. Recognizes that one shelter receives twice as much as the other. Calculates the total correctly. Might not designate answers, and might omit units. Describes some steps of the solution strategy for each part of the problem.

2 — Demonstrates some understanding of the problem, but there might be errors. Might not apply the concept of *twice as much as*, but the work and explanation make some sense in the context of the problem. The explanations might be incomplete or incorrect.

1 — Demonstrates little or no understanding of the problem. Might have multiplied some numbers, but the work might not make sense in the context of the problem.

0 — Does not attempt to solve the problem.

Sample Student Responses

This Level 4 paper illustrates the following features: The total for each class is calculated based on the relationships described in the problem. For Problem 2, after finding $\frac{1}{3}$ of the total, subtraction yielded the total for the second shelter. The answers are stated with units in the explanations.

This Level 4 paper illustrates the following features: The total for each class is calculated based on the relationships described in the problem. For Problem 2, after finding $\frac{1}{3}$ of the total for the first shelter, multiplying $\frac{1}{3}$ by 2 yielded the total for the second shelter. The work and explanations are clear and well-labeled.

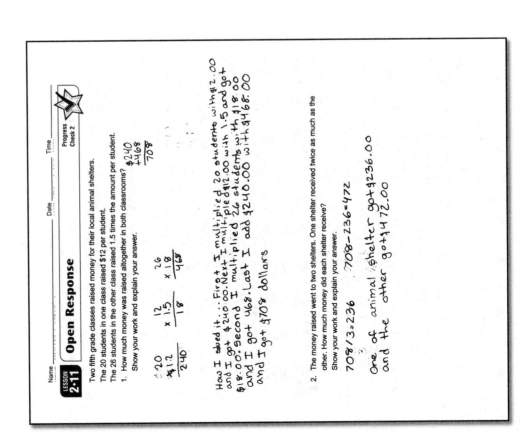

This Level 3 paper illustrates the following features: The work is not well organized but does show all the steps. The answers are correct but not clearly designated in the work. There is an attempt at an explanation, but the explanation consists primarily of number sentences used to solve the problem.

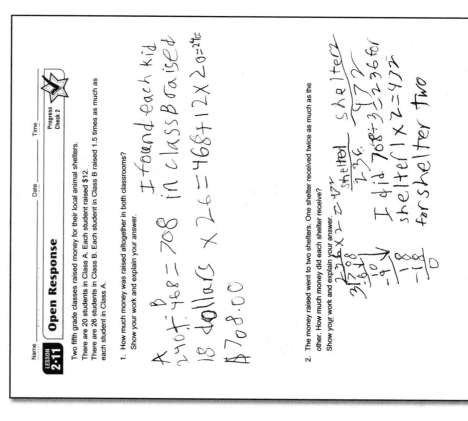

Two fifth grade classes raised money for their local animal shelters.
There are 20 students in Class A. Each student raised $12.
There are 26 students in Class B. Each student in Class B raised 1.5 times as much as each student in Class A.

1. How much money was raised altogether in both classrooms?
Show your work and explain your answer.

A   B
240 + 468 = 708   I found each kid in class B raised
18 dollars × 26 = 468 + 12 × 20 = 240
$708.00

2. The money raised went to two shelters. One shelter received twice as much as the other. How much money did each shelter receive?
Show your work and explain your answer.

708 ÷ 3 = 236
shelter 1 × 2 = 472
236   shelter 1   shelter 2
3)708   472   236 for
-6   I did 708 ÷ 3 = 236 for
10   shelter 1 × 2 = 472
-9   for shelter two
18
-18
0

This Level 3 paper illustrates the following features: The calculations are easy to follow. The answers are correct but not designated in the work. There is an attempt at an explanation, but the explanation provides little additional information.

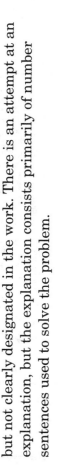

Two fifth grade classes raised money for their local animal shelters.
The 20 students in one class raised $12 per student.
The 26 students in the other class raised 1.5 times the amount per student.

1. How much money was raised altogether in both classrooms?
Show your work and explain your answer.

$12   20   26
×15   ×12   ×18
18   240   468

240
+468
708

My answer is that I add 240 × 468 and I got 708

I solve it I first multipli. 12×15 then I multipli again 12× 20 then I multipli 18×26 then for my final answer I add 240 + 468 = 708

2. The money raised went to two shelters. One shelter received twice as much as the other. How much money did each shelter receive?
Show your work and explain your answer.

I first devided 708 ÷ 3 = 236 then I subtract
708 – 236 = 472
∴ 708 ÷ 3 = 236

I solve it this way because to find the answer because I knew that I had to first find out how much money was raised altogether per student and I first multiply 12 and 15 and I got 16 second 20 × 12 = 240 third I multiply 26 × 18 = 468 Finali add 240 + 468 = 708 that is why I did it this way.

66   Assessment Handbook

This Level 2 paper illustrates the following features: The total is calculated for each class by multiplying the number of students in each class by 12. The total for the second class is multiplied by 1.5 to find the grand total. There is no solution to Problem 2. Instead, the information from Problem 1 is repeated.

This Level 1 paper illustrates the following features: The total is calculated for the first class by multiplying the number of students by 12. For the second class, the number of students is multiplied by 1.5 to find the grand total. In Problem 2, the solution described makes no sense in the context of the problem.

Assessment Overview

In this unit, students begin the American Tour and further explore plane figures and tessellations. Use the information in this section to develop your assessment plan for Unit 3.

Ongoing Assessment

Opportunities for using and collecting ongoing assessment information are highlighted in Informing Instruction and Recognizing Student Achievement notes. Student products, along with observations and suggested writing prompts, provide a range of useful assessment information.

Informing Instruction

The Informing Instruction notes highlight students' thinking and point out common misconceptions. Informing Instruction in Unit 3: Lessons 3-4, 3-5, 3-7, and 3-10.

Recognizing Student Achievement

The Recognizing Student Achievement notes highlight specific tasks from which teachers can collect assessment data to monitor and document student progress toward meeting Grade-Level Goals.

Lesson	Content Assessed	Where to Find It
3•1	Read and write large whole numbers. [Number and Numeration Goal 1]	*TLG*, p. 155
3•2	Add and subtract whole numbers and decimals. [Operations and Computation Goal 1]	*TLG*, p. 162
3•3	Use the relationship between circles and polygons to identify angle measures. [Geometry Goal 1]	*TLG*, p. 167
3•4	Use full-circle and half-circle protractors to measure angles. [Measurement and Reference Frames Goal 1]	*TLG*, p. 175
3•5	Solve extended multiplication facts mentally. [Operations and Computation Goal 2]	*TLG*, p. 178
3•6	Compare decimals. [Number and Numeration Goal 6]	*TLG*, p. 187
3•7	Use attributes to identify polygons. [Geometry Goal 2]	*TLG*, p. 190
3•8	Classify quadrangles. [Geometry Goal 2]	*TLG*, p. 197
3•9	Use the sum of angles in triangles to find the sums of angles in other polygons. [Geometry Goal 1]	*TLG*, p. 203
3•10	Make reasonable magnitude estimates for division problems. [Operations and Computation Goal 6]	*TLG*, p. 207

Math Boxes

Math Boxes, one of several types of tasks highlighted in the Recognizing Student Achievement notes, have an additional useful feature. Math Boxes in most lessons are paired or linked with Math Boxes in one or two other lessons that have similar problems. Paired or linked Math Boxes in Unit 3: 3-1 and 3-3; 3-2 and 3-4; 3-5 and 3-7; 3-6 and 3-9; and 3-8 and 3–10.

Writing/Reasoning Prompts

In Unit 3, a variety of writing prompts encourage students to explain their strategies and thinking, to reflect on their learning, and to make connections to other mathematics or life experiences. Here are some of the Unit 3 suggestions:

Lesson	Writing/Reasoning Prompts	Where to Find It
3◆3	Explain how you know which figure is congruent to Figure 2.	*TLG*, p. 168
3◆5	Explain if 48 will have an even or odd number of factors.	*TLG*, p. 181
3◆6	Maddie drew a trapezoid. What's wrong with that answer? How would you help Maddie know the correct figure to draw and name?	*TLG*, p. 187
3◆7	Explain how you determined the first number pattern.	*TLG*, p. 192
3◆8	Write similar statements for "How many 5s are in 35,000?"	*TLG*, p. 197
3◆9	John called his drawing a parallelogram, and Jack called his drawing a rhombus. Who was correct?	*TLG*, p. 204

Portfolio Opportunities

Portfolios are a versatile tool for assessment. They help students reflect on their mathematical growth and help teachers understand and document that growth. Each unit identifies several student products that can be selected and stored in a portfolio. Here are some of the Unit 3 suggestions:

Lesson	Portfolio Opportunities	Where to Find It
3◆3	Students explain how to identify congruent triangles.	*TLG*, p. 168
3◆5	Students inscribe a regular hexagon in a circle.	*TLG*, p. 182
3◆8	Students compare the size of the product to the size of one factor based on the size of the other factor.	*TLG*, p. 197
3◆9	Students identify a figure as a parallelogram and a rhombus.	*TLG*, p. 204
3◆10	Students apply their understanding of polygons and angles to solve problems.	*TLG*, p. 210
3◆11	Students apply their understanding of types of angles and their measures to solve a problem.	*TLG*, p. 214

Periodic Assessment

Every Progress Check lesson includes opportunities to observe student progress and to collect student products in a variety of ways—Self Assessment, Oral and Slate Assessment, Written Assessment, and an Open Response task. For more details, see the first page of Progress Check 3, Lesson 3-11 on page 211, of the *Teacher's Lesson Guide*.

Progress Check Modifications

Written Assessments are one way students demonstrate what they know. The table below shows modifications for the Written Assessment in this unit. Use these to maximize opportunities for students to demonstrate what they know. Modifications can be given individually or written on the board for the class.

Problem(s)	Modifications for Written Assessment
1–4, 17c	For Problems 1–4 and 17c, refer to the angle definitions on *Student Reference Book*, p. 139, to solve these problems. Use the corner of a sheet of paper to estimate whether each angle measures more, or less, than 90° before measuring with your protractor.
5	For Problem 5, place each digit in a place-value chart before recording your final number.
15	For Problem 15, explain how you found the angle measure for one of the angles around Point *H*.
19	For Problem 19, use pattern blocks to build a tessellating pattern. Then use your Geometry Template to record the pattern you created.

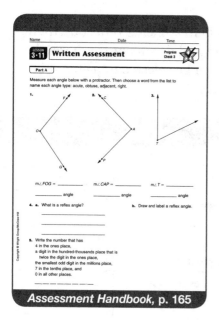

Assessment Handbook, p. 165

The Written Assessment for the Unit 3 Progress Check is on pages 165–168.

Open Response, *Adding Angles*

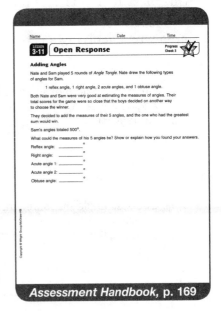

35-45 Min.

Description

For this task, students list five specific types of angles that measure a total of 500 degrees.

Focus

◆ **Use mental arithmetic and paper-and-pencil algorithms to solve problems involving the addition and subtraction of whole numbers.** [Operations and Computation Goal 1]

◆ **Identify, describe, compare, name, and draw right, acute, obtuse, straight, and reflex angles.** [Geometry 1]

Implementation Tips

◆ Review the rules for *Angle Tangle.*

◆ Encourage students to explore the possible angles using their templates.

Assessment Handbook, p. 169

Modifications for Meeting Diverse Needs

◆ Have students look up the types of angles in the *Student Reference Book.* Once they know the range of measures for each angle, have students record measures for all but the acute angles, subtracting from 500 one at a time for the right angle, the reflex angle, and the obtuse angle measures. Encourage students to use numbers that are easy to work with. Have them decide on the measures of their acute angles last.

◆ First, have students draw the angles they have listed using estimation. Then have them measure the angles using a template to record the actual measures. Have them explain the strategies they used to estimate reflex and obtuse angles.

Improving Open Response Skills

After students complete the task, have them share their strategies in small groups. Have students describe and compare their strategies for choosing measures that totaled 500 degrees. Have each group share some of their strategies with the whole class. Have students discuss which of the strategies presented might be easier to work with or more efficient.

Note: The wording and formatting of the text on the student samples that follow may vary slightly from the actual task your children will complete. These minor discrepancies will not affect the implementation of the task.

Rubric

This rubric is designed to help you assess levels of mathematical performance on this task. It emphasizes mathematical understanding with only a mention of clarity of explanation. Consider the expectations of standardized tests in your area when applying a rubric. Modify this sample rubric as appropriate.

4	Chooses angle measures that are correct for each specified type of angle. Identifies angles with a total measure of 500 degrees. Clearly explains all of the steps of a strategy for choosing the angle measures.
3	Chooses angle measures that are correct for each specified type of angle. Identifies angles with a total measure of 500 degrees. Explains some steps of a strategy for choosing the angle measures.
2	Chooses angle measures that are correct for most specified type of angles. Identifies angles with a total measure of about 500 degrees. Might make computation errors. Might attempt to explain some steps of a strategy, but the explanation might not make sense.
1	Chooses angles that provide little evidence of understanding the definitions for the specified types of angles. Might not identify angles with a total measure of about 500 degrees. The explanation might be missing or incomplete.
0	Does not attempt to solve the problem.

Sample Student Responses

This Level 4 paper illustrates the following features: All the specified angle measures are correct. The explanation clearly describes a strategy that begins with listing and finding the totals for the right angle, obtuse angle, and acute angles, and subtracting the subtotal from 500. The difference becomes the reflex angle measure.

This Level 4 paper illustrates the following features: All the specified angle measures are correct. The explanation describes a strategy that begins with a right angle and a reflex angle to bring the total to almost 400 degrees. The obtuse angle is chosen next since it is the next largest, and finally the acute angles split the difference.

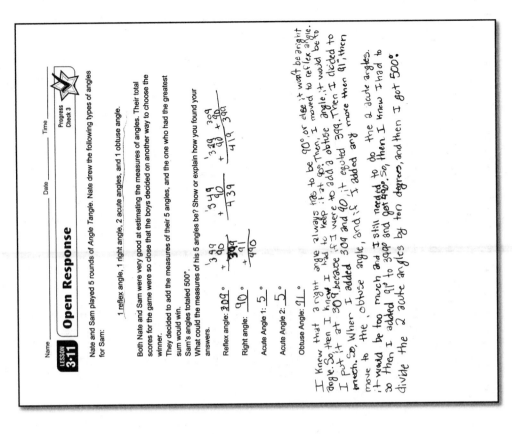

This Level 3 paper illustrates the following features: All the specified angle measures are correct. The explanation describes a strategy of first choosing and totaling the angle measures. Then the individual angle measures are adjusted according to the definition for each angle to reach a total of 500 degrees.

This Level 3 paper illustrates the following features: All the specified angle measures are correct. The explanation describes steps of a strategy that uses easy numbers beginning with the right angle and reflex angle. The reflex angle is given a measure of 200 degrees and the measures of the right angle and obtuse angle total 200 degrees. The final 100 degrees is split between the 2 acute angles.

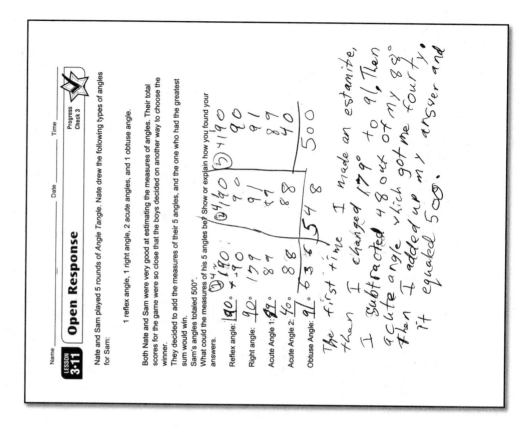

This Level 1 paper illustrates the following features: The angle measures are recorded, but there is no evidence of understanding the definitions for the specified types of angles. Four of the five angles are listed as 90 degrees.

This Level 2 paper illustrates the following features: The angles are correctly described and the measures are chosen according to descriptions. The total of the angle measures is not close to 500 degrees.

Level 1 paper:

Name _____ Date _____ Time _____

LESSON 3·11 **Open Response**

Progress Check 3

Nate and Sam played 5 rounds of *Angle Tangle*. Nate drew the following types of angles for Sam:

1 reflex angle, 1 right angle, 2 acute angles, and 1 obtuse angle.

Both Nate and Sam were very good at estimating the measures of angles. Their total scores for the game were so close that the boys decided on another way to choose the winner.

They decided to add the measures of their 5 angles, and the one who had the greatest sum would win.

Sam's angles totaled 500°.

What could the measures of his 5 angles be? Show or explain how you found your answers.

Reflex angle: 140 °

Right angle: 90 °

Acute Angle 1: 90 °

Acute Angle 2: 90 °

Obtuse Angle: 90 °

I got my answer by using angles that I am sure that that add up to 500

I got my answer by uses the measures of the angles and not so sure that my answer is accurate.

My answer is 500 and I added.

I solved ot this way because we knowing that obtuse, acute, right and reflex angle you know what they measure then I sad maybe 90,180 well without I got my answer, my reference book worried that. Because also I know no other way to solve it.

Level 2 paper:

Name _____ Date _____ Time _____

LESSON 3·11 **Open Response**

Progress Check 3

Nate and Sam played 5 rounds of *Angle Tangle*. Nate drew the following types of angles for Sam:

1 reflex angle, 1 right angle, 2 acute angles, and 1 obtuse angle.

Both Nate and Sam were very good at estimating the measures of angles. Their total scores for the game were so close that the boys decided on another way to choose the winner.

They decided to add the measures of their 5 angles, and the one who had the greatest sum would win.

Sam's angles totaled 500°.

What could the measures of his 5 angles be? Show or explain how you found your answers.

Reflex angle: 300 ° A reflex angle is between 180°-360° so I said 300 useing ploteacter

Right angle: 90 ° A right angle is always 90 and I useing ploteacter

Acute Angle 1: 60 ° Acute is less than 90°

Acute Angle 2: 60 ° is less than 90°

Obtuse Angle: 120 ° A obtuse is greater than 90°.

Frist for all of them I did is read it. Then I look at my notes. Next I look in my book. last I look at my plotracter to see if I was write.

Assessment Overview

In this unit, students review division facts and the partial-quotients division algorithm, and they extend the algorithm to division of decimals. Use the information in this section to develop your assessment plan for Unit 4.

Ongoing Assessment

Opportunities for using and collecting ongoing assessment information are highlighted in Informing Instruction and Recognizing Student Achievement notes. Student products, along with observations and suggested writing prompts, provide a range of useful assessment information.

Informing Instruction

The Informing Instruction notes highlight student thinking and point out common misconceptions. Informing Instruction in Unit 4: Lessons 4-1, 4-2, 4-3, and 4-4.

Recognizing Student Achievement

The Recognizing Student Achievement notes highlight specific tasks from which teachers can collect assessment data to monitor and document student progress toward meeting Grade-Level Goals.

Lesson	Content Assessed	Where to Find It
4•1	Use multiplication and division facts to solve division problems with 1-digit divisors. [Operations and Computation Goal 3]	*TLG*, p. 233
4•2	Use the partial quotients algorithm to solve division problems. [Operations and Computation Goal 3]	*TLG*, p. 239
4•3	Identify place value in decimals. [Number and Numeration Goal 1]	*TLG*, p. 246
4•4	Write a number story. [Operations and Computation Goal 3]	*TLG*, p. 252
4•5	Make magnitude estimates for division problems. [Operations and Computation Goal 6]	*TLG*, p. 256
4•6	Interpret the remainder in division problems. [Operations and Computation Goal 3]	*TLG*, p. 262
4•7	Find the value of an algebraic expression. [Patterns, Functions, and Algebra Goal 2]	*TLG*, p. 267

Math Boxes

Math Boxes, one of several types of tasks highlighted in the Recognizing Student Achievement notes, have an additional useful feature. Math Boxes in most lessons are paired or linked with Math Boxes in one or two other lessons that have similar problems. Paired or linked Math Boxes in Unit 4: 4-1 and 4-3; 4-2, 4-4, and 4-6; and 4-5 and 4-7.

Writing/Reasoning Prompts

In Unit 4, a variety of writing prompts encourage students to explain their strategies and thinking, to reflect on their learning, and to make connections to other mathematics or life experiences. Here are some of the Unit 4 suggestions:

Lesson	Writing/Reasoning Prompts	Where to Find It
4•1	Explain how you solved the money number story.	TLG, p. 234
4•2	Explain how you found the missing angle measure.	TLG, p. 240
4•5	Explain how you used the data table to make your prediction. Include the number models for your calculations.	TLG, p. 257
4•6	Compare the prime factorization for 200 with the prime factorization for 400.	TLG, p. 263
4•7	Explain how you determined the placement of the decimal.	TLG, p. 269

Portfolio Opportunities

Portfolios are a versatile tool for assessment. They help students reflect on their mathematical growth and help teachers understand and document that growth. Each unit identifies several student products that can be selected and stored in a portfolio. Here are some of the Unit 4 suggestions:

Lesson	Portfolio Opportunities	Where to Find It
4•2	Students use factors to find numbers that meet certain divisibility criteria.	TLG, p. 241
4•3	Students use factor rainbows, factor trees, and factor strings to practice factoring numbers.	TLG, p. 245
4•3	Students explore strategies for measuring and rounding to the nearest fraction of an inch.	TLG, p. 246
4•6	Students write and solve their own division number stories.	TLG, p. 264
4•7	Students play *First to 100*.	TLG, p. 267
4•7	Students explain how they determine the placement of the decimal point.	TLG, p. 269
4•8	Students apply rules of divisibility to solve a problem.	TLG, p. 275

Periodic Assessment

Every Progress Check lesson includes opportunities to observe student progress and to collect student products in a variety of ways—Self Assessment, Oral and Slate Assessment, Written Assessment, and an Open Response task. For more details, see the first page of Progress Check 4, Lesson 4-8 on page 272, of the *Teacher's Lesson Guide*.

Progress Check Modifications

Written Assessments are one way students demonstrate what they know. The table below shows modifications for the Written Assessment in this unit. Use these to maximize opportunities for students to demonstrate what they know. Modifications can be given individually or written on the board for the class.

Problem(s)	Modifications for Written Assessment
1–3	For Problems 1–3, draw a line segment between the two locations listed. Use a ruler and the map key to figure out the distance.
10, 11	For Problems 10 and 11, break the problem down into two steps. Record the value of x in the first problem; then rewrite the second problem inserting the value of x.
12, 19, 20	For Problems 12, 19, and 20, draw pictures to help you solve the problems.
18	For Problem 18, tell what the remainder is and explain what you could do with the remainder if the problem had been 2.99 divided by 14.

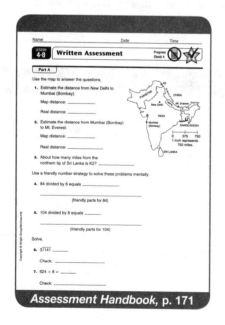

Assessment Handbook, p. 171

The Written Assessment for the Unit 4 Progress Check is on pages 171–173.

Open Response, *Missing Digits*

30-40 Min.

Description

For this task, students use divisibility rules to find missing digits in a 5-digit number.

Focus

◆ **Use rules of divisibility.**
[Number and Numeration Goal 3]

Implementation Tips

◆ Since divisibility by 4 is not explicit in lessons, discuss it with students (they can divide by 2 and then by 2 again).

◆ Review that A and B stand for missing digits.

Modifications for Meeting Diverse Needs

◆ Record and post the divisibility rules with examples for students' reference.

◆ Have students write their own divisibility problem similar to this one.

Assessment Handbook, p. 174

Improving Open Response Skills

After students complete the task, have them compare their explanations for finding the missing digit. In small groups, have them write a complete list on chart paper of all of the steps they used to solve the problem. Display the lists. Discuss and compare the group lists, generating one final list. Have volunteers explain why each step on the final list is necessary.

Note: The wording and formatting of the text on the student samples that follow may vary slightly from the actual task your children will complete. These minor discrepancies will not affect the implementation of the task.

Rubric

This rubric is designed to help you assess levels of mathematical performance on this task. It emphasizes mathematical understanding with only a mention of clarity of explanation. Consider the expectations of standardized tests in your area when applying a rubric. Modify this sample rubric as appropriate.

4 — Uses divisibility rules to solve the problem. Chooses two different digits to create a 5-digit number that is divisible by both 4 and 9. Clearly and completely describes all the solution steps, including how divisibility rules are applied to solve the problem.

3 — Uses divisibility rules to solve the problem. Chooses two different digits to create a 5-digit number that is divisible by both 4 and 9. Describes some of the solution steps and might include a description of how divisibility rules are applied to solve the problem.

2 — Chooses two different digits to create a 5-digit number that is divisible by both 4 and 9. Describes some of the solution steps. Provides some evidence of awareness of the importance of divisibility rules, but it is unclear how the rules are applied.

1 — Chooses two different digits to create a 5-digit number that might be divisible by both 4 and 9. Attempts to describe some of the solution steps. The explanation might be confusing or have errors.

0 — Does not attempt to solve the problem.

Sample Student Responses

This Level 4 paper illustrates the following features: The correct answer is shown with a clear explanation of the steps used to solve the problem. The explanation begins with a discussion of finding a 2-digit number divisible by 4 with a 3 in the tens place. The five digits are totaled, and the last digit is chosen to bring the sum of the digits to 9, so the number is divisible by 9.

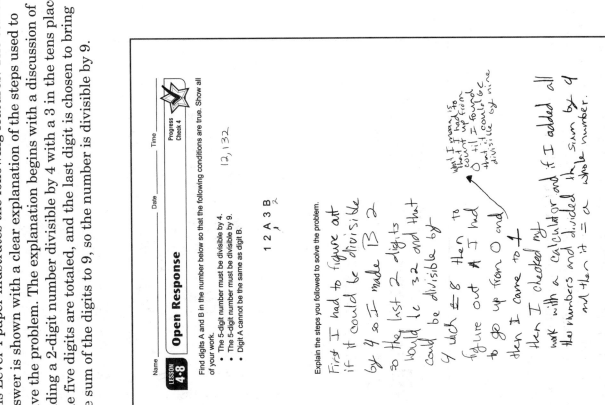

This Level 4 paper illustrates the following features: The correct answer is shown with a clear explanation of the steps used to solve the problem. The explanation begins with a discussion of knowing that the last digit must be either a 2 or a 6, so that the number is divisible by 4. Trial and error is used to solve the problem. There is a complete explanation of how to check the number for divisibility by 4 and 9.

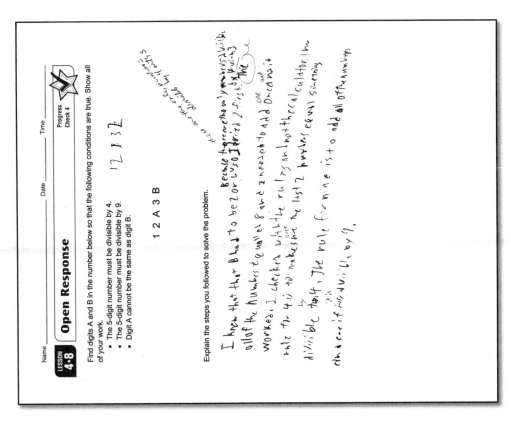

This Level 3 paper illustrates the following features: The answer is is correct. Most of the solution steps are listed in the description, but the language is imprecise. The description makes sense and refers to the divisibility rule for 9, but the explanation of the steps needs to be clarified.

LESSON 4·8

Open Response

Progress
Check 4

Find digits A and B in the number below so that the following conditions are true. Show all of your work.

- The 5-digit number must be divisible by 4.
- The 5-digit number must be divisible by 9.
- Digit A cannot be the same as digit B.

1 2 A 3 B
1 2 4 3 2

Explain the steps you followed to solve the problem.

1. First I looked at all the numbers that start with 3 and B2 was one of them so B was 2.

2. Then I add 12+3+2=8 what pluse 8 can be divided by 9.

3. The first # I tried was 6 that didn't work than 2, 3 and 1.

4. 12+1+3+2=9 and 9÷9=1 and thats the answer.

This Level 3 paper illustrates the following features: The answer is correct. The description explains some steps of a trial-and-error strategy of plugging in different digits and checking to see if they work. Since the solution is 1 and 2, only one incorrect solution is displayed before the correct answer is found.

LESSON 4·8

Open Response

Progress
Check 4

Find digits A and B in the number below so that the following conditions are true. Show all of your work.

- The 5-digit number must be divisible by 4.
- The 5-digit number must be divisible by 9.
- Digit A cannot be the same as digit B.

4
2
1
1 2 A 3 B

Explain the steps you followed to solve the problem.

A— 1 because

B— 2
I put the numbers above each letter and started out with 0–1 then I went to 1–2 and I divided it by 9 and 4 and it worked.

This Level 1 paper illustrates the following features: There is no indication of how the missing digits were determined. There are two number sentences that show checking the final number for divisibility by 4 and by 9, but there is no evidence of how the number is determined. The last statement makes no sense in the context of the problem.

This Level 2 paper illustrates the following features: The explanation describes the final solution rather than the steps followed to reach a solution. There is a discussion of dividing the final number by 4 and 9 to check for divisibility.

Name _____ Date _____ Time _____

LESSON 4·8   **Open Response**   Progress Check 4

Find digits A and B in the number below so that the following conditions are true. Show all of your work.

- The 5-digit number must be divisible by 4.
- The 5-digit number must be divisible by 9.
- Digit A cannot be the same as digit B.

1 2 A 3 B
↑ ↑
1 2

Explain the steps you followed to solve the problem.

1. 12132 ÷ 4 = 3033
2. 12132 ÷ 9 = 1348
I estimates going from 12138 to 12132

Name _____ Date _____ Time _____

LESSON 4·8   **Open Response**   Progress Check 4

Find digits A and B in the number below so that the following conditions are true. Show all of your work.

- The 5-digit number must be divisible by 4.
- The 5-digit number must be divisible by 9.
- Digit A cannot be the same as digit B.

1 2 A 3 B

Explain the steps you followed to solve the problem.

A found that 12132 is ÷ble
By 9 and 4 By using a calaulator to
figare out what the ahsor ts By
taking the number1 in the place
of A and 2 in the place of
B and added the digets up and
got 12,132 wich is divisible
By 4 and 9.

Assessment Overview

In this unit, students review the meanings of fraction, decimal, and percent notations for rational numbers and explore the relationships among these notations. Use the information in this section to develop your assessment plan for Unit 5.

Ongoing Assessment

Opportunities for using and collecting ongoing assessment information are highlighted in Informing Instruction and Recognizing Student Achievement notes. Student products, along with observations and suggested writing prompts, provide a range of useful assessment information.

Informing Instruction

The Informing Instruction notes highlight students' thinking and point out common misconceptions. Informing Instruction in Unit 5: Lessons 5-1, 5-2, 5-3, 5-7, 5-8, 5-10, and 5-11.

Recognizing Student Achievement

The Recognizing Student Achievement notes highlight specific tasks from which teachers can collect assessment data to monitor and document student progress toward meeting Grade-Level Goals.

Lesson	Content Assessed	Where to Find It
5◆1	**Find the unit fraction of a set.** [Operations and Computation Goal 7]	*TLG*, p. 293
5◆2	**Find the value of a region based on a defined unit fraction.** [Operations and Computation Goal 7]	*TLG*, p. 300
5◆3	**Explain the relationship between the numerator and denominator of a fraction.** [Number and Numeration Goal 6]	*TLG*, p. 303
5◆4	**Find equivalent fractions.** [Number and Numeration Goal 5]	*TLG*, p. 312
5◆5	**Convert between fractions and decimals.** [Number and Numeration Goal 5]	*TLG*, p. 315
5◆6	**Compare fractions.** [Number and Numeration Goal 6]	*TLG*, p. 323
5◆7	**Convert between fractions and decimals.** [Number and Numeration Goal 5]	*TLG*, p. 328
5◆8	**Identify percent equivalents for fractions.** [Number and Numeration Goal 5]	*TLG*, p. 335
5◆9	**Compare features of bar and circle graphs.** [Data and Chance Goal 1]	*TLG*, p. 338
5◆10	**Estimate and find the measure of circle-graph sectors.** [Measurement and Reference Frames Goal 1]	*TLG*, p. 346
5◆11	**Use fractions to draw circle-graph sectors.** [Data and Chance Goal 1]	*TLG*, p. 351
5◆12	**Estimate answers to +, −, ∗, and ÷ problems.** [Operations and Computation Goal 6]	*TLG*, p. 358

Math Boxes

Math Boxes, one of several types of tasks highlighted in the Recognizing Student Achievement notes, have an additional useful feature. Math Boxes in most lessons are paired or linked with Math Boxes in one or two other lessons that have similar problems. Paired or linked Math Boxes in Unit 5: 5-1 and 5-3; 5-2 and 5-4; 5-5 and 5-7; 5-6 and 5-8; 5-9 and 5-11; and 5-10 and 5-12.

Writing/Reasoning Prompts

In Unit 5, a variety of writing prompts encourage students to explain their strategies and thinking, reflect on their learning, and make connections to other mathematics or life experiences. Here are some of the Unit 1 suggestions:

Lesson	Writing/Reasoning Prompts	Where to Find It
5◆3	Explain how you changed the fraction to mixed numbers.	*TLG*, p. 306
5◆7	Explain how you round 0.725 to the nearest hundredth.	*TLG*, p. 329
5◆8	Explain the strategies you used to compare and order fractions.	*TLG*, p. 335
5◆9	You have been asked to report the results of the preferred lunch survey. Which graph would you use in your presentation? Explain why.	*TLG*, p. 340
5◆11	Explain how you solved Problem 4.	*TLG*, p. 353

Portfolio Opportunities

Portfolios are a versatile tool for assessment. They help students reflect on their mathematical growth and help teachers understand and document that growth. Each unit identifies several student products that can be selected and stored in a portfolio. Here are some of the Unit 5 suggestions:

Lesson	Portfolio Opportunities	Where to Find It
5◆1	Students find the fraction of a collection of objects.	*TLG*, p. 293
5◆2	Students model relationships between pattern-block fractions.	*TLG*, p. 301
5◆4	Students find equivalent fractions.	*TLG*, p. 312
5◆11	Students practice measuring sectors of a circle graph with the Percent Circle.	*TLG*, p. 353
5◆12	Students construct circle graphs from bar graphs.	*TLG*, p. 359
5◆13	Students solve a problem using fractions of a region.	*TLG*, p. 362

Periodic Assessment

Every Progress Check lesson includes opportunities to observe student progress and to collect student products in a variety of ways—Self Assessment, Oral and Slate Assessment, Written Assessment, and an Open Response task. For more details, see the first page of Progress Check 5, Lesson 5-13 on page 360, of the *Teacher's Lesson Guide*.

Progress Check Modifications

Written Assessments are one way students demonstrate what they know. The table below shows modifications for the Written Assessment in this unit. Use these to maximize opportunities for students to demonstrate what they know. Modifications can be given individually or written on the board for the class.

Problem(s)	Modifications for Written Assessment
5	For Problem 5, explain how you identified the equivalent mixed number(s).
14–19	For Problems 14–19, use the Fraction-Stick Chart on *Math Masters,* page 130, to compare the fractions.
21	For Problem 21, use the corner of a sheet of paper to estimate whether each sector of the graph is greater than or less than 25%. Place the corner of the paper on the center point. The paper covers a 25% sector of the circle.
24–26	For Problems 24–26, begin by recording each percent in the graph as a fraction with a denominator of 100.

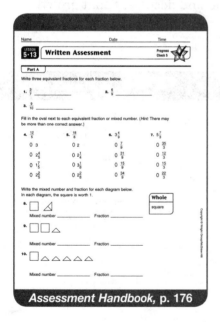

Assessment Handbook, p. 176

The Written Assessment for the Unit 5 Progress Check is on pages 176–178.

Open Response, *Finding Fractions*

Description

For this task, students identify fractions of a region by using relationships between the fractional parts.

Focus

◆ **Use numerical expressions to represent equivalent names for fractions.**
[Number and Numeration Goal 5]

◆ **Use mental math and paper-and-pencil algorithms to solve addition and subtraction problems involving fractions; describe the strategies used and explain how they work.**
[Operations and Computation Goal 4]

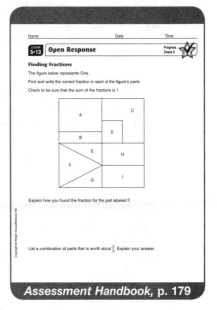

Assessment Handbook, p. 179

Implementation Tips

◆ Relate the fraction of a region exploration to students' experiences with pattern blocks for exploring fractions. Relate the *fraction of a fraction* idea to making fraction strips.

◆ Remind students that for the last problem, they are looking for a total of about $\frac{2}{3}$.

Modifications for Meeting Diverse Needs

◆ Provide students with an additional copy of the figure and a pair of scissors so they can manipulate the individual pieces. For the last part, convert all fractions to percents, using a calculator if necessary.

◆ Have students provide at least three different solutions to the last part of the problem. Record their solutions with letters and as number sentences.

Improving Open Response Skills

Before students begin the task, have them read the problem together. Review Level 4 of the rubric using the board or overhead projector. Have them restate Level 4 of the rubric; record the students' version on chart paper; and display this during the task. Have students compare their work with the posted Level 4 description before turning in their papers.

Note: The wording and formatting of the text on the student samples that follow may vary slightly from the actual task your children will complete. These minor discrepancies will not affect the implementation of the task.

Rubric

This rubric is designed to help you assess levels of mathematical performance on this task. It emphasizes mathematical understanding with only a mention of clarity of explanation. Consider the expectations of standardized tests in your area when applying a rubric. Modify this sample rubric as appropriate.

4 Clearly labels all regions with the correct fraction. Clearly explains how to use a relationship between regions to determine the fraction name for Region F. In the last part of the problem, chooses regions that total about $\frac{2}{3}$ and clearly justifies how the regions are chosen.

3 Labels most regions with the correct fraction. Explains how to use a relationship between regions to determine the fraction name for Region F. In the last part of the problem, chooses regions that total more than $\frac{1}{2}$. Attempts to justify how the regions are chosen, but the explanation might be unclear.

2 Labels all regions demonstrating some understanding of how to find the fraction of a region. Makes reference to some relationship between regions to determine a fraction name for Region F. Might attempt to solve the last part of the problem.

1 Attempts to label regions. Attempts to explain how to find the fraction name for Region F, but the explanation might be incorrect or makes no sense in the context of the problem. Might attempt to solve the last part of the problem.

0 Does not attempt to solve the problem.

This Level 4 paper illustrates the following features: All regions are named correctly with a common denominator of 16. Two regions are also renamed with an equivalent fraction of $\frac{1}{8}$. The explanation refers to Region F being equal to the area of Regions E and G together. In the last part of the problem, the areas of the selected regions total $\frac{10}{16}$, and this total is justified because $\frac{10}{15}$ equals $\frac{2}{3}$ and $\frac{10}{16}$ is close to $\frac{10}{15}$.

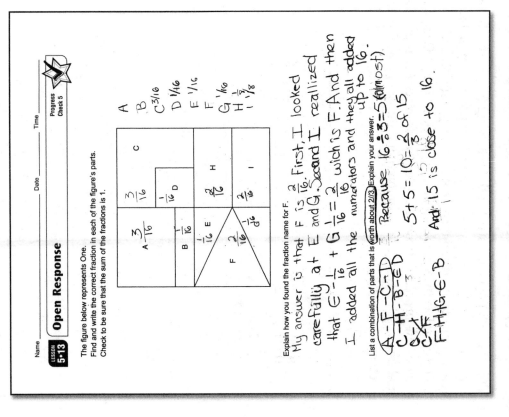

This Level 4 paper illustrates the following features: All regions are named correctly with a common denominator of 16. Two regions are also renamed with an equivalent fraction of $\frac{1}{8}$. The explanation refers to Region F being twice the area of Regions E or G. In the last part of the problem, the areas of the selected regions total $\frac{10}{16}$ which, as stated, is about $\frac{2}{3}$.

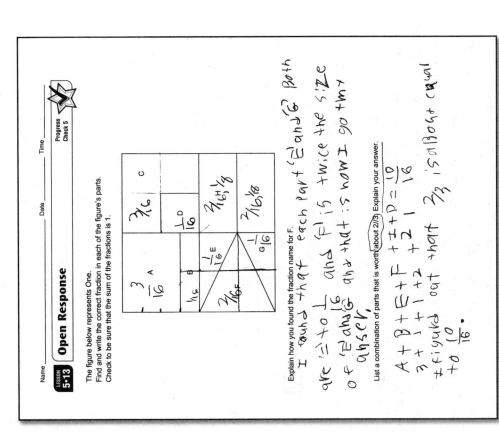

This Level 3 paper illustrates the following features: All regions are named correctly with a common denominator of 16. The explanation refers to finding the total area for all of the known regions and subtracting that from 1 to find the value of Region F. In the last part of the problem, the regions are chosen because the total of the areas is greater than $\frac{1}{2}$ and less than $\frac{10}{16}$.

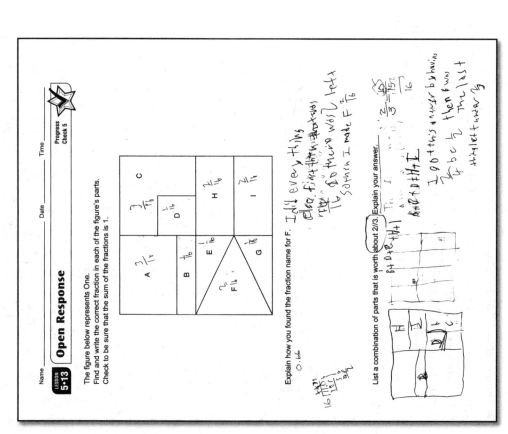

This Level 3 paper illustrates the following features: All regions are named correctly, most with a common denominator of 16. Two regions are correctly named as $\frac{1}{8}$. The explanation refers to Region F being equal to the combined area of Regions E and G. In the last part of the problem, a common denominator of 48 is found for thirds and sixteenths. How the common denominator is used to solve the problem is not clear.

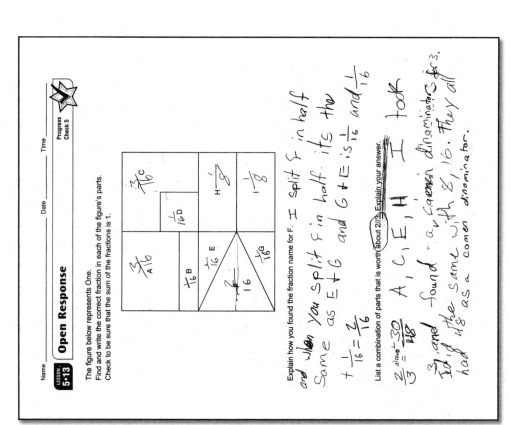

This Level 2 paper illustrates the following features: All regions named correctly with a common denominator of 16. The explanation refers to dividing Region F in half so it looks like Regions E and G. In the last part of the problem, no answer is given, and the explanation makes no sense in the context of the problem.

This Level 1 paper illustrates the following features: Some of the regions are named with fractions, but there are errors. The explanation describes how Region F looks like the shapes around it when it is divided in half. There is no apparent strategy for solving the last part of the problem.

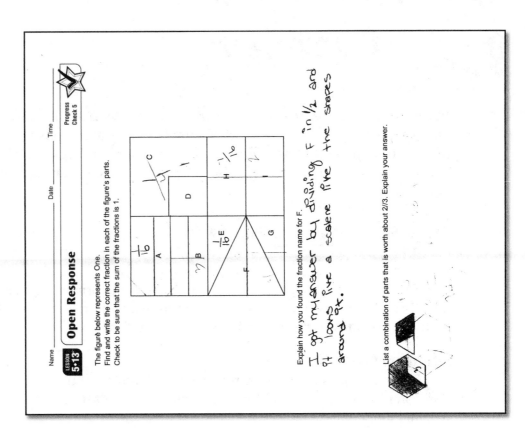

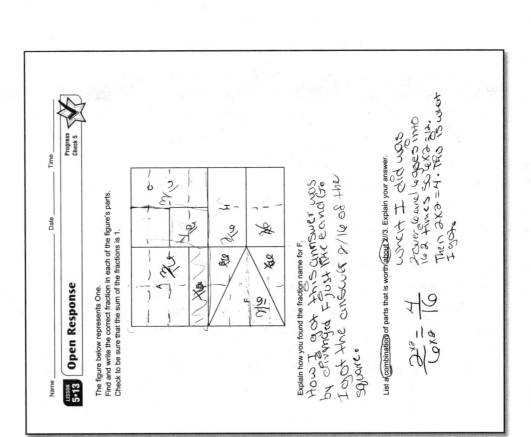

Assessment Overview

In this unit, students extend their work with data to make and interpret displays, and investigate the effect of sample size. Students also review fraction concepts including adding, subtracting, and finding equivalent fractions. Use the information in this section to develop your assessment plan for Unit 6.

Ongoing Assessment

Opportunities for using and collecting ongoing assessment information are highlighted in Informing Instruction and Recognizing Student Achievement notes. Student products, along with observations and suggested writing prompts, provide a range of useful assessment information.

Informing Instruction
The Informing Instruction notes highlight students' thinking and point out common misconceptions. Informing Instruction in Unit 6: Lessons: 6-3, 6-4, 6-6, and 6-8.

Recognizing Student Achievement
The Recognizing Student Achievement notes highlight specific tasks from which teachers can collect assessment data to monitor and document student progress toward meeting Grade-Level Goals.

Lesson	Content Assessed	Where to Find It
6◆1	**Display data on a line plot and identify the data landmarks.** [Data and Chance Goals 1 and 2]	*TLG*, p. 381
6◆2	**Measure lengths to the nearest centimeter and $\frac{1}{4}$-inch.** [Measurement and Reference Frame Goal 1]	*TLG*, p. 386
6◆3	**Explain the advantages of displaying data in stem-and-leaf plots.** [Data and Chance Goal 1]	*TLG*, p. 393
6◆4	**Interpret data displayed in line plots.** [Data and Chance Goal 2]	*TLG*, p. 397
6◆5	**Describe how to find the percent of a number.** [Number and Numeration Goal 2]	*TLG*, p. 401
6◆6	**Name fraction-decimal equivalents.** [Number and Numeration Goal 5]	*TLG*, p. 409
6◆7	**Rename fractions as decimals and percents.** [Number and Numeration Goal 5]	*TLG*, p. 412
6◆8	**Use benchmarks to estimate sums and differences.** [Operations and Computation Goal 6]	*TLG*, p. 421
6◆9	**Add and subtract fractions with unlike denominators.** [Operations and Computation Goal 4]	*TLG*, p. 424
6◆10	**Find common denominators.** [Number and Numeration Goal 5]	*TLG*, p. 432

Math Boxes

Math Boxes, one of several types of tasks highlighted in the Recognizing Student Achievement notes, have an additional useful feature. Math Boxes in most lessons are paired or linked with Math Boxes in one or two other lessons that have similar problems. Paired or linked lessons: 6-1 and 6-3; 6-2 and 6-4; 6-5 and 6-7; 6-6 and 6-9; and 6-8 and 6-10.

Writing/Reasoning Prompts

In Unit 6, a variety of writing prompts encourage students to explain their strategies and thinking, to reflect on their learning, and to make connections to other mathematics or life experiences. Here are some of the Unit 6 suggestions:

Lesson	Writing/Reasoning Prompts	Where to Find It
6◆1	If you extended the top number line, would 100 be one of the missing numbers?	*TLG,* p. 382
6◆4	Explain your method for finding the savings based on discounts.	*TLG,* p. 398
6◆5	Explain your strategy for solving a decimal division problem.	*TLG,* p. 404
6◆7	Explain your strategy for solving a decimal division problem.	*TLG,* p. 415
6◆9	Explain why 53 cannot be the average, and how you chose the values for the data set.	*TLG,* p. 427
6◆10	Using 9^3 as an example, explain the words *base* and *exponent*.	*TLG,* p. 432

Portfolio Opportunities

Portfolios are a versatile tool for assessment. They help students reflect on their mathematical growth and help teachers understand and document that growth. Each unit identifies several student products that can be selected and stored in a portfolio. Here are some of the Unit 6 suggestions:

Lesson	Portfolio Opportunities	Where to Find It
6◆3	Students construct a stem-and-leaf plot.	*TLG,* p. 394
6◆5	Students conduct and design probability experiments.	*TLG,* p. 404
6◆6	Students identify individual values in stem-and-leaf plots.	*TLG,* p. 410
6◆7	Students explain their strategies for solving a decimal division problem.	*TLG,* p. 415
6◆7	Students interpret a contour map.	*TLG,* p. 416
6◆9	Students identify the values for a data set.	*TLG,* p. 427
6◆11	Students use the mean to solve a problem.	*TLG,* p. 436

Periodic Assessment

Every Progress Check lesson includes opportunities to observe student progress and to collect student products in a variety of ways—Self Assessment, Oral and Slate Assessment, Written Assessment, and an Open Response task. For more details, see the first page of Progress Check 6, Lesson 6-11 on page 432, of the *Teacher's Lesson Guide*.

Progress Check Modifications

Written Assessments are one way students demonstrate what they know. The table below shows modifications for the Written Assessment in this unit. Use these to maximize opportunities for students to demonstrate what they know. Modifications can be given individually or written on the board for the class.

Problem(s)	Modifications for Written Assessment
5	For Problem 5, write each number on a stick-on note and arrange the stick-on notes to find the median.
6–11, 13	For Problems 6–11 and 13, use the Fraction-Stick Chart on *Math Journal*, page 130, and a straightedge to add and subtract the fractions. (Hint: Line up your straightedge with the fraction where you want to start the problem and count on or back from there.)
14	For Problem 14, explain why the drawings cannot represent the fraction pairs that you did not circle.
18	For Problem 18, reorganize the numbers of jellybeans in the list so that they are in order, and then you can compare each number to those in the stem-and-leaf plot.

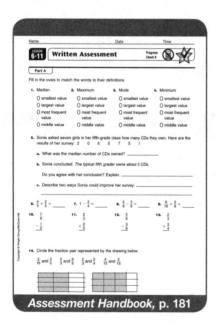

Assessment Handbook, p. 181

The Written Assessment for the Unit 6 Progress Check is on pages 181–183.

Open Response, *Mean Age*

Description

For this task, students describe a data set for a given mean.

Focus

◆ **Use paper-and-pencil algorithms to solve problems involving whole numbers.**
[Operations and Computation Goals 1 and 3]

◆ **Use the mean to answer questions and draw conclusions.**
[Data and Chance Goal 2]

Implementation Tips

◆ Generate a list of who could be included as a family member in hypothetical families with realistic age ranges: for example, parents (30–55), grandparents (40–75), aunts/uncles (10–60), siblings (1–30), and so on.

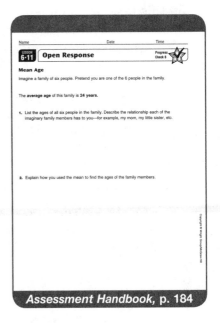

Assessment Handbook, p. 184

Modifications for Meeting Diverse Needs

◆ Have students use six half-sheets of paper and base-10 blocks to model the average age of 24, six times. (Each page will have two longs and four cubes.) Students redistribute the blocks among the six sheets to create new numbers of blocks on each sheet. When they have finished, have them label each sheet with the family member it represents and the age represented by the blocks.

◆ Have students write a general rule for how the average age of the family of six changes if one member's age is different. For example, if one parent were ten years older, how would that change the average? *(Sample answer: The increase or decrease in age divided by six has to be added or subtracted from the previous average.)*

Improving Open Response Skills

Before students begin the task, have them read the problem. As a class, have students create a list of the components that are necessary for a complete response. *(Sample answer: The list must include six ages and the average age must be 24. Label each age with the family member it represents. The ages must make sense for each family member. The explanation must include how the mean is used to solve the problem.)* Post the list for the students to refer to as they work through the problem.

Note: The wording and formatting of the text on the student samples that follow may vary slightly from the actual task your children will complete. These minor discrepancies will not affect the implementation of the task.

Rubric

This rubric is designed to help you assess levels of mathematical performance on this task. It emphasizes mathematical understanding with only a mention of clarity of explanation. Consider the expectations of standardized tests in your area when applying a rubric. Modify this sample rubric as appropriate.

4	Lists six ages totaling 144, including self. The age of each family member is reasonable. Clearly explains the role of the mean in solving the problem. Refers to either using the mean of 24 or the total of the ages based on the mean in the solution strategy.
3	Lists six ages totaling 144, including self. The age of most of the family members is reasonable. Explains how the problem was solved using the mean, but the explanation might refer only to adding or dividing.
2	Lists six ages. Might include self in the list. The explanation includes some reference to using the mean to solve the problem, but there might be steps missing or incorrect. The process for solving the problem is not clear.
1	Might list six ages. There is little evidence of an understanding of mean or how to apply the concept of mean to solving the problem.
0	Does not attempt to solve the problem.

Sample Student Responses

This Level 4 paper illustrates the following features: There are six family members listed and labeled. The explanation clearly describes multiplying the average by 6 to find the target total for the six ages. The next step describes assigning random ages to family members and, finally, adjusting the remaining ages for a total of 144.

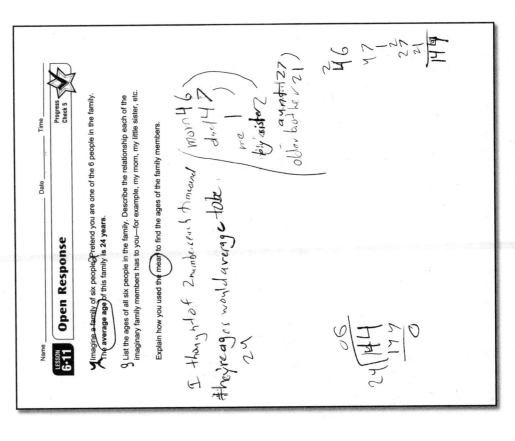

This Level 4 paper illustrates the following features: There are six family members listed and labeled. The explanation clearly describes pairing numbers so that the average for each pair is 24. The answer is checked by finding the average of the ages—finding a sum and dividing the sum by 6. The work on the page matches the explanation.

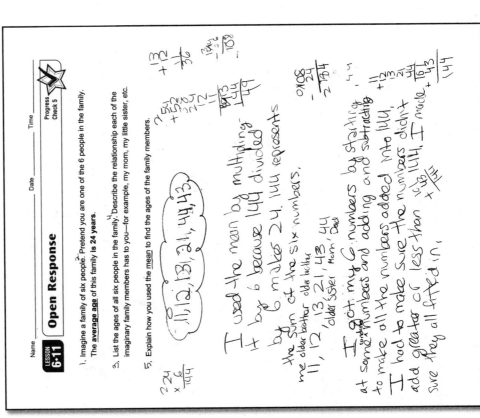

This Level 3 paper illustrates the following features: There are six family members listed and labeled. The explanation describes picking random numbers to start and then adding numbers to total 144. The first step telling where the target number 144 comes from is missing from the explanation. The answer is checked by finding the average for the six ages.

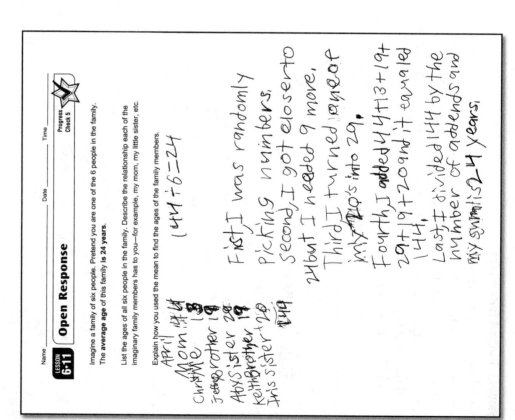

This Level 3 paper illustrates the following features: There are six family members listed and labeled. The explanation describes the list of numbers that total 144. The first step telling where the target number 144 comes from is missing from the explanation. The explanation indicates that the answer can be checked by finding the average.

This Level 1 paper illustrates the following features: There are six family members listed and labeled. There is some evidence of understanding the concept of mean, but no indication of knowing how to use it to solve the problem.

This Level 2 paper illustrates the following features: There are six family members listed and labeled. The explanation refers to multiplying the mean by 6 and then dividing the product of 144 by 6. The division is incorrect, resulting in an average that is different from the original average. This quotient seems to be ignored.

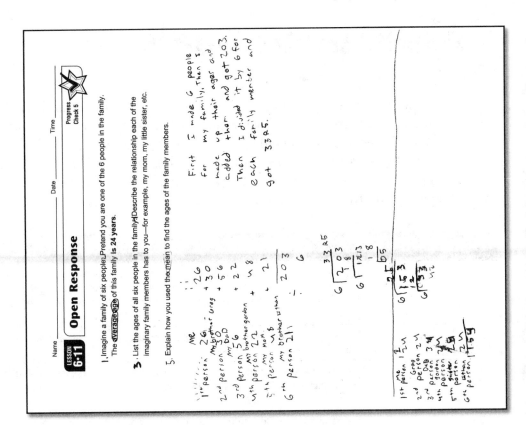

Name _____ Date _____ Time _____

LESSON 6·11 **Open Response** Progress Check 5

1. Imagine a family of six people. Pretend you are one of the 6 people in the family. The **average age** of this family is **24 years**.

3. List the ages of all six people in the family. Describe the relationship each of the imaginary family members has to you—for example, my mom, my little sister, etc.

5. Explain how you used the **mean** to find the ages of the family members.

Mid-Year
Assessment Goals

The Mid-Year Assessment (pages 228–233B) provides an additional opportunity that you may use as part of your balanced assessment plan. It covers some of the important concepts and skills presented in *Fifth Grade Everyday Mathematics*. It should be used to complement the ongoing and periodic assessments that appear within lessons and at the end of units. The following table provides the goals for all the problems in the Mid-Year Assessment.

Problem(s)	Grade-Level Goal
1	**Operations and Computation Goal 1:** Use manipulatives, mental arithmetic, paper-and-pencil algorithms and models, and calculators to solve problems involving the addition and subtraction of whole numbers, decimals, and signed numbers; describe the strategies used and explain how they work.
2	**Operations and Computation Goal 2:** Demonstrate automaticity with multiplication and division fact extensions.
3, 4	**Number and Numeration Goal 1:** Read and write whole numbers and decimals; identify places in such numbers and the values of the digits in those places; use expanded notation to represent whole numbers and decimals.
5	**Operations and Computation Goal 7:** Use repeated addition, arrays, area, and scaling to model multiplication and division; use ratios expressed as words, fractions, percents, and with colons; solve problems involving ratios of parts of a set to the whole set.
6a, 6b	**Measurement and Reference Frames Goal 1:** Estimate length with and without tools; measure length with tools to the nearest $\frac{1}{8}$ inch and millimeter; estimate the measure of angles with and without tools; use tools to draw angles with given measures.
6c, 6d	**Geometry Goal 1:** Identify, describe, compare, name, and draw right, acute, obtuse, straight, and reflex angles; determine angle measures in vertical and supplementary angles and by applying properties of sums of angle measures in triangles and quadrangles.
7, 13	**Measurement and Reference Frames Goal 2:** Describe and use strategies to find the perimeter of polygons and the area of circles; choose and use appropriate methods, including formulas, to find the areas of rectangles, parallelograms, and triangles, and the volume of a prism; define *pi* as the ratio of a circle's circumference to its diameter.
8	**Geometry Goal 2:** Describe, compare, and classify plane and solid figures using appropriate geometric terms; identify congruent figures and describe their properties.
9	**Geometry Goal 1:** Identify, describe, compare, name, and draw right, acute, obtuse, straight, and reflex angles; determine angle measures in vertical and supplementary angles and by applying properties of sums of angle measures in triangles and quadrangles.

Problem(s)	Grade-Level Goal
10	**Operations and Computation Goal 1:** Use manipulatives, mental arithmetic, paper-and-pencil algorithms and models, and calculators to solve problems involving the addition and subtraction of whole numbers, decimals, and signed numbers; describe the strategies used and explain how they work.
11	**Measurement and Reference Frames Goal 1:** Estimate length with and without tools; measure length with tools to the nearest $\frac{1}{8}$ inch and millimeter; estimate the measure of angles with and without tools; use tools to draw angles with given measures.
12a, 12b	**Geometry Goal 1:** Identify, describe, compare, name, and draw right, acute, obtuse, straight, and reflex angles; determine angle measures in vertical and supplementary angles and by applying properties of sums of angle measures in triangles and quadrangles.
12c	**Measurement and Reference Frames Goal 1:** Estimate length with and without tools; measure length with tools to the nearest $\frac{1}{8}$ inch and millimeter; estimate the measure of angles with and without tools; use tools to draw angles with given measures.
13	**Measurement and Reference Frames Goal 2:** Describe and use strategies to find the perimeter of polygons and the area of circles; choose and use appropriate methods, including formulas, to find the areas of rectangles, parallelograms, and triangles, and the volume of a prism; define *pi* as the ratio of a circle's circumference to its diameter.
14	**Operations and Computation Goal 7:** Use repeated addition, arrays, area, and scaling to model multiplication and division; use ratios expressed as words, fractions, percents, and with colons; solve problems involving ratios of parts of a set to the whole set.
15	**Data and Chance Goal 1:** Collect and organize data or use given data to create graphic displays with reasonable titles, labels, keys, and intervals.
16	**Number and Numeration Goal 1:** Read and write whole numbers and decimals; identify places in such numbers and the values of the digits in those places; use expanded notation to represent whole numbers and decimals.
17	**Operations and Computation Goal 2:** Demonstrate automaticity with multiplication and division fact extensions.
18	**Operations and Computation Goal 1:** Use manipulatives, mental arithmetic, paper-and-pencil algorithms and models, and calculators to solve problems involving the addition and subtraction of whole numbers, decimals, and signed numbers; describe the strategies used and explain how they work.
19	**Operations and Computation Goal 1:** Use manipulatives, mental arithmetic, paper-and-pencil algorithms and models, and calculators to solve problems involving the addition and subtraction of whole numbers, decimals, and signed numbers; describe the strategies used and explain how they work.
20	**Number and Numeration Goal 1:** Read and write whole numbers and decimals; identify places in such numbers and the values of the digits in those places; use expanded notation to represent whole numbers and decimals.

In this unit, students further develop their prealgebra skills, use of parentheses, and work with negative numbers. Use the information in this section to develop your assessment plan for Unit 7.

Ongoing Assessment

Opportunities for using and collecting ongoing assessment information are highlighted in Informing Instruction and Recognizing Student Achievement notes. Student products, along with observations and suggested writing prompts, provide a range of useful assessment information.

Informing Instruction

The Informing Instruction notes highlight students' thinking and point out common misconceptions. Informing Instruction in Unit 7: Lessons 7-2, 7-5, 7-6, 7-8 and 7-11.

Recognizing Student Achievement

The Recognizing Student Achievement notes highlight specific tasks from which teachers can collect assessment data to monitor and document student progress toward meeting Grade-Level Goals.

Lesson	Content Assessed	Where to Find It
7♦1	Identify and correct mistakes in writing numbers using exponential notation. [Number and Numeration Goal 4]	TLG, p. 544
7♦2	Use powers of ten to write equivalent names for numbers. [Number and Numeration Goal 4]	TLG, p. 548
7♦3	Use place value to convert numbers written in scientific notation to standard notation. [Number and Numeration Goal 1]	TLG, p. 554
7♦4	Write expressions containing parentheses to represent a number story. [Patterns, Functions, and Algebra Goal 3]	TLG, p. 559
7♦5	Compare decimals. [Number and Numeration Goal 6]	TLG, p. 566
7♦6	Add and subtract fractions with like and unlike denominators. [Operations and Computation Goal 4]	TLG, p. 569
7♦7	Use order of operations to solve problems. [Patterns, Functions, and Algebra Goal 3]	TLG, p. 575
7♦8	Model problems with positive and negative counters. [Operations and Computation Goal 1]	TLG, p. 581
7♦9	Write and compare decimals. [Number and Numeration Goals 1 and 6]	TLG, p. 588
7♦10	Add and compare fractions. [Number and Numeration Goal 6 and Operations and Computation Goal 4]	TLG, p. 594
7♦11	Convert fractions to whole numbers or mixed numbers in simplest form. [Number and Numeration Goal 5]	TLG, p. 597

Math Boxes

Math Boxes, one of several types of tasks highlighted in the Recognizing Student Achievement notes, have an additional useful feature. Math Boxes in most lessons are paired or linked with Math Boxes in one or two other lessons that have similar problems. Paired or linked Math Boxes in Unit 7: 7-1 and 7-3; 7-2, 7-4 and 7-6; 7-5 and 7-8; 7-7 and 7-10; and 7-9 and 7-11.

Writing/Reasoning Prompts

In Unit 7, a variety of writing prompts encourage students to explain their strategies and thinking, to reflect on their learning, and to make connections to other mathematics or life experiences. Here are some of the Unit 7 suggestions:

Lesson	Writing/Reasoning Prompts	Where to Find It
7•1	Explain how to use division to find equivalent fractions.	*TLG*, p. 545
7•4	Explain how to read a stem-and-leaf plot.	*TLG*, p. 560
7•11	Explain your strategy for solving an open-number sentence.	*TLG*, p. 599

Portfolio Opportunities

Portfolios are a versatile tool for assessment. They help students reflect on their mathematical growth and help teachers understand and document that growth. Each unit identifies several student products that can be selected and stored in a portfolio. Here are some of the Unit 7 suggestions:

Lesson	Portfolio Opportunities	Where to Find It
7•2	Students investigate patterns in powers of 10 and describe them.	*TLG*, p. 550
7•2	Students explore the patterns and notation of negative exponents.	*TLG*, p. 550
7•3	Students identify the value of digits in a number written in standard form.	*TLG*, p. 555
7•7	Students use the correct order of operations to solve problems.	*TLG*, p. 575
7•12	Students use order of operations to solve a problem.	*TLG*, p. 603

Periodic Assessment

Every Progress Check lesson includes opportunities to observe students' progress and to collect student products in a variety of ways—Self Assessment, Oral and Slate Assessment, Written Assessment, and an Open Response task. For more details, see the first page of Progress Check 7, Lesson 7-12 on page 600, of the *Teacher's Lesson Guide*.

Progress Check Modifications

Written Assessments are one way students demonstrate what they know. The table below shows modifications for the Written Assessment in this unit. Use these to maximize opportunities for students to demonstrate what they know. Modifications can be given individually or written on the board for the class.

Problem(s)	Modifications for Written Assessment
1–6	For Problems 1–6, use a number line to help you compare the numbers. Rewrite the numbers in standard notation as needed.
10	For Problem 10, explain how you know if an expression is a number sentence.
12–17	Record each number sentence on another sheet of paper so that there is space between the numbers and symbols. Use craft sticks or strips of paper to model the parentheses. Move the parentheses around in each number sentence until you find the position that will make the sentence true.
34	For Problem 34, draw a place-value chart and record the numbers in standard notation in the chart before writing them in number-and-word notation.

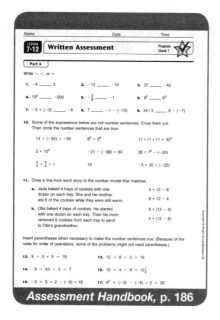

Assessment Handbook, p. 186

The Written Assessment for the Unit 7 Progress Check is on pages 186–188.

Open Response, *Operations in the Klasies Caves*

Description

For this task, students use order of operations to determine the missing operations in number sentences with parentheses.

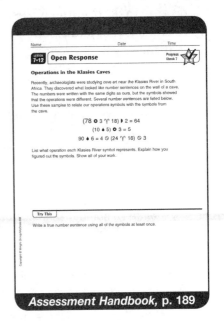

Assessment Handbook, p. 189

Focus

◆ **Use mental arithmetic and paper-and-pencil algorithms to solve problems involving whole numbers.**
[Operations and Computation Goals 1 and 3]

◆ **Evaluate numeric expressions containing grouping symbols.** [Patterns, Functions, and Algebra Goal 3]

Implementation Tips

◆ Remind students that this is like playing a game of *Name That Number*. They have to find the missing operations so that a series of numbers will help them hit the target.

◆ Remind students about order of operations before beginning the task.

Modifications for Meeting Diverse Needs

◆ Provide a set of number cards that contains numbers, operation symbols, and parentheses. Have students model the equations with the cards. When they find an operation to match a symbol, have them record the symbol on a small stick-on note and attach it to the matching operation card. Then they can check their findings by using the card in the other sentences.

◆ Have students explain how the first number sentence changes when the parentheses are removed. Have them use the operations they identified for each symbol and the order of operations to figure out what must be either added to or subtracted from 64 to make the new number sentence without parentheses true. For example, *I have to subtract 362 from 64 to equal –298, the total for the operations without parentheses.*

Improving Open Response Skills

Before students begin the task, read it together. Give students a minute or two to think about how they will solve the problem. Have them share ideas in small groups on how to organize their work.

Note: The wording and formatting of the text on the student samples that follow may vary slightly from the actual task your children will complete. These minor discrepancies will not affect the implementation of the task.

Rubric

This rubric is designed to help you assess levels of mathematical performance on this task. It emphasizes mathematical understanding with only a mention of clarity of explanation. Consider the expectations of standardized tests in your area when applying a rubric. Modify this sample rubric as appropriate.

4 Identifies all of the symbols correctly. Clearly and completely describes all the steps of the solution strategy. Writes a true number sentence using each symbol at least once. Applies the rules for order of operations. Uses number sentence conventions correctly.

3 Identifies all of the symbols correctly. Describes some steps of the solution strategy. Writes a number sentence using 2 or more symbols, but might not apply the rules for order of operations. Uses number sentence conventions with only minor errors.

2 Identifies most of the symbols correctly. Attempts to describe or show some steps of the solution strategy, but there might be minor errors. Might attempt to write a number sentence using some of the symbols, but there might be errors.

1 Attempts to identify some symbols. There is little evidence of understanding either the problem context or the application of the rules for order of operations.

0 Does not attempt to solve the problem.

Sample Student Responses

This Level 4 paper illustrates the following features: The correct operations are written above the symbols in the number sentences. The solution strategy described involves figuring out the operations in the first number sentence and then using these operations to work through the remaining number sentences. The number sentence in the second part uses each symbol once, and uses order of operations correctly.

This Level 4 paper illustrates the following features: The correct operations are listed for the symbols. The solution strategy described involves first figuring out the operations in the middle number sentence. The number sentence in the second part uses each symbol at least once, and uses order of operations correctly.

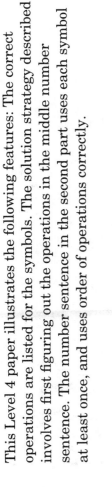

Name _____ Date _____ Time _____

LESSON
7·12
Open Response

Progress
Check 7

Recently, archaeologists were studying cave art near the Klasies River in South Africa. They discovered what looked like number sentences on the wall of a cave. The numbers were written with the same digits as ours, but the symbols that showed the operations were different. Several number sentences are listed below. Use these samples to relate our operations symbols with the symbols from the cave.

$$(78 \ \bullet \ 3 \ \curlyvee \ 18) \ \triangleright \ 2 = 64$$

$$(10 \ \blacklozenge \ 5) \ \bullet \ 3 = 5$$

$$90 \ \blacklozenge \ 6 = 4 \ \oslash \ (24 \ \curlyvee \ 16) \ \oslash \ 3$$

List what operation each Klasies River symbol represents. Show all of your work.

$$\bullet = \div$$
$$\blacklozenge = +$$
$$\triangleright = x$$
$$\curlyvee = -$$
$$\oslash = \bullet$$

you first have to do 78÷3 which
equals 26. 26−18=8 and 8 to the
power of 2 = 64. 2nd #sentence
15
(10 + 5) ÷ 3 = 5
3rd # sentence

90÷6 = 4 x (24−16)x³

Try This
Write a true number sentence using all of the symbols at least once.

$$(6 \ \triangleright 2) \ \oslash \ 2 \ \bullet \ 9 \ \blacklozenge \ 2 \ \curlyvee \ 5 = 5$$

Name _____ Date _____ Time _____

LESSON
7·12
Open Response

Progress
Check 7

Recently, archaeologists were studying cave art near the Klasies River in South Africa. They discovered what looked like number sentences on the wall of a cave. The numbers were written with the same digits as ours, but the symbols that showed the operations were different. Several number sentences are listed below. Use these samples to relate our operations symbols with the symbols from the cave.

$$(78 \ \bullet \ 3 \ \curlyvee \ 18) \ \triangleright \ 2 = 64$$

$$(10 \ \blacklozenge \ 5) \ \bullet \ 3 = 5$$

$$90 \ \blacklozenge \ 6 = 4 \ \oslash \ (24 \ \curlyvee \ 16) \ \oslash \ 3$$

List what operation each Klasies River symbol represents. Explain how you figured out the symbols. Show all of your work.

$$\bullet = \div$$
$$\blacklozenge = +$$
$$\triangleright = x$$
$$\curlyvee = -$$
$$\oslash = \bullet$$

I started to mix up and try different operation with the different symbols, and finally I figured the second one with the variable is the ÷ sign. and the donut as division. Then I tryed the × sign first ome and came up with the half circles and exponent and the V looking thing as subtraction. so that left me with multiplication.

Try This
Write a true number sentence using all of the symbols at least once.

$$(50 \ \oslash \ 10 \ \blacklozenge \ 6) \ \triangleright \ 2 \ \curlyvee \ 100 \ \bullet \ 3 = 1,323$$

This Level 3 paper illustrates the following features: The correct operations are listed above the symbols in the number sentences. The computation shown is correct, but a description of the solution strategy is not provided. The number sentence in the second part uses each symbol at least once and uses the order of operations correctly.

This Level 3 paper illustrates the following features: The correct operations are listed for the symbols. The explanation does not provide information about the solution strategy. The number sentence in the second part uses each symbol at least once, but the order of operations is ignored in finding the answer.

LESSON 7·12 Open Response Progress Check 7

Recently, archaeologists were studying cave art near the Klasies River in South Africa. They discovered what looked like number sentences on the wall of a cave. The numbers were written with the same digits as ours, but the symbols that showed the operations were different. Several number sentences are listed below. Use these samples to relate our operations symbols with the symbols from the cave.

$(78 \div 3 \curlyvee 18) \triangleright 2 = 64$

$(10 \bullet 5) \odot 3 = 5$

$90 \bullet 6 = 4 \oslash (24 \curlyvee 16) \oslash 3$
16

List what operation each Klasies River symbol represents. Explain how you figured out the symbols. Show all of your work.

$(78 \div 3 - 18) = 64$

$\curlyvee \odot -\div$
$\triangleright = -$
$\triangleright = 4$

$(10 \div 5) \odot 3 = 5$

$90 \div 6 = 4 \times (24 \curlyvee 16 \curlyvee \times 3 \oslash = \div \times$
I went $(78 \times 3 - 18) \triangleright 2 = \textcircled{x} = \div \times$
no then I kept trying until I
I got it $\curlyvee$ ish + an d did J

Try This
Write a true number sentence using all of the symbols at least once.

I kept trying.

$30 \div 2 \times 2 + 5 - 6 - 1$
$30 \bullet 2 \oslash 2 \bullet 5 = 6 \triangleright^2 \curlyvee \triangleright$

LESSON 7·12 Open Response Progress Check 7

Recently, archaeologists were studying cave art near the Klasies River in South Africa. They discovered what looked like number sentences on the wall of a cave. The numbers were written with the same digits as ours, but the symbols that showed the operations were different. Several number sentences are listed below. Use these samples to relate our operations symbols with the symbols from the cave.

$(78 \div 3 \curlyvee 18) \triangleright 2 = 64$

$(10 \bullet 5) \odot 3 = 5$

$90 \bullet 6 = 4 \oslash (24 \curlyvee 16) \oslash 3$
8

List what operation each Klasies River symbol represents. Explain how you figured out the symbols. Show all of your work.

$\bullet = \div$
$\triangleright = +$
$\oslash = \times$
$\curlyvee = -$

On all of the problems I read what the problems be and I filled them in. Then I went back to see if there were other ways to fit the solution and I found the solution.

Try This
Write a true number sentence using all of the symbols at least once.

$90 \bullet 8 \curlyvee 10 \oslash 2 \bullet 0 \div 4 = 44$

$90 + 8 = 98 - 10 = 88 \times 2 = 172 \div 4 = 44$

This Level 1 paper illustrates the following features: No number sentence is recorded using the symbols.

LESSON 7·12 | **Open Response**

Progress Check 7

Recently, archaeologists were studying cave art near the Klasies River in South Africa. They discovered what looked like number sentences on the wall of a cave. The numbers were written with the same digits as ours, but the symbols that showed the operations were different. Several number sentences are listed below. Use these samples to relate our operations symbols with the symbols from the cave.

$(78 \; ● \; 3 \; ϒ \; 18) \; ◗ \; 2 = 64$
$(10 \; ● \; 5) \; ● \; 3 = 5 \quad 10 ÷ 5 + 3 = 5$
$90 \; ● \; 6 = 4 \; ∅ \; (24 \; ϒ \; 16) \; ∅ \; 3$

List what operation each Klasies River symbol represents. Explain how you figured out the symbols. Show all of your work.

$(78 ÷ 3 - (8) \; 2^2 = 64$
$(10 + 5) \; ÷ \; 3 = 5$
$90 ÷ 6 = 4 × (24 - 16) × 3$

Try This

Write a true number sentence using all of the symbols at least once.

$64 - 2 + 8 - 3 = 77$
$18 ÷ 3 - 18 + 2 = 65$

This Level 2 paper illustrates the following features: The correct operations are listed for the symbols. The explanation describes beginning with the easier one, but the easier one is not identified. The number sentence in the second part is incorrect.

LESSON 7·12 | **Open Response**

Progress Check 7

Recently, archaeologists were studying cave art near the Klasies River in South Africa. They discovered what looked like number sentences on the wall of a cave. The numbers were written with the same digits as ours, but the symbols that showed the operations were different. Several number sentences are listed below. Use these samples to relate our operations symbols with the symbols from the cave.

$(78 \; ● \; 3 \; ϒ \; 18) \; ◗ \; 2 = 64$
$(10 \; ● \; 5) \; ● \; 3 = 5$
$90 \; ● \; 6 = 4 \; ∅ \; (24 \; ϒ \; 16) \; ∅ \; 3$

List what operation each Klasies River symbol represents. Explain how you figured out the symbols. Show all of your work.

$ϒ ?$
$◗ ?$
$- ?$
$÷ ●$
$× ∅$

$(10 - 5) ÷ 3 = 5$ I figured it out by figuring out the easier ones

$(78 ÷ 3 - 18) \; 8^2 = 64$ first and then I used those symbols to the next

$90 ÷ 6 = 4 × (24 - 16) × 3$ problem and figured out the other symbol then on the third problem I just had to figure out one more

Try This

Write a true number sentence using all of the symbols at least once.

$32 ϒ 2 ∅ 65 ● 2 ◗ ∅ 12$

Unit 8

Assessment Overview

In this unit, students review finding equivalent fractions and further develop their computation skills with fractions and percents. Use the information in this section to develop your assessment plan for Unit 8.

Ongoing Assessment

Opportunities for using and collecting ongoing assessment information are highlighted in Informing Instruction and Recognizing Student Achievement notes. Student products, along with observations and suggested writing prompts, provide a range of useful assessment information.

Informing Instruction
The Informing Instruction notes highlight students' thinking and point out common misconceptions. Informing Instruction in Unit 8: Lessons 8-1, 8-2, 8-3, 8-6, 8-8, and 8-12.

Recognizing Student Achievement
The Recognizing Student Achievement notes highlight specific tasks from which teachers can collect assessment data to monitor and document student progress toward meeting Grade-Level Goals.

Lesson	Content Assessed	Where to Find It
8•1	**Compare fractions using benchmarks.** [Number and Numeration Goal 6]	*TLG*, p. 619
8•2	**Rename fractions to have common denominators and be in simplest form.** [Number and Numeration Goal 5; Operations and Computation Goal 4]	*TLG*, p. 627
8•3	**Estimate sums and differences of mixed numbers using benchmarks.** [Operations and Computation Goals 4 and 6]	*TLG*, p. 633
8•4	**Order fractions using benchmarks.** [Number and Numeration Goal 6]	*TLG*, p. 637
8•5	**Use a number-line model to solve fraction multiplication problems.** [Operations and Computation Goal 5]	*TLG*, p. 643
8•6	**Use an area model to solve fraction multiplication problems.** [Operations and Computation Goal 5]	*TLG*, p. 651
8•7	**Convert fractions to decimals and percents.** [Number and Numeration Goal 5]	*TLG*, p. 657
8•8	**Multiply mixed numbers.** [Operations and Computation Goal 5]	*TLG*, p. 662
8•9	**Convert between fractions, decimals, and percents.** [Number and Numeration Goal 5]	*TLG*, p. 665
8•10	**Use unit fractions and unit percents to solve problems.** [Number and Numeration Goal 2]	*TLG*, p. 670
8•11	**Add fractions.** [Number and Numeration Goal 5; Operations and Computation Goal 4]	*TLG*, p. 678
8•12	**Use a visual model to divide fractions.** [Operations and Computation Goal 5]	*TLG*, p. 683

Math Boxes

Math Boxes, one of several types of tasks highlighted in the Recognizing Student Achievement notes, have an additional useful feature. Math Boxes in most lessons are paired or linked with Math Boxes in one or two other lessons that have similar problems. Paired or linked Math Boxes in Unit 8: 8-1 and 8-3; 8-2 and 8-4; 8-5 and 8-7; 8-6 and 8-8; 8-9 and 8-11; and 8-10 and 8-12.

Writing/Reasoning Prompts

In Unit 8, a variety of writing prompts encourage students to explain their strategies and thinking, to reflect on their learning, and to make connections to other mathematics or life experiences. Here are some of the Unit 8 suggestions:

Lesson	Writing/Reasoning Prompts	Where to Find It
8◆3	Explain one advantage and one disadvantage using number-and-word notation.	*TLG*, p. 634
8◆3	Explain why some parallelograms are squares.	*TLG*, p. 634
8◆5	Write one of the false number sentences. Then write it correctly so it is true and explain your solution.	*TLG*, p. 647
8◆8	Explain how to use the division rule for finding equivalent fractions.	*TLG*, p. 662
8◆9	Explain how to identify perpendicular sides and how to make a set of lines parallel by plotting new ordered pairs.	*TLG*, p. 667
8◆9	Explain how to rename an improper fraction as a mixed number.	*TLG*, p. 668

Portfolio Opportunities

Portfolios are a versatile tool for assessment. They help students reflect on their mathematical growth and help teachers understand and document that growth. Each unit identifies several student products that can be selected and stored in a portfolio. Here are some of the Unit 8 suggestions:

Lesson	Portfolio Opportunities	Where to Find It
8◆2	Students explain how to find the values of variables.	*TLG*, p. 628
8◆3	Students explain why some parallelograms are squares.	*TLG*, p. 634
8◆4	Students use a flowchart to find common denominators before solving fraction addition problems.	*TLG*, p. 640
8◆9	Students solve number stories by calculating the percent discount and the discounted total.	*TLG*, p. 668
8◆11	Students interpret a data display to make a table and a line graph.	*TLG*, p. 679
8◆12	Students use what they know about fractions, fraction multiplication, and their calculators to find reciprocals of numbers.	*TLG*, p. 685
8◆13	Students solve a problem using equivalent fractions and adding fractions.	*TLG*, p. 689

Periodic Assessment

Every Progress Check lesson includes opportunities to observe students' progress and to collect student products in a variety of ways—Self Assessment, Oral and Slate Assessment, Written Assessment, and an Open Response task. For more details, see the first page of Progress Check 8, Lesson 8-13 on page 686, of the *Teacher's Lesson Guide*.

Progress Check Modifications

Written Assessments are one way students demonstrate what they know. The table below shows modifications for the Written Assessment in this unit. Use these to maximize opportunities for students to demonstrate what they know. Modifications can be given individually or written on the board for the class.

Problem(s)	Modifications for Written Assessment
1, 2	For Problems 1 and 2, use a laminated copy of the 100-grid on *Math Masters,* p. 435 and shade the fraction of the hundred grid. Use this to help you figure out the decimal and percent names for the fraction.
7, 8, 10, 11	For Problems 7, 8, 10 and 11, use a number line from *Math Masters* p. 434 to help you solve the problems. You may want to use a colored pencil or highlighter and trace over the tick marks that represent the division of the number line into quarter segments.
24	For Problem 24, record a number sentence(s) to show the steps for how you solved the problem.
25	For Problem 25, convert 75% to a fraction and draw a picture to help you solve the problem.

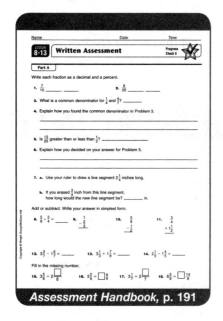

Assessment Handbook, p. 191

The Written Assessment for the Unit 8 Progress Check is on pages 191–192.

Open Response, *Writing Egyptian Fractions*

Description

For this task, students write equivalent expressions for fractions using unit fractions and addition.

Focus

◆ **Use numerical expressions to find and represent equivalent names for fractions.**
[Number and Numeration Goal 5]

◆ **Use mental arithmetic and paper-and-pencil algorithms to solve problems involving the addition of fractions; describe the strategies used and explain how they work.**
[Operations and Computation Goal 4]

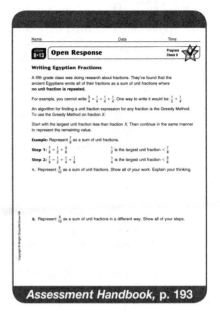

Assessment Handbook, p. 193

Implementation Tips

◆ Remind students that they do not always have to start with the next largest unit fraction that will work. Once they have followed the process through the first time, they will have to look for another combination the second time.

Modifications for Meeting Diverse Needs

◆ Suggest a tree-diagram structure that students can use to organize their work. Have them begin with $\frac{9}{10}$. They can break $\frac{9}{10}$ into $\frac{1}{2}$ and $\frac{4}{10}$. Encourage them to simplify fractions each step of the way. (Simplify $\frac{4}{10}$ to $\frac{2}{5}$.) When they have a unit fraction at the end of any branch, have them circle it so they can keep track of the unit fractions.

◆ Have students describe how they might find multiple ways of writing $\frac{9}{10}$ as a sum of unit fractions. For example, *Each time I will start with a unit fraction that I have not used. Then I know the combination will be different.*

Improving Open Response Skills

After students complete the task, have them analyze several sample written explanations for Problem 1. Consider using some of the explanations included in the Sample Student Responses beginning on page 115 of this book. Record each explanation and the number sentence it describes on a piece of chart paper and give one to each group. Have students determine and record what information is missing from the explanation. Have them work together to write a clearer and more complete explanation.

Note: The wording and formatting of the text on the student samples that follow may vary slightly from the actual task your children will complete. These minor discrepancies will not affect the implementaton of the task.

Rubric

This rubric is designed to help you assess levels of mathematical performance on this task. It emphasizes mathematical understanding with only a mention of clarity of explanation. Consider the expectations of standardized tests in your area when applying a rubric. Modify this sample rubric as appropriate.

4 Records two fraction-addition number sentences that total $\frac{9}{10}$, and uses only unit-fraction addends. Does not repeat a unit fraction within a number sentence. Completely explains or shows how to determine which unit fraction combinations make the target sum of $\frac{9}{10}$.

3 Records at least one fraction-addition number sentence that totals $\frac{9}{10}$, and uses only unit-fraction addends. Does not repeat a unit fraction in the number sentence. Attempts to explain how to determine the fraction combination, but the explanation might need clarification. For Problem 2, shows work related to the problem, but it might be incomplete or have errors.

2 Attempts to record a fraction-addition number sentence that totals $\frac{9}{10}$ using unit-fraction addends, and does not repeat a unit fraction in the number sentence. There might be minor errors. Attempts to explain or show how to determine the fraction combination, but the explanation might be incomplete or have errors.

1 Attempts to record a fraction-addition number sentence that totals $\frac{9}{10}$. Might attempt to explain how to determine the fraction combination, but the explanation might not make sense in the context of the problem.

0 Does not attempt to solve the problem.

Sample Student Responses

This Level 4 paper illustrates the following features: The fraction $\frac{9}{10}$ is represented in 2 different ways using unit fractions. In Problem 1, the explanation describes how to use the Greedy Method. The work shows keeping track of tenths. One half is $\frac{5}{10}$, $\frac{1}{3}$ is $3\frac{1}{3}$ tenths, and $\frac{1}{15}$ is $\frac{2}{3}$ tenths for a total of $\frac{9}{10}$. The second solution is derived in a similar way.

This Level 4 paper illustrates the following features: The fraction $\frac{9}{10}$ is represented in 2 different ways using unit fractions. In Problem 1, the explanation describes starting with $\frac{1}{2}$ (the largest unit fraction) and taking $\frac{1}{10}$ out of the remaining $\frac{4}{10}$. Three tenths is converted to a decimal to make it easier to compare the unit fractions—that is, $\frac{1}{3}$ is larger than $\frac{3}{10}$, but $\frac{1}{4}$ will fit. Decimals are finally converted back into fractions.

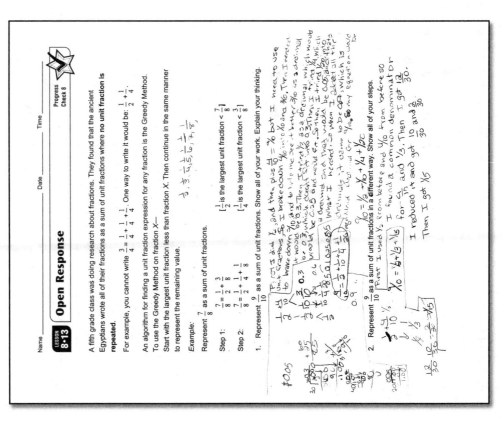

This Level 3 paper illustrates the following features: The fraction $\frac{9}{10}$ is represented in 2 different ways using unit fractions. The first explanation for the first problem describes working with $\frac{4}{10}$ and finding what is left to be subtracted. Some of the steps are missing, but the work and the explanation together support the final sums.

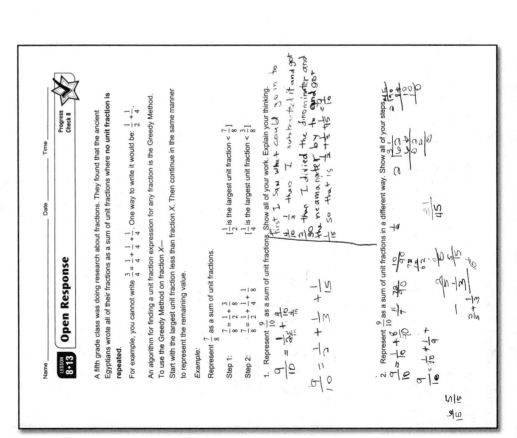

This Level 3 paper illustrates the following features: The fraction $\frac{9}{10}$ is represented in 2 different ways using unit fractions. The first strategy involves trying to use an area fraction model (circles and rectangle), but it is quickly deserted. The explanation describes estimating and using equivalent fractions, but needs some clarification. The explanation does not match the work shown on the page.

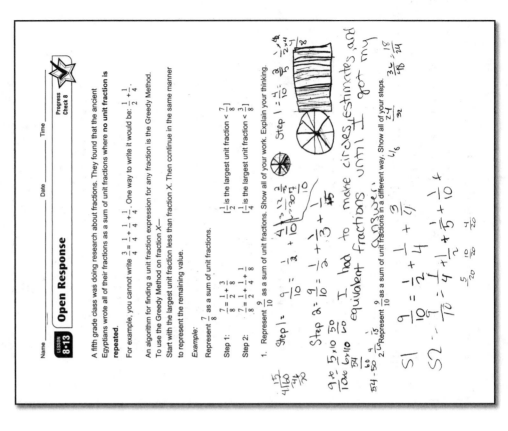

This Level 1 paper illustrates the following features: There is evidence of some understanding that unit fractions have numerators of 1, but there is no evidence of understanding how to use fraction concepts to solve the problem.

This Level 2 paper illustrates the following features: The fraction $\frac{9}{10}$ is represented in 2 different ways using unit fractions. The explanation is missing. The work shown for Problem 1 supports the final number sentence. For Problem 2, the solution repeats tenths.

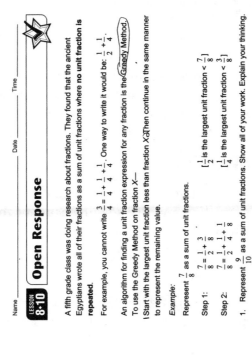

Name _____ Date _____ Time _____

LESSON 8·10 Open Response

A fifth grade class was doing research about fractions. They found that the ancient Egyptians wrote all of their fractions as a sum of unit fractions where **no unit fraction is repeated.**

For example, you cannot write $\frac{3}{4} = \frac{1}{4} + \frac{1}{4} + \frac{1}{4}$. One way to write it would be: $\frac{1}{2} + \frac{1}{4}$.

An algorithm for finding a unit fraction expression for any fraction is the Greedy Method.
To use the Greedy Method on fraction X—
Start with the largest unit fraction less than fraction X. Then continue in the same manner to represent the remaining value.

Example:
Represent $\frac{7}{8}$ as a sum of unit fractions.

Step 1: $\frac{7}{8} = \frac{1}{2} + \frac{3}{8}$ $[\frac{1}{2}$ is the largest unit fraction $< \frac{7}{8}]$
Step 2: $\frac{7}{8} = \frac{1}{2} + \frac{1}{4} + \frac{1}{8}$ $[\frac{1}{4}$ is the largest unit fraction $< \frac{3}{8}]$

1. Represent $\frac{9}{10}$ as a sum of unit fractions. Show all of your work. Explain your thinking.

$\frac{9}{10} = \frac{8}{10} + \frac{1}{10}$
$\frac{9}{10} = \frac{1}{2} + \frac{1}{5} + \frac{1}{5}$
$\frac{9}{10} = \frac{1}{2} + \frac{1}{5} + \frac{1}{5}$

$\frac{5}{10} \quad \frac{2}{10} \quad \frac{2}{10}$

2. Represent $\frac{9}{10}$ as a sum of unit fractions in a different way. Show all of your steps.

$\frac{9}{10} = \frac{5}{10} + \frac{2}{10} + \frac{2}{10}$
$= \frac{1}{2} + \frac{1}{5} + \frac{1}{5}$

Name _____ Date _____ Time _____

LESSON 8·10 Open Response

A fifth grade class was doing research about fractions. They found that the ancient Egyptians wrote all of their fractions as a sum of unit fractions where **no unit fraction is repeated.**

For example, you cannot write $\frac{3}{4} = \frac{1}{4} + \frac{1}{4} + \frac{1}{4}$. One way to write it would be: $\frac{1}{2} + \frac{1}{4}$.

An algorithm for finding a unit fraction expression for any fraction is the Greedy Method.
To use the Greedy Method on fraction X—
Start with the largest unit fraction less than X. Then continue in the same manner to represent the remaining value.

Example:
Represent $\frac{7}{8}$ as a sum of unit fractions.

Step 1: $\frac{7}{8} = \frac{1}{2} + \frac{3}{8}$ $[\frac{1}{2}$ is the largest unit fraction $< \frac{7}{8}]$
Step 2: $\frac{7}{8} = \frac{1}{2} + \frac{1}{4} + \frac{1}{8}$ $[\frac{1}{4}$ is the largest unit fraction $< \frac{3}{8}]$

1. Represent $\frac{9}{10}$ as a sum of unit fractions. Show all of your work. Explain your thinking.

$\frac{9}{10} = \frac{4}{10} = \frac{4}{10} - \frac{1}{4} = \frac{3}{20} - \frac{1}{8} = \frac{1}{40}$
$\frac{1}{4} + \frac{1}{8} + \frac{1}{40} = \frac{1}{7} \cdot \frac{1}{4} \cdot \frac{1}{8} \cdot \frac{1}{40}$
$\frac{1}{2} + \frac{1}{4} + \frac{1}{8} + \frac{1}{40} = \frac{9}{10}$
10

2. Represent $\frac{9}{10}$ as a sum of unit fractions in a different way. Show all of your steps.

$\frac{1}{10} + \frac{1}{10} + \frac{1}{10} + \frac{1}{10} + \frac{1}{10} + \frac{1}{10} + \frac{1}{10} + \frac{1}{10} + \frac{1}{10} = \frac{9}{10}$

Assessment Overview

In this unit, students explore coordinate graphs, extend area concepts, and develop a formula for volume. Use the information in this section to develop your assessment plan for Unit 9.

Ongoing Assessment

Opportunities for using and collecting ongoing assessment information are highlighted in Informing Instruction and Recognizing Student Achievement notes. Student products, along with observations and suggested writing prompts, provide a range of useful assessment information.

Informing Instruction

The Informing Instruction notes highlight students' thinking and point out common misconceptions. Informing Instruction in Unit 9: Lessons 9-4, 9-8, and 9-10.

Recognizing Student Achievement

The Recognizing Student Achievement notes highlight specific tasks from which teachers can collect assessment data to monitor and document student progress toward meeting Grade-Level Goals.

Lesson	Content Assessed	Where to Find It
9◆1	**Translate numbers written in scientific notation to standard notation and number-and-word notation** [Number and Numeration Goal 1]	*TLG*, p. 705
9◆2	**Plot ordered number pairs and identify decimals on a number line.** [Number and Numeration Goal 1; Measurement and Reference Frames Goal 4]	*TLG*, p. 711
9◆3	**Plot points on a coordinate grid.** [Measurement and Reference Frames Goal 4]	*TLG*, p. 718
9◆4	**Calculate area.** [Measurement and Reference Frames Goal 2]	*TLG*, p. 726
9◆5	**Draw line segments and explain that congruent line segments have the same length.** [Geometry Goal 2]	*TLG*, p. 733
9◆6	**Write formulas for finding the area of triangles and parallelograms.** [Measurement and Reference Frames Goal 2]	*TLG*, p. 738
9◆7	**Solve fraction of problems.** [Number and Numeration Goal 2]	*TLG*, p. 742
9◆8	**Find common denominators and write fractions in simplest form.** [Number and Numeration Goal 5]	*TLG*, p. 751
9◆9	**Match polygons with their properties.** [Geometry Goal 2]	*TLG*, p. 757
9◆10	**Distinguish between volume and capacity.** [Measurement and Reference Frames Goal 3]	*TLG*, p. 763

Math Boxes

Math Boxes, one of several types of tasks highlighted in the Recognizing Student Achievement notes, have an additional useful feature. Math Boxes in most lessons are paired or linked with Math Boxes in one or two other lessons that have similar problems. Paired or linked Math Boxes in Unit 9: 9-1 and 9-3; 9-2 and 9-4; 9-5 and 9-7; 9-6 and 9-9; 9-8 and 9-10.

Writing/Reasoning Prompts

In Unit 9, a variety of writing prompts encourage students to explain their strategies and thinking, to reflect on their learning, and to make connections to other mathematics or life experiences. Here are some of the Unit 9 suggestions:

Lesson	Writing/Reasoning Prompts	Where to Find It
9◆1	Explain how you solved the mixed-number multiplication problem. How might you check your answer?	*TLG*, p. 708
9◆2	Explain your solution strategy for completing the table and finding the rule.	*TLG*, p. 713
9◆3	Explain how to find the volume of a rectangular prism by counting unit cubes.	*TLG*, p. 719
9◆5	Explain how to find equivalents for linear metric units.	*TLG*, p. 733
9◆6	Explain the transformation formed by plotting a new set of ordered pairs.	*TLG*, p. 738
9◆7	Write a fraction multiplication number story.	*TLG*, p. 744
9◆9	Draw a preimage and rotate 180°.	*TLG*, p. 757
9◆10	Explain how you found the least common denominator.	*TLG*, p. 764

Portfolio Opportunities

Portfolios are a versatile tool for assessment. They help students reflect on their mathematical growth and help teachers understand and document that growth. Each unit identifies several student products that can be selected and stored in a portfolio. Here are some of the Unit 9 suggestions:

Lesson	Portfolio Opportunities	Where to Find It
9◆2	Students explain their solution strategy for finding the rule and completing a function table.	*TLG*, p. 713
9◆3	Students explain how to find the volume of a rectangular prism by counting unit cubes.	*TLG*, p. 719
9◆6	Students explain what rule they would use to change ordered pairs to transform a figure.	*TLG*, p. 738
9◆7	Students write a fraction multiplication number story.	*TLG*, p. 744
9◆8	Students shade the square in a net that would be on the bottom of a cube to demonstrate their understanding of geometric solids.	*TLG*, p. 752
9◆8	Students record their strategies and solutions for comparing the volume of a stick-on note and a centimeter cube.	*TLG*, p. 752
9◆11	Students solve an area problem.	*TLG*, p. 769

Periodic Assessment

Every Progress Check lesson includes opportunities to observe students' progress and to collect student products in a variety of ways—Self Assessment, Oral and Slate Assessment, Written Assessment, and an Open Response task. For more details, see the first page of Progress Check 9, Lesson 9-11 on page 766, of the *Teacher's Lesson Guide*.

Progress Check Modifications

Written Assessments are one way students demonstrate what they know. The table below shows modifications for the Written Assessment in this unit. Use these to maximize opportunities for students to demonstrate what they know. Modifications can be given individually or written on the board for the class.

Problem(s)	Modifications for Written Assessment
5	For Problem 5, redraw the rectangle on centimeter grid paper. Use the scale 1 centimeter represents 1 foot.
9	For Problem 9, explain how you could use the rectangle method to find the area.
14–17	For Problems 14–17, build the prism with centimeter cubes.
18–21	For Problems 18–21, record the formula you will use for each problem. Then replace the variables with the given dimensions.

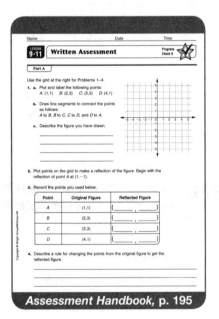

Assessment Handbook, p. 195

The Written Assessment for the Unit 9 Progress Check is on pages 195–197.

Open Response, *Countertop Tiles*

Description

For this task, students solve an area problem involving covering a countertop with tiles of a specified size.

Focus

◆ **Factor numbers.**
[Number and Numeration Goal 3]

◆ **Describe and use strategies and formulas to calculate the areas of rectangles.**
[Measurement and Reference Frames Goal 2]

Implementation Tips

◆ Review how you would find the area of a desktop using Everything Math Deck cards.

Assessment Handbook, p. 198

Modifications for Meeting Diverse Needs

◆ Provide chart paper and construction paper cut into 3" × 6" rectangles so that students can model the problem. Have them draw the larger rectangles, and experiment with placing the smaller rectangles inside the larger rectangles to cover the surface completely.

◆ Have students find tiles with dimensions that would work for both countertops, and explain how to determine quickly if any tile will fit; for example, will a 1.5" × 3" tile work for both countertops?

Improving Open Response Skills

After students complete the task, have them reflect on and write about what was easy and what was difficult about the task and what they think they could improve. When they have finished, have them share their reflections in small groups. After the discussion, return their papers and have them attempt to improve their work.

Note: The wording and formatting of the text on the student samples that follow may vary slightly from the actual task your children will complete. These minor discrepancies will not affect the implementaton of the task.

Rubric

This rubric is designed to help you assess levels of mathematical performance on this task. It emphasizes mathematical understanding with only a mention of clarity of explanation. Consider the expectations of standardized tests in your area when applying a rubric. Modify this sample rubric as appropriate.

4   Illustrates both countertops and includes countertop and tile dimensions. For Problem 1, clearly explains how the tiles will fit. For Problem 2, determines that the tiles will not fit and provides a rationale based on countertop and tile dimensions. Clearly states a rule explaining that when the countertop dimensions are multiples of the tile dimensions, the tiles cover the countertop.

3   Illustrates both countertops and labels or indicates the tiles in the countertop. Determines that for Problem 1, the tiles will fit, and for Problem 2, that they will not fit. Explains a rationale, but the explanation might not relate to countertop and tile dimensions. States a rule related to the problems and to divisibility or multiples, but the rule might need clarification.

2   Illustrates at least one countertop and labels or indicates tiles in the countertop. Determines that for Problem 1, the tiles will fit, and for Problem 2, that they will not fit. Attempts to explain or show reasoning for both problems, but the explanations might require clarification or be incomplete. Attempts to state a rule, but it might not relate to the problems or it might be incorrect.

1   Attempts to illustrate at least one countertop with some representation of tiles. Attempts to determine if tiles will fit. The explanation might demonstrate little understanding of the problem. Might attempt to write a rule but it might not relate to the context of the problem.

0   Does not attempt to solve the problem.

Sample Student Responses

This Level 4 paper illustrates the following features: The drawing in Problem 1 shows 3-inch increments on the 15-inch by 18-inch countertop. The tile dimensions are multiplied by the number of tiles which shows the tiles fit. The drawing in Problem 2 shows 4 tiles fitting into the countertop with a fraction of a tile missing. The rule clearly states that one dimension of the countertop must be divisible by 3 and the other by 6.

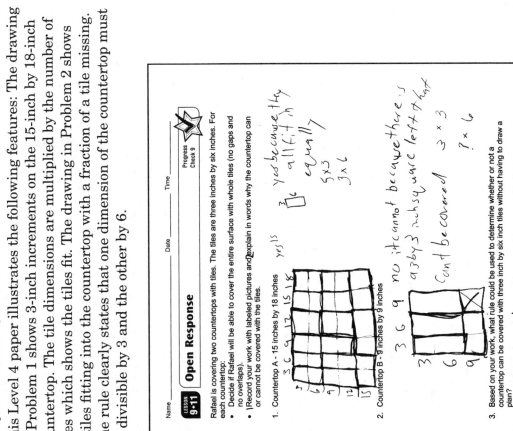

This Level 4 paper illustrates the following features: Problem 1 shows the total area of the 15-inch by 18-inch countertop. The total area is divided by the area of a tile. There is no remainder, so it is concluded that the tiles fit. In Problem 2, the quotient has a remainder, so it is concluded that the tiles will not fit. The rule states that you have to divide the total area by the area of the tiles.

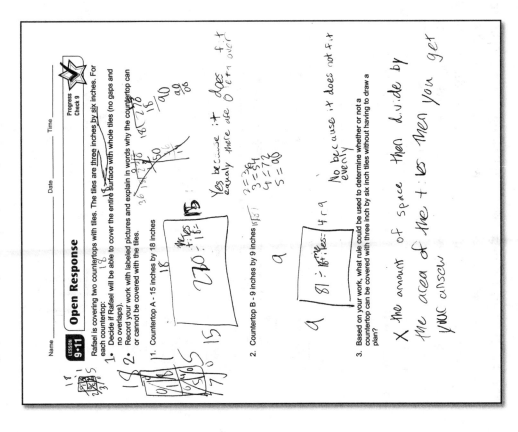

This Level 3 paper illustrates the following features: The drawing in Problem 1, shows how the tiles fit in the 15-inch by 18-inch countertop. It is concluded the tiles fit because the countertop dimensions are multiples of the tile dimensions. Problem 2 appears to show that the tiles will not fit evenly because 6 cannot go into 9. The rule seems to suggest an understanding of dividing the dimensions of the tile into the countertop.

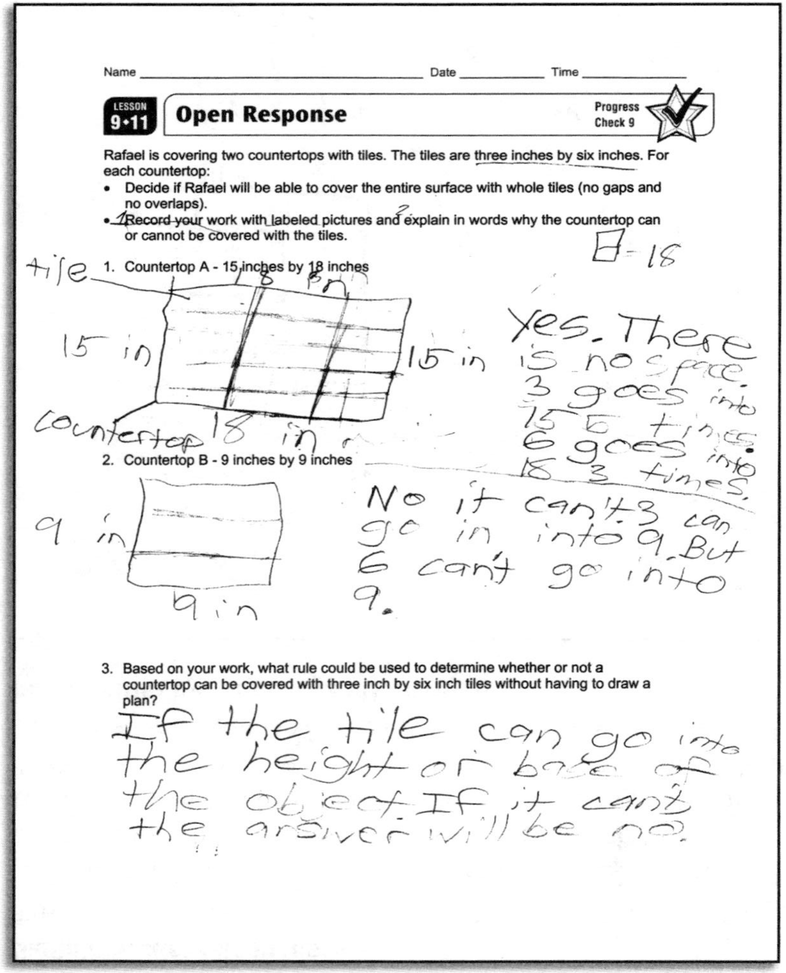

Name ______ Date ______ Time ______

LESSON 9•11 **Open Response** Progress Check 9

Rafael is covering two countertops with tiles. The tiles are three inches by six inches. For each countertop:

- Decide if Rafael will be able to cover the entire surface with whole tiles (no gaps and no overlaps).
- Record your work with labeled pictures and explain in words why the countertop can or cannot be covered with the tiles.

1. Countertop A - 15 inches by 18 inches

tile 15 in 15 in countertop 18 in

Yes. There is no space. 3 goes into 15 5 times. 6 goes into 18 3 times.

2. Countertop B - 9 inches by 9 inches

9 in 9 in

No it can't 3 can go in into 9. But 6 can't go into 9.

3. Based on your work, what rule could be used to determine whether or not a countertop can be covered with three inch by six inch tiles without having to draw a plan?

If the tile can go into the height or base of the object. If it can't the answer will be no.

This Level 3 paper illustrates the following features: The drawing in Problem 1 is clearly labeled to show how the tiles fit. The explanation describes that the tiles fit because the countertop dimensions are multiples of the tile dimensions. The drawing for Problem 2 has no labels, but the explanation suggests that 6 cannot go into 9 "evenly." The rule suggests an understanding of the use of multiples in this context, but it requires clarification.

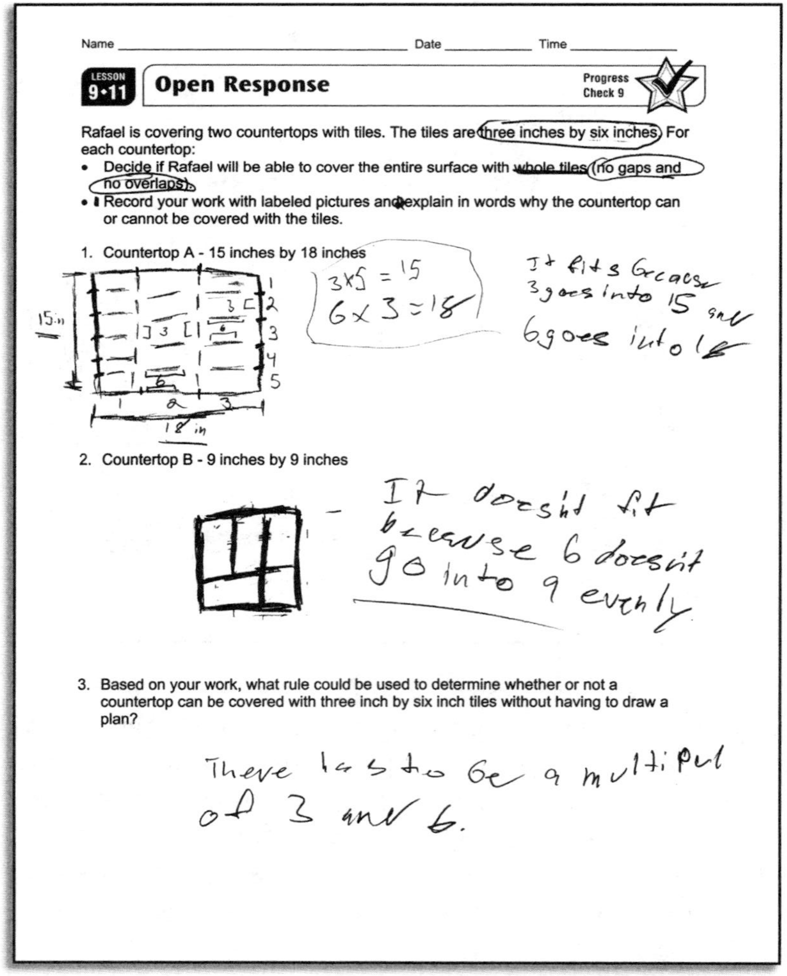

Name ______ Date ______ Time ______

LESSON 9•11 **Open Response** Progress Check 9

Rafael is covering two countertops with tiles. The tiles are three inches by six inches. For each countertop:

- Decide if Rafael will be able to cover the entire surface with whole tiles (no gaps and no overlaps).
- Record your work with labeled pictures and explain in words why the countertop can or cannot be covered with the tiles.

1. Countertop A - 15 inches by 18 inches

15 in 18 in

3x5 = 15
6x3 = 18

It fits because 3 goes into 15 and 6 goes into 18

2. Countertop B - 9 inches by 9 inches

It doesn't fit because 6 doesn't go into 9 evenly

3. Based on your work, what rule could be used to determine whether or not a countertop can be covered with three inch by six inch tiles without having to draw a plan?

There has to be a multipul of 3 and 6.

This Level 1 paper illustrates the following features: The drawings are not labeled, but they appear to make sense for both problems. There is an attempt to use the total area to solve the problems, but there is no evidence of understanding the specifics of the problems.

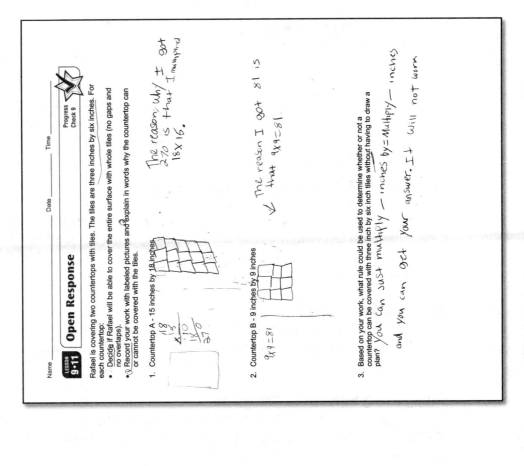

This Level 2 paper illustrates the following features: The drawing in Problem 1 shows how the tiles fit in the 15-inch by 18-inch countertop. It seems to be suggested that the tiles fit because the countertop dimensions are multiples of the tile dimensions. The explanation for Problem 2 describes that a tile has to be broken because 3 and 6 both do not go into 9. The rule makes sense in the context of the problem but requires clarification.

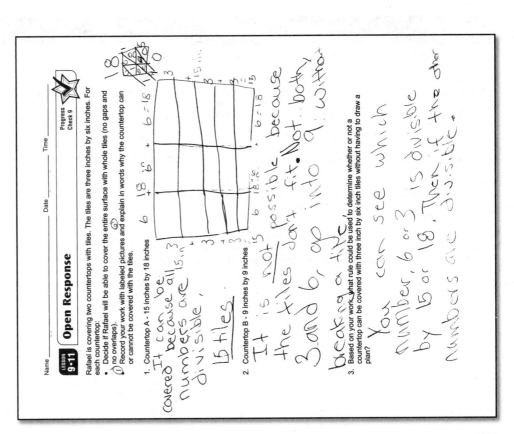

Assessment Overview

In this unit, students solve equations using a pan-balance metaphor and explore representing relationships as algebraic expressions containing variables. Use the information in this section to develop your assessment plan for Unit 10.

Ongoing Assessment

Opportunities for using and collecting ongoing assessment information are highlighted in Informing Instruction and Recognizing Student Achievement notes. Student products, along with observations and suggested writing prompts, provide a range of useful assessment information.

Informing Instruction

The Informing Instruction notes highlight students' thinking and point out common misconceptions. Informing Instruction in Unit 10: Lessons 10-1, 10-6, 10-7, and 10-9.

Recognizing Student Achievement

The Recognizing Student Achievement notes highlight specific tasks from which teachers can collect assessment data to monitor and document student progress toward meeting Grade-Level Goals.

Lesson	Content Assessed	Where to Find It
10•1	**Apply a formula to find the volume of a rectangular prism.** [Measurement and Reference Frames Goal 2]	*TLG*, p. 788
10•2	**Solve equations using a pan-balance model.** [Patterns, Functions, and Algebra Goal 2]	*TLG*, p. 792
10•3	**Write algebraic expressions that model situations.** [Patterns, Functions, and Algebra Goal 2]	*TLG*, p. 800
10•4	**Use table data to plot points on a graph.** [Data and Chance Goal 1]	*TLG*, p. 806
10•5	**Solve addition and subtraction open sentences containing negative and positive numbers.** [Patterns, Functions, and Algebra Goal 2]	*TLG*, p. 812
10•6	**Read and interpret graphs.** [Data and Chance Goal 2]	*TLG*, p. 818
10•7	**Interpret line graphs.** [Data and Chance Goal 2]	*TLG*, p. 821
10•8	**Describe area and perimeter.** [Measurement and Reference Frames Goal 2]	*TLG*, p. 826
10•9	**Replace variables in number sentences and solve problems.** [Patterns, Functions, and Algebra Goal 2]	*TLG*, p. 835

Math Boxes

Math Boxes, one of several types of tasks highlighted in the Recognizing Student Achievement notes, have an additional useful feature. Math Boxes in most lessons are paired or linked with Math Boxes in one or two other lessons that have similar problems. Paired or linked Math Boxes in Unit 10: 10-1 and 10-3; 10-2 and 10-4; 10-5, 10-7, and 10-9; and 10-6 and 10-8.

Writing/Reasoning Prompts

In Unit 10, a variety of writing prompts encourage students to explain their strategies and thinking, to reflect on their learning, and to make connections to other mathematics or life experiences. Here are some of the Unit 10 suggestions:

Lesson	Writing/Reasoning Prompts	Where to Find It
10◆1	Explain how you would use a number line to solve $-7 + (-3) =$ ____.	*TLG*, p. 788
10◆2	Explain how you compared the areas of the rectangle and the triangle.	*TLG*, p. 795
10◆3	Explain how to find the volume of a rectangular prism when given the base and the height.	*TLG*, p. 801
10◆4	Explain how to determine whether 3,735 is divisible by 9, without actually dividing.	*TLG*, p. 807
10◆6	Explain your strategies and reasoning for subtraction with decimals.	*TLG*, p. 818A
10◆9	Exchange the exponent and base for each of the numbers, write the standard notation, and explain which number is larger than the original number and why.	*TLG*, p. 835

Portfolio Opportunities

Portfolios are a versatile tool for assessment. They help students reflect on their mathematical growth and help teachers understand and document that growth. Each unit identifies several student products that can be selected and stored in a portfolio. Here are some of the Unit 10 suggestions:

Lesson	Portfolio Opportunities	Where to Find It
10◆3	Students explain how to find the volume of a rectangular prism when given the base.	*TLG*, p. 801
10◆5	Students complete and graph "What's My Rule?" tables.	*TLG*, p. 812
10◆6	Students identify the relationship between parts of a table and parts of a graph.	*TLG*, p. 818B
10◆7	Students discuss and then write a description of the object or event for silhouettes.	*TLG*, p. 824
10◆7	Students construct tables from graph data and then write the rule for each table and graph.	*TLG*, p. 824
10◆8	Students share their mystery graphs and the situations they portray.	*TLG*, p. 826
10◆10	Students solve an algebra problem.	*TLG*, p. 840

Periodic Assessment

Every Progress Check lesson includes opportunities to observe students' progress and to collect student products in a variety of ways—Self Assessment, Oral and Slate Assessment, Written Assessment, and an Open Response task. For more details, see the first page of Progress Check 10, Lesson 10-10 on page 837, of the *Teacher's Lesson Guide*.

Progress Check Modifications

Written Assessments are one way students demonstrate what they know. The table below shows modifications for the Written Assessment in this unit. Use these to maximize opportunities for students to demonstrate what they know. Modifications can be given individually or written on the board for the class.

Problem(s)	Modifications for Written Assessment
1, 2	For Problems 1 and 2, record sample values in a What's My Rule? table to help you determine the correct expression. For example, enter $3, $4, and $5 in the table for Marge and figure out what Tom would have in each case.
4–6	For Problems 4–6, draw a picture for each step as you solve the problems.
7	For Problem 7, use counters to help you solve the problem.
8	For Problem 8, explain how data landmarks helped you figure out which line plot matched the data set for How Many Books You Read Last Summer.

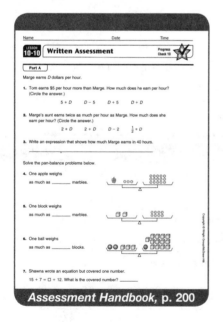

Assessment Handbook, p. 200

The Written Assessment for the Unit 10 Progress Check is on pages 200–203.

Open Response, *An Age Puzzle*

⏱ 30-40 Min.

Description

For this task, students solve an algebra problem involving relationships between numbers and write an algebraic expression representing this relationship.

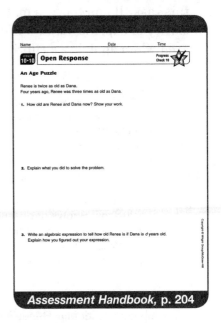

Assessment Handbook, p. 204

Focus

◆ **Use algebraic expressions to write rules involving the four basic arithmetic operations.**
   [Patterns, Functions, and Algebra Goal 1]

◆ **Write and solve algebraic expressions.**
   [Patterns, Functions, and Algebra Goal 2]

Implementation Tips

◆ Review writing algebraic expressions in the *Student Reference Book*.

◆ Review the meaning of *twice as old* and *three times as old*.

Modifications for Meeting Diverse Needs

◆ Have students draw two tables. The first table should show Renee's age in one column and Dana's age in the other column if Renee is *twice as old* as Dana. The second table should show Renee's age in one column and Dana's age in the other column if Renee is *three times as old* as Dana. Students compare the table entries until they find a pair of numbers that differs on both sides by 4 years.

◆ Have students use variables to record both number models they can use to check their answers; for example, $2 * D = R$ and $(D - 4) * 3 = R - 4$. Then have students prove their answers are correct.

Improving Open Response Skills

After students complete the task, have them organize their answers into two columns on a separate sheet of paper—What to do for each step, and Why each step is necessary. A possible entry for the What column is *I made a list of pairs of numbers that have a double relationship*. The corresponding entry for the Why column is *because I know that Renee's age is double Dana's age*. Have them attach this organization to their original task. Remind students that when they explain their answers, the explanation should include both of these parts—What and Why.

Note: The wording and formatting of the text on the student samples that follow may vary slightly from the actual task your children will complete. These minor discrepancies will not affect the implementaton of the task.

Rubric

This rubric is designed to help you assess levels of mathematical performance on this task. It emphasizes mathematical understanding with only a mention of clarity of explanation. Consider the expectations of standardized tests in your area when applying a rubric. Modify this sample rubric as appropriate.

4 — Identifies Renee's and Dana's ages. Might show work that supports the conclusions. Clearly shows or describes steps for solving the problem that demonstrate an understanding of both the "twice as" and "three times as" relationships. Writes and explains the expression that represents Renee's age in terms of Dana's age.

3 — Identifies Renee's and Dana's ages. Might show work that is related to the conclusions. Shows or describes some steps for solving the problem that demonstrate an understanding of both the "twice as" and "three times as" relationships. Writes an expression that represents some relationship between Renee's and Dana's ages.

2 — Attempts to identify Renee's and Dana's ages. Attempts to use relationships between Renee's and Dana's ages to solve the problem but there might be errors. Might describe some steps for solving the problem. Attempts to write an expression.

1 — Attempts to identify Renee's and Dana's ages. Might attempt to describe some steps for solving the problem, but there is no evidence of using the relationships between Renee's and Dana's ages.

0 — Does not attempt to solve the problem.

Sample Student Responses

This Level 4 paper illustrates the following features: Renee's and Dana's ages are determined. The work illustrates a strategy that begins with identifying pairs of numbers with one number that is double the other. The next step is to find 4 less than both numbers in each pair. Finally, the resulting pair is checked to see if one number is triple the other. The algebraic expression is correct and correctly described.

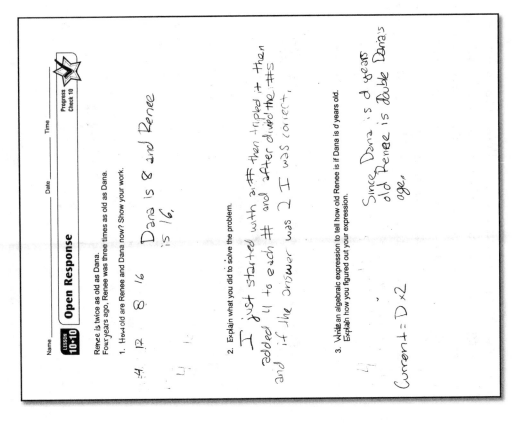

This Level 4 paper illustrates the following features: Renee's and Dana's ages are determined. Although no real work is shown in the solution for Problem 1, the explanation clearly describes a trial-and-error strategy of tripling numbers and adding 4 until a pair of numbers with a half-double relationship is found. The algebraic expression is correct and correctly described.

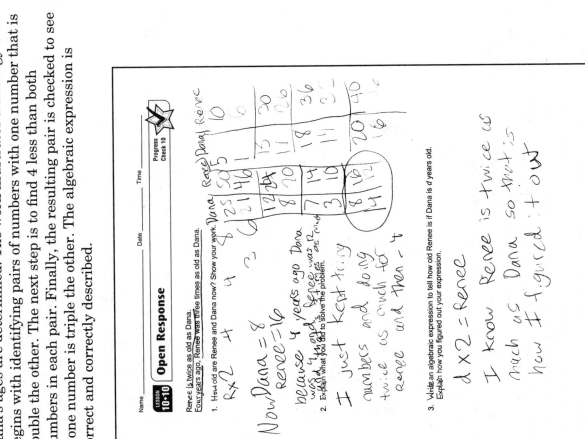

This Level 3 paper illustrates the following features: Renee's and Dana's ages are determined. The explanation describes trying numbers and adding 4 years to them. The only pair tried in the explanation is 12 and 4. The explanation states that this works because when you add 4, the resulting pair of numbers (16 and 8) includes one that is double the other. The algebraic expression is correct and correctly described.

This Level 3 paper illustrates the following features: Renee's and Dana's ages are determined. The work illustrates a strategy that begins with identifying pairs of numbers with one number that is double the other. The explanation describes beginning with even numbers and finding half of each number. There is a reference to using a "4 years ago rule" but this is not explained. The algebraic expression is correct and correctly described.

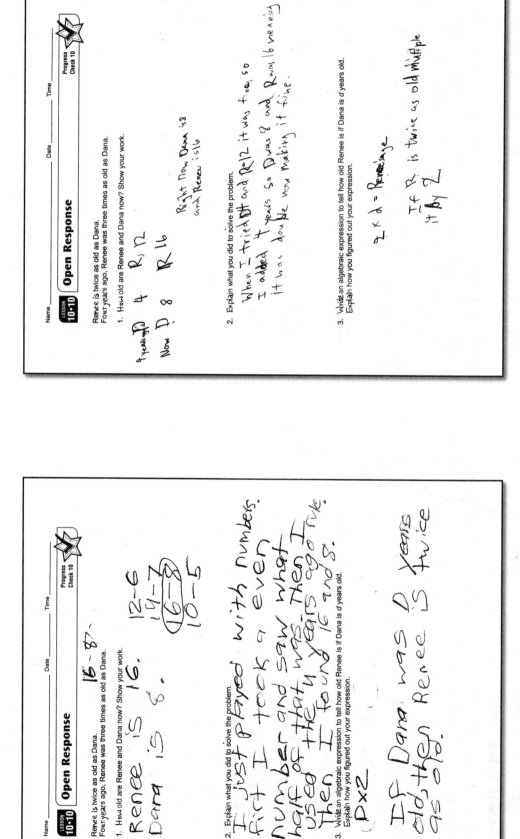

This Level 2 paper illustrates the following features: Renee's and Dana's ages are determined and use correct algebraic expression. There is no work shown and the explanation in Problem 2 only describes playing around with numbers. There is no description of a strategy. The algebraic expressions correctly describe the relationship between Renee's and Dana's ages.

This Level 1 paper illustrates the following features: Renee's and Dana's ages are determined. The explanation does not relate to the work that is shown in Problem 1, and it makes no sense in the context of the problem. The algebraic expression uses numbers related to the problem but does not correctly represent Renee's age.

Name _____ Date _____ Time _____

LESSON 10·10 Open Response   Progress Check 10

Renee is twice as old as Dana.
Four years ago, Renee was three times as old as Dana.

1. How old are Renee and Dana now? Show your work.

16
Renee is d×2 years old = 16
Four years ago, Renee is d×3 years old = 12

2. Explain what you did to solve the problem.

I played around with the numbers

3. Write an algebraic expression to tell how old Renee is if Dana is d years old. Explain how you figured out your expression.

Renee is d×2 years old
four years ago Renee was d×3 years old.
because if Renee is twice as old, then it is told.

Assessment Overview

In this unit, students review properties of 3-dimensional shapes and explore volume formulas for prisms, pyramids, cylinders, and cones. Use the information in this section to develop your assessment plan for Unit 11.

Ongoing Assessment

Opportunities for using and collecting ongoing assessment information are highlighted in Informing Instruction and Recognizing Student Achievement notes. Student products, along with observations and suggested writing prompts, provide a range of useful assessment information.

Informing Instruction

The Informing Instruction notes highlight students' thinking and point out common misconceptions. Informing Instruction in Unit 11: Lessons 11-1, 11-2, and 11-7.

Recognizing Student Achievement

The Recognizing Student Achievement notes highlight specific tasks from which teachers can collect assessment data to monitor and document student progress toward meeting Grade-Level Goals.

Lesson	Content Assessed	Where to Find It
11♦1	Identify the properties of geometric solids. [Geometry Goal 2]	*TLG*, p. 858
11♦2	Compare prisms, pyramids, cylinders, and cones. [Geometry Goal 2]	*TLG*, p. 863
11♦3	Explain what is similar and what is different between finding the volume of cylinders and finding the volume of prisms. [Measurement and Reference Frames Goal 2]	*TLG*, p. 869
11♦4	Calculate a fraction of a whole. [Number and Numeration Goal 2]	*TLG*, p. 876
11♦5	Compare fractions. [Number and Numeration Goal 6]	*TLG*, p. 879
11♦6	Write number sentences using the order of operations. [Number and Numeration Goal 4; Patterns, Functions, and Algebra Goal 3]	*TLG*, p. 887
11♦7	Measure to the nearest $\frac{1}{4}$ inch and centimeter and find the area of circles, triangles, and rectangles. [Measurement and Reference Frames Goals 1 and 2]	*TLG*, p. 893

Math Boxes

Math Boxes, one of several types of tasks highlighted in the Recognizing Student Achievement notes, have an additional useful feature. Math Boxes in most lessons are paired or linked with Math Boxes in one or two other lessons that have similar problems. Paired or linked Math Boxes in Unit 11: 11-1 and 11-3; 11-2, 11-4 and 11-6; and 11-5 and 11-7.

Writing/Reasoning Prompts

In Unit 11, a variety of writing prompts encourage students to explain their strategies and thinking, to reflect on their learning, and to make connections to other mathematics or life experiences. Here are some of the Unit 11 suggestions:

Lesson	Writing/Reasoning Prompts	Where to Find It
11♦2	Explain how to use a factor tree to find the prime factorization for a number.	*TLG*, p. 864
11♦5	Explain how you found the simplest form of $\frac{29}{3}$.	*TLG*, p. 882
11♦6	Explain how you found the value for the width of the base of the rectangular prism.	*TLG*, p. 888

Portfolio Opportunities

Portfolios are a versatile tool for assessment. They help students reflect on their mathematical growth and help teachers understand and document that growth. Each unit identifies several student products that can be selected and stored in a portfolio. Here are some of the Unit 11 suggestions:

Lesson	Portfolio Opportunities	Where to Find It
11♦3	Students explain what is similar and what is different about finding the volume of cylinders and prisms.	*TLG*, p. 869
11♦5	Students explain how they found the simplest form of $\frac{29}{3}$.	*TLG*, p. 882
11♦5	Students solve a thought experiment about a boat and a stone, discuss their solution strategies, and make a model of the problem.	*TLG*, p. 883
11♦8	Students solve a volume problem.	*TLG*, p. 898

Periodic Assessment

Every Progress Check lesson includes opportunities to observe students' progress and to collect student products in a variety of ways—Self Assessment, Oral and Slate Assessment, Written Assessment, and an Open Response task. For more details, see the first page of Progress Check 11, Lesson 11-8 on page 895, of the *Teacher's Lesson Guide*.

Progress Check Modifications

Written Assessments are one way students demonstrate what they know. The table below shows modifications for the Written Assessment in this unit. Use these to maximize opportunities for students to demonstrate what they know. Modifications can be given individually or written on the board for the class.

Problem(s)	Modifications for Written Assessment
1–4	For Problems 1–4, use models of a pyramid, cone, rectangular prism, and cylinder to help you solve the riddles.
7–10	For Problems 7–10, use the glossary in *Student Reference Book* as a reference to identify the radius, diameter, and circumference of the circle.
11	For Problem 11, Javier said the volume of the cylinder is 10 in^2. Explain what mistake Javier might have made and how he could correct his mistake.
12–15	For Problems 12–15, build the prism with centimeter cubes.

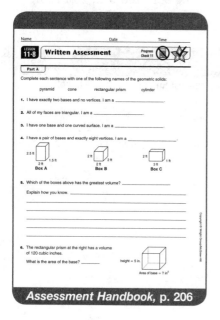

The Written Assessment for the Unit 11 Progress Check is on pages 206–208.

Open Response, *A Treasure Hunt*

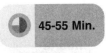

45-55 Min.

Description

For this task, students solve a volume problem where the volume changes as one dimension changes.

Focus

◆ **Use mental arithmetic and paper-and-pencil algorithms to solve problems involving multiplication.**
[Operations and Computation Goal 3]

◆ **Use appropriate formulas to calculate the volume of a prism.**
[Measurement and Reference Frames Goal 2]

◆ **Solve open number sentences.**
[Patterns, Functions, and Algebra Goal 2]

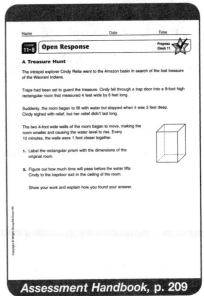

Assessment Handbook, p. 209

Implementation Tips

◆ Review formulas for finding the area of a rectangle and the volume of a rectangular prism.

◆ Have students describe the problem situation in their own words before beginning the problem.

Modifications for Meeting Diverse Needs

◆ Set up a table like the following to help students organize their work:

Time	Length of Room	Width of Room	Height of Water	Volume of Water
0 min	6 ft	4 ft	3 ft	72 ft³
10 min		4 ft		72 ft³

Discuss and record the volume formula. Draw and label pictures for each 10-minute interval. Have students record the height of the water for which they must determine the time. *(Sample answer: 9 feet)*

◆ Have students figure out a way to solve the problem that does not involve calculating the total for every 10-minute increment. For example, *I know that the final height of the water is 9 feet, that the 4-foot length stays the same, and that the final volume is 72 cubic feet. I can set up a number sentence (9 * 4 * width of remaining wall = 72) and solve for the missing dimension.*

Improving Open Response Skills

After students complete the task, have them translate Level 4 of the rubric into their own words. Record the information on chart paper, and display it. Have students discuss in their groups what the statements in the rubric mean. After the discussion, have students take their own papers and try to improve or enhance their work according to the rubric.

Rubric

This rubric is designed to help you assess levels of mathematical performance on this task. It emphasizes mathematical understanding with only a mention of clarity of explanation. Consider the expectations of standardized tests in your area when applying a rubric. Modify this sample rubric as appropriate.

4 Determines how long it takes for the water to reach the ceiling. Labels the drawing with the dimensions including units. Shows all work. Clearly and completely explains the steps for solving the problem. Explains how to find the original volume and describes how to use that information with the changing dimensions of the room. Notation is used correctly.

3 Determines how long it takes for the water to reach the ceiling. Labels the drawing with the dimensions, and might include units. Shows some work. Explains or shows some steps for solving the problem, including a reference to finding the volume. Might have minor errors in notation.

2 Attempts to determine how long it takes for the water to reach the ceiling. Labels parts of the drawing. Shows some work related to the problem. Explains some steps involving volume, but it might be incorrect. Might not connect the explanation or the answer to the work shown. Might have errors in notation.

1 Attempts to solve the problem using time or volume, but there might be errors. Shows work that might make no sense in the context of the problem.

0 Does not attempt to solve the problem.

Sample Student Responses

This Level 4 paper illustrates the following features: The dimensions of the room are labeled. The explanation describes finding the volume of water and dividing the volume by each set of dimensions as the room size decreases. The work shown is systematic and neatly organized. There is a number reversal in the step for 30 minutes. The final answer is 40 minutes.

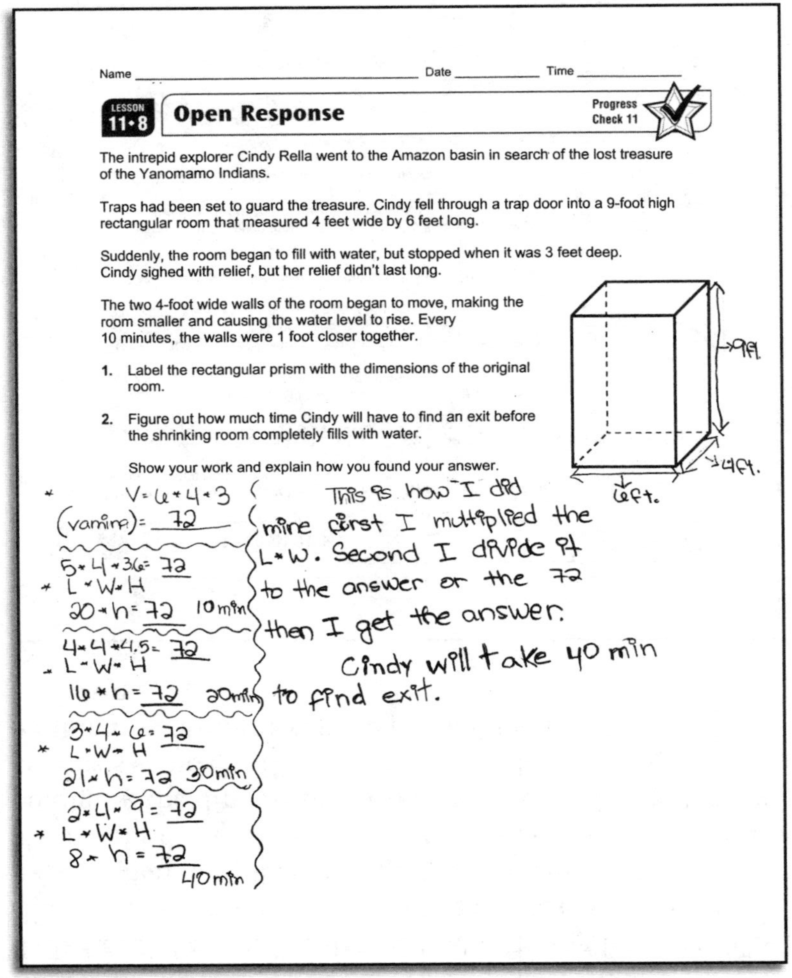

Name ______ Date ______ Time ______

LESSON 11•8 **Open Response** Progress Check 11

The intrepid explorer Cindy Rella went to the Amazon basin in search of the lost treasure of the Yanomamo Indians.

Traps had been set to guard the treasure. Cindy fell through a trap door into a 9-foot high rectangular room that measured 4 feet wide by 6 feet long.

Suddenly, the room began to fill with water, but stopped when it was 3 feet deep. Cindy sighed with relief, but her relief didn't last long.

The two 4-foot wide walls of the room began to move, making the room smaller and causing the water level to rise. Every 10 minutes, the walls were 1 foot closer together.

1. Label the rectangular prism with the dimensions of the original room.
2. Figure out how much time Cindy will have to find an exit before the shrinking room completely fills with water.

Show your work and explain how you found your answer.

9ft.
4ft.
6ft.
V= 6*4*3
(vamine)= 72
5*4*3.6= 72
L*W*H
20*h= 72 10min
4*4*4.5= 72
L*W*H
16*h= 72 20min
3*4*6= 72
L*W*H
21*h= 72 30min
2*4*9= 72
L*W*H
8*h= 72
40min
This is how I did mine first I multiplied the L*W. Second I divide it to the answer or the 72 then I get the answer.
Cindy will take 40 min to find exit.

This Level 4 paper illustrates the following features: The dimensions of the room are labeled on the drawing. The explanation describes finding the original volume of the water in the room and then working with the changing dimensions for each 10-minute interval. The work shown is neatly organized, and clearly justifies the final answer of 40 minutes.

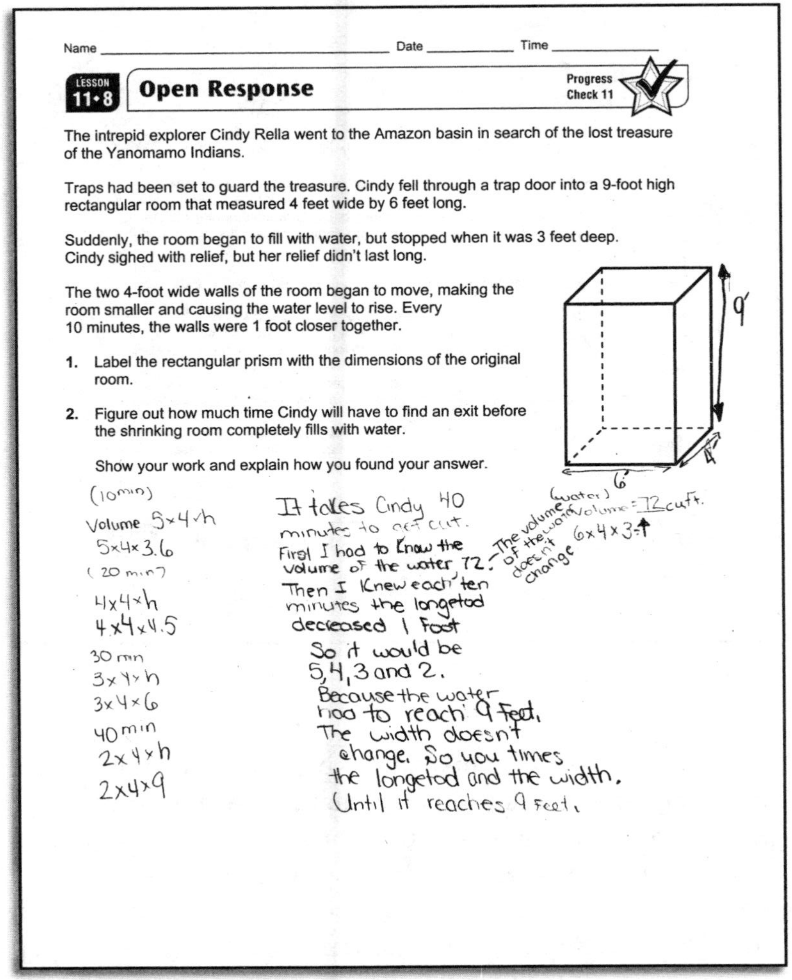

Name ______ Date ______ Time ______

LESSON 11•8 **Open Response** Progress Check 11

The intrepid explorer Cindy Rella went to the Amazon basin in search of the lost treasure of the Yanomamo Indians.

Traps had been set to guard the treasure. Cindy fell through a trap door into a 9-foot high rectangular room that measured 4 feet wide by 6 feet long.

Suddenly, the room began to fill with water, but stopped when it was 3 feet deep. Cindy sighed with relief, but her relief didn't last long.

The two 4-foot wide walls of the room began to move, making the room smaller and causing the water level to rise. Every 10 minutes, the walls were 1 foot closer together.

1. Label the rectangular prism with the dimensions of the original room.
2. Figure out how much time Cindy will have to find an exit before the shrinking room completely fills with water.

Show your work and explain how you found your answer.

9'
4
6'
(water) volume = 72 cu ft.
6x4x3=↑
The volume of the water doesn't change
(10min)
Volume 5x4xh
5x4x3.6
(20 min)
4x4xh
4x4x4.5
30 min
3x4xh
3x4x6
40 min
2x4xh
2x4x9
It takes Cindy 40 minutes to get out.
First I had to know the volume of the water 72.
Then I knew each ten minutes the longetod decreased 1 foot
So it would be 5,4,3 and 2.
Because the water had to reach 9 feet.
The width doesn't change. So you times the longetod and the width.
Until it reaches 9 feet.

This Level 3 paper illustrates the following features: The dimensions of the room are labeled on the drawing. The starting point is shown but not clearly stated. Subsequent steps are shown. The explanation describes the computation but does not explain exactly what is happening in the problem. The final answer is 40 minutes, and the work shown justifies this conclusion.

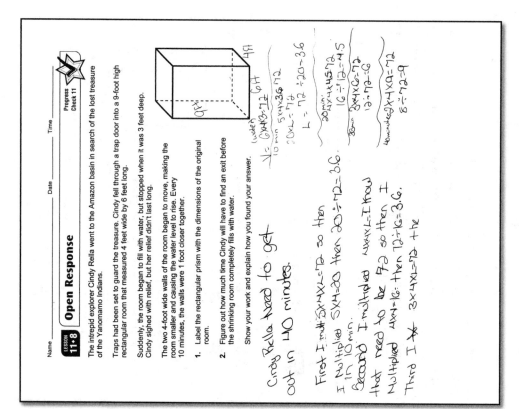

This Level 3 paper illustrates the following features: The dimensions of the room are labeled on the drawing. The explanation describes multiplying the dimensions of the room by the height of the water to find the volume and then describes changing the dimensions "over and over." The explanation requires some clarification. Some work that supports the explanation and the conclusion of 40 minutes is shown.

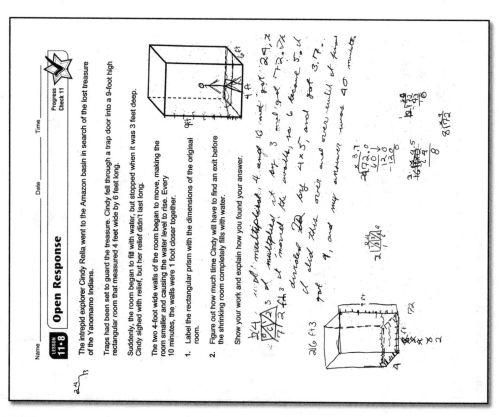

This Level 1 paper illustrates the following features: The dimensions of the room are labeled, but there is other extraneous information that make the labels difficult to read. The explanation demonstrates an understanding that the walls are moving, but the steps described are not correct. The final answer of 40 minutes has nothing to do with the volume of water in the room but is related to the moving walls—10 minutes by 4 feet is 40 minutes.

This Level 2 paper illustrates the following features: The dimensions of the room are labeled imprecisely. The explanation and work describe arriving at the final volume by computing with the original dimensions and water height. The final width of the room is calculated by solving for the missing dimension. There is no final answer for the time.

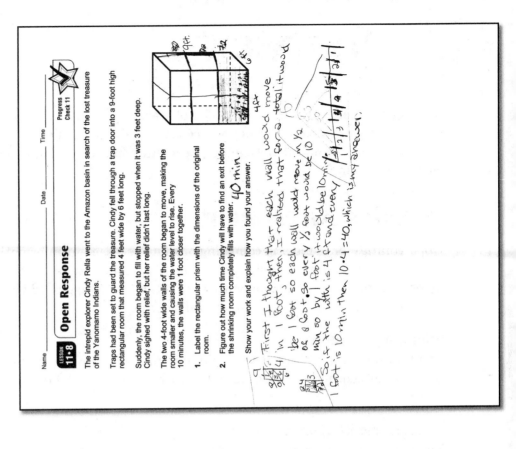

LESSON 11·8 Open Response

The intrepid explorer Cindy Rella went to the Amazon basin in search of the lost treasure of the Yanomamo Indians.

Traps had been set to guard the treasure. Cindy fell through a trap door into a 9-foot high rectangular room that measured 4 feet wide by 6 feet long.

Suddenly, the room began to fill with water, but stopped when it was 3 feet deep. Cindy sighed with relief, but her relief didn't last long.

The two 4-foot wide walls of the room began to move, making the room smaller and causing the water level to rise. Every 10 minutes, the walls were 1 foot closer together.

1. Label the rectangular prism with the dimensions of the original room.

2. Figure out how much time Cindy will have to find an exit before the shrinking room completely fills with water.

Show your work and explain how you found your answer.

Unit 12 Assessment Overview

In this unit, students explore using factor trees to find prime factorization and using tree diagrams to represent and count combinations of choices, and review the uses of ratios and rates. Use the information in this section to develop your assessment plan for Unit 12.

Ongoing Assessment

Opportunities for using and collecting ongoing assessment information are highlighted in Informing Instruction and Recognizing Student Achievement notes. Student products, along with observations and suggested writing prompts, provide a range of useful assessment information.

Informing Instruction
The Informing Instruction notes highlight students' thinking and point out common misconceptions. Informing Instruction in Unit 12: Lessons 12-2, 12-4, and 12-5.

Recognizing Student Achievement
The Recognizing Student Achievement notes highlight specific tasks from which teachers can collect assessment data to monitor and document student progress toward meeting Grade-Level Goals.

Lesson	Content Assessed	Where to Find It
12♦1	Factor numbers and identify the prime factorizations. [Number and Numeration Goal 3]	*TLG*, p. 917
12♦2	Express probability using fractions and basic probability terms. [Data and Chance Goal 4]	*TLG*, p. 921
12♦3	Solve fraction division problems. [Operations and Computation Goal 5]	*TLG*, p. 927
12♦4	Solve ratio problems. [Operations and Computation Goal 7]	*TLG*, p. 934
12♦5	Estimate and solve multidigit multiplication problems. [Operations and Computation Goal 6]	*TLG*, p. 939
12♦6	Identify equivalent expressions. [Number and Numeration Goal 4]	*TLG*, p. 944
12♦7	Round numbers. [Number and Numeration Goal 1]	*TLG*, p. 947
12♦8	Plot points in all four quadrants of a coordinate grid. [Measurement and Reference Frames Goal 4]	*TLG*, p. 955

Math Boxes

Math Boxes, one of several types of tasks highlighted in the Recognizing Student Achievement notes, have an additional useful feature. Math Boxes in most lessons are paired or linked with Math Boxes in one or two other lessons that have similar problems. Paired or linked Math Boxes in Unit 12: 12-1 and 12-3; 12-2 and 12-4; 12-5 and 12-7; and 12-6 and 12-8.

Writing/Reasoning Prompts

In Unit 12, a variety of writing prompts encourage students to explain their strategies and thinking, to reflect on their learning, and to make connections to other mathematics or life experiences. Here are some of the Unit 12 suggestions:

Lesson	Writing/Reasoning Prompts	Where to Find It
12•1	Explain how you used the sale price and percent discount to calculate the original price.	*TLG*, p. 918
12•4	Explain what value you would use for π if you didn't have a calculator.	*TLG*, p. 934
12•6	Explain how you found equivalent fractions.	*TLG*, p. 944
12•7	Explain how your ratio could be expressed as a fraction and a percent.	*TLG*, p. 950

Portfolio Opportunities

Portfolios are a versatile tool for assessment. They help students reflect on their mathematical growth and help teachers understand and document that growth. Each unit identifies several student products that can be selected and stored in a portfolio. Here are some of the Unit 12 suggestions:

Lesson	Portfolio Opportunities	Where to Find It
12•1	Students explain how they used the sale price and percent discount to calculate the original price.	*TLG*, p. 918
12•1	Students factor four- and five-digit numbers.	*TLG*, p. 918
12•3	Students write a story about what life would be like if everything were suddenly 10 times more/greater or 10 times less/smaller.	*TLG*, p. 930
12•6	Students explain how they can express their ratio as a fraction and a percent.	*TLG*, p. 944
12•9	Students use ratios to solve a problem.	*TLG*, p. 960

Periodic Assessment

Every Progress Check lesson includes opportunities to observe students' progress and to collect student products in a variety of ways—Self Assessment, Oral and Slate Assessment, Written Assessment, and an Open Response task. For more details, see the first page of Progress Check 12, Lesson 12-9 on page 957, of the *Teacher's Lesson Guide*.

Progress Check Modifications

Written Assessments are one way students demonstrate what they know. The table below shows modifications for the Written Assessment in this unit. Use these to maximize opportunities for students to demonstrate what they know. Modifications can be given individually or written on the board for the class.

Problem(s)	Modifications for Written Assessment
1, 2	For Problems 1 and 2, list the prime numbers through 11 before finding the prime factorization.
9–13	For Problems 9–13, draw pictures or use your square tiles to help you solve the problems.
12	For Problem 12, Lucinda figured out that 21 of the cars were red. Explain what Lucinda might have done and how she could correct her mistake.
15	For Problem 15, make a list of all possible outcomes to help you figure out the probabilities—for example, 1-H would be a 1 on the die and a head on the coin.

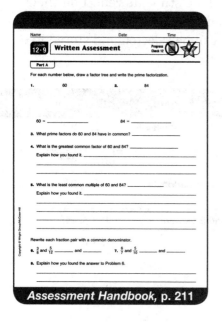

Assessment Handbook, p. 211

The Written Assessment for the Unit 12 Progress Check is on pages 211–214.

Open Response, *Counting Cars*

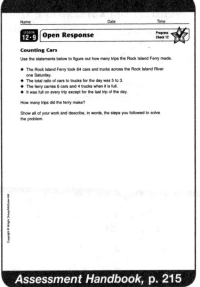

Assessment Handbook, p. 215

Description

For this task, students use ratios to solve a problem.

Focus

◆ **Use ratios expressed as words and fractions to solve problems; use scaling to model multiplication; solve problems involving ratios.**
[Operations and Computation Goal 7]

Implementation Tips

◆ Remind students to focus on the essential elements of the problem they are trying to solve. They need to find how many trips the ferry must make to get all the cars and trucks across.

Modifications for Meeting Diverse Needs

◆ Have students use 64 counters to model the problem. Label one sheet of paper *Cars* and one sheet *Trucks*. Students place the counters on the papers, moving 5 cars for every 3 trucks. When they have figured out how many vehicles there are of each type, they can then construct ferries with the counters by making groups with a ratio of 6 from the *Car* sheet, and 4 from the *Truck* sheet for each ferry.

◆ Have students calculate the number of cars and the number of trucks that traveled on the ferry. Have them prove that their answers are correct using a variety of ratios from the problem; for example, 5 cars to 3 trucks; 5 cars out of 8 vehicles; or 3 trucks out of 8 vehicles.

Improving Open Response Skills

After students complete the task, give them a few minutes to discuss the four levels of the rubric. As a class, determine and record the important features at each level based on the rubric. Provide small groups of students with 2 or 3 papers to score according to the rubric. Consider using anonymous papers from another class or enlarge copies of the Sample Student Responses beginning on page 147 of this book. For each sample paper, have them write a brief description of what features of the paper helped them decide on the score.

Note: The wording and formatting of the text on the student samples that follow may vary slightly from the actual task your children will complete. These minor discrepancies will not affect the implementaton of the task.

Rubric

This rubric is designed to help you assess levels of mathematical performance on this task. It emphasizes mathematical understanding with only a mention of clarity of explanation. Consider the expectations of standardized tests in your area when applying a rubric. Modify this sample rubric as appropriate.

4   Uses both ratios from the problem to determine the number of ferry trips required. Clearly shows all of the solution steps. Explains or shows how both ratios (3 to 5 and 6 to 4) are used in solving the problem.

3   Uses ratios from the problem to determine the number of ferry trips required. Shows some solution steps. Work might not be clearly organized. Explains parts of the solution steps in words. Explains or shows the use of ratios (3 to 5 and 6 to 4) in solving the problem.

2   Demonstrates some understanding of and the use of ratios, but might not correctly apply ratios to solving the problem. Might use only one of the stated ratios, or might not completely solve the problem. Might attempt to explain the solution strategy, but the explanation might not match the work shown, or it might be incomplete.

1   Attempts to solve the problem using some of the stated information, but there is little evidence of an understanding or of an application of ratios. Might attempt to explain the solution strategy. The explanation might ignore the specified ratios or might not make sense in the context of the problem.

0   Does not attempt to solve the problem.

This Level 4 paper illustrates the following features: The first array shows a ratio of 5 cars for every 3 trucks in each column until a total of 64 is reached. The second array illustrates the vehicles that the ferry carried on each trip in a 6-cars to 4-trucks ratio with each trip circled. The explanation describes these 2 steps.

This Level 4 paper illustrates the following features: The illustration shows a ratio of 5 cars for every 3 trucks until a total of 64 is reached. The table shows the vehicles that the ferry carried on each trip in a 6-cars to 4-trucks ratio. The table stops when the total of each vehicle has been reached. The explanation clearly describes these 2 steps.

Name _____ Date _____ Time _____

LESSON 12·9 **Open Response**   Progress Check 12

Use the statements below to figure out how many trips the Rock Island ferry made.

- The Rock Island ferry took 64 cars and trucks across the Rock Island River one Saturday.
- The total ratio of cars to trucks for the day was 5 to 3.
- The ferry carries 6 cars and 4 trucks when it is full.
- It was full on every trip except the last trip of the day.

How many trips did the ferry make? 7 trips

Show all of your work and describe, in words, the steps you followed to solve the problem.

Name _____ Date _____ Time _____

LESSON 12·9 **Open Response**   Progress Check 12

Use the statements below to figure out how many trips the Rock Island ferry made.

- The Rock Island ferry took 64 cars and trucks across the Rock Island River one Saturday.
- The total ratio of cars to trucks for the day was 5 to 3.
- The ferry carries 6 cars and 4 trucks when it is full.
- It was full on every trip except the last trip of the day.

How many trips did the ferry make? 7 trips

Show all of your work and describe, in words, the steps you followed to solve the problem.

This Level 3 paper illustrates the following features: The first table shows a ratio of 5 cars for every 3 trucks until a total of 40 cars and 24 trucks is reached. The second table is less clear, but appears to be the repeated ferry trips. The explanation describes the contents of the two tables, but there are some statements that need to be clarified.

This Level 3 paper illustrates the following features: The table shows a ratio of 5 cars for every 3 trucks until a total of 64 cars and vehicles is reached. The explanation describes repeatedly subtracting 6 cars and 4 trucks from the totals, but fraction notation is incorrectly used. When one of the totals reaches 0, the number of repeated subtractions is counted to determine the number of ferry trips.

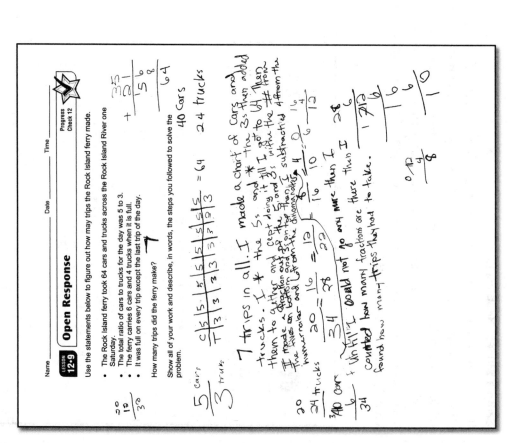

LESSON 12·9 Open Response

Name _____ Date _____ Time _____

Progress Check 12

Use the statements below to figure out how may trips the Rock Island ferry made.

- The Rock Island ferry took 64 cars and trucks across the Rock Island River one Saturday.
- The total ratio of cars to trucks for the day was 5 to 3.
- The ferry carries 6 cars and 4 trucks when it is full.
- It was full on every trip except the last trip of the day.

How many trips did the ferry make? **7**

Show all of your work and describe, in words, the steps you followed to solve the problem.

This Level 2 paper illustrates the following features: There is a table with a ratio of 5 cars for every 3 trucks until a total of 64 is reached. The explanation describes finding the number of cars and trucks. There is no mention of the ferry or the number of ferry trips.

This Level 1 paper illustrates the following features: The answer is correct, but it is derived through a strategy that does not involve the use of the ratios. There is no indication that ratios were considered in solving the problem.

Name _____ Date _____ Time _____

Open Response

Progress Check 12

Use the statements below to figure out how many trips the Rock Island ferry made.

- The Rock Island ferry took 64 cars and trucks across the Rock Island River one Saturday.
- The total ratio of cars to trucks for the day was 5 to 3.
- The ferry carries 6 cars and 4 trucks when it is full.
- It was full on every trip except the last trip of the day.

How many trips did the ferry make?

Show all of your work and describe, in words, the steps you followed to solve the problem.

trucks	cars
3	5
3	5
3	5
3	5
3	5
3	5
3	5
3	5

My answer is 24 truck and 40 cars.
I got it by I know that 3+5 = 8
and 8×8=64 so I had to do 8 cars
and 8 trucks.

I knew that th 3trucks there is 5 cars-So I
knew that was 8 so1 multiplie 8×8=64 And thats
how I got my answer.

Name _____ Date _____ Time _____

Open Response

Progress Check 12

Use the statements below to figure out how may trips the Rock Island ferry made.

- The Rock Island ferry took 64 cars and trucks across the Rock Island River one Saturday.
- The total ratio of cars to trucks for the day was 5 to 3.
- The ferry carries 6 cars and 4 trucks when it is full.
- It was full on every trip except the last trip of the day.

How many trips did the ferry make?

Show all of your work and describe, in words, the steps you followed to solve the problem.

7 trips becuase they said it was
full on every ride but the last one,
and it can hold 10 vehicles each ride
so divide 60 by 10 and it is
6 but add one more because they
said it was full on every one
but the last one.

End-of-Year Assessment Goals

The End-of-Year Assessment (pages 234–241) provides an additional opportunity that you may use as part of your balanced assessment plan. It covers some of the important concepts and skills presented in *Fifth Grade Everyday Mathematics*. It should be used to complement the ongoing and periodic assessments that appear within lessons and at the end of units. The following table provides the goals for all the problems in the End-of-Year Assessment.

Problem(s)	Grade-Level Goal
1	**Number and Numeration Goal 1:** Read and write whole numbers and decimals; identify places in such numbers and the values of the digits in those places; use expanded notation to represent whole numbers and decimals.
2, 3	**Number and Numeration Goal 1:** Read and write whole numbers and decimals; identify places in such numbers and the values of the digits in those places; use expanded notation to represent whole numbers and decimals.
4, 5	**Number and Numeration Goal 5:** Use numerical expressions to find and represent equivalent names for fractions, decimals, and percents; use and explain multiplication and division rules to find equivalent fractions and fractions in simplest form; convert between fractions and mixed numbers; convert between fractions, decimals, and percents.
6	**Number and Numeration Goal 3:** Identify prime and composite numbers; factor numbers; find prime factorizations.
7a	**Data and Chance Goal 1:** Collect and organize data or use given data to create graphic displays with reasonable titles, labels, keys, and intervals.
7b–7e	**Data and Chance Goal 2:** Use the maximum, minimum, range, median, mode, and mean and graphs to ask and answer questions, draw conclusions, and make predictions.
8	**Operations and Computation Goal 1:** Use manipulatives, mental arithmetic, paper-and-pencil algorithms and models, and calculators to solve problems involving the addition and subtraction of whole numbers, decimals, and signed numbers; describe the strategies used and explain how they work.
9	**Geometry Goal 2:** Describe, compare, and classify plane and solid figures using appropriate geometric terms; identify congruent figures and describe their properties.
10	**Measurement and Reference Frames Goal 2:** Describe and use strategies to find the perimeter of polygons and the area of circles; choose and use appropriate methods, including formulas, to find the areas of rectangles, parallelograms, and triangles, and the volume of a prism; define *pi* as the ratio of a circle's circumference to its diameter.
11	**Patterns, Functions, and Algebra Goal 3:** Evaluate numeric expressions containing grouping symbols and nested grouping symbols; insert grouping symbols and nested grouping symbols to make number sentences true; describe and use the precedence of multiplication and division over addition and subtraction.
12	**Operations and Computation Goal 4:** Use mental arithmetic, paper-and-pencil algorithms and models, and calculators to solve problems involving the addition and subtraction of fractions and mixed numbers; describe the strategies used and explain how they work.

Problem(s)	Grade-Level Goal
13	**Measurement and Reference Frames Goal 2:** Describe and use strategies to find the perimeter of polygons and the area of circles; choose and use appropriate methods, including formulas, to find the areas of rectangles, parallelograms, and triangles, and the volume of a prism; define *pi* as the ratio of a circle's circumference to its diameter.
14, 15	**Operations and Computation Goal 5:** Use area models, mental arithmetic, paper-and-pencil algorithms and models, and calculators to solve problems involving the multiplication of fractions and mixed numbers; use visual models, paper-and-pencil methods, and calculators to solve problems involving the division of fractions; describe the strategies used.
16	**Patterns, Functions, and Algebra Goal 4:** Describe and apply properties of arithmetic.
17	**Operations and Computation Goal 6:** Make reasonable estimates for whole number and decimal addition, subtraction, multiplication, and division problems and fraction and mixed number addition and subtraction problems; explain how the estimates were obtained.
18	**Operations and Computation Goal 7:** Use repeated addition, arrays, area, and scaling to model multiplication and division; use ratios expressed as words, fractions, percents, and with colons; solve problems involving ratios of parts of a set to the whole set.
19a	**Data and Chance Goal 1:** Collect and organize data or use given data to create graphic displays with reasonable titles, labels, keys, and intervals.
19b	**Number and Numeration Goal 2:** Solve problems involving percents and discounts; describe and explain strategies used; identify the unit whole in situations involving fractions.
20	**Number and Numeration Goal 6:** Compare and order rational numbers; use area models, benchmark fractions, and analyses of numerators and denominators to compare and order fractions and mixed numbers; describe strategies used to compare fractions and mixed numbers.
21	**Number and Numeration Goal 4:** Use numerical expressions involving one or more of the basic four arithmetic operations, grouping symbols, and exponents to give equivalent names for whole numbers; convert between base-10, exponential, and repeated-factor notations.
22	**Data and Chance Goal 3:** Describe events using *certain, very likely, likely, unlikely, very unlikely, impossible,* and other basic probability terms; use *more likely, equally likely, same chance, 50-50, less likely,* and other basic probability terms to compare events; explain the choice of language.
23	**Operations and Computation Goal 3:** Use manipulatives, mental arithmetic, paper-and-pencil algorithms and models, and calculators to solve problems involving the multiplication of whole numbers and decimals and the division of multidigit whole numbers and decimals by whole numbers; express remainders as whole numbers or fractions as appropriate; describe the strategies used and explain how they work.
24	**Data and Chance Goal 4:** Predict the outcomes of experiments, test the predictions using manipulatives, and summarize the results; compare predictions based on theoretical probability with experimental results; use summaries and comparisons to predict future events; express the probability of an event as a fraction, decimal, or percent.
25	**Measurement and Reference Frames Goal 3:** Describe relationships among U.S. customary units of measure and among metric units of measure.
26	**Patterns, Functions, and Algebra Goal 2:** Determine whether number sentences are true or false; solve open number sentences and explain the solutions; use a letter variable to write an open sentence to model a number story; use a pan-balance model to solve linear equations in one unknown.
27	**Operations and Computation Goal 2:** Demonstrate automaticity with multiplication and division fact extensions.

Problem(s)	Grade-Level Goal
28	**Operations and Computation Goal 1:** Use manipulatives, mental arithmetic, paper-and-pencil algorithms and models, and calculators to solve problems involving the addition and subtraction of whole numbers, decimals, and signed numbers; describe the strategies used and explain how they work.
29	**Operations and Computation Goal 7:** Use repeated addition, arrays, area, and scaling to model multiplication and division; use ratios expressed as words, fractions, percents, and with colons; solve problems involving ratios of parts of a set to the whole set.
30	**Measurement and Reference Frames Goal 1:** Estimate length with and without tools; measure length with tools to the nearest $\frac{1}{8}$ inch and millimeter; estimate the measure of angles with and without tools; use tools to draw angles with given measures.
31	**Geometry Goal 1:** Identify, describe, compare, name, and draw right, acute, obtuse, straight, and reflex angles; determine angle measures in vertical and supplementary angles and by applying properties of sums of angle measures in triangles and quadrangles.
32a, 32b	**Measurement and Reference Frames Goal 4:** Use ordered pairs of numbers to name, locate, and plot points in all four quadrants of a coordinate grid.
32c	**Geometry Goal 3:** Identify, describe, and sketch examples of reflections, translations, and rotations.
32d	**Geometry Goal 2:** Describe, compare, and classify plane and solid figures using appropriate geometric terms; identify congruent figures and describe their properties.
33	**Measurement and Reference Frames Goal 2:** Describe and use strategies to find the perimeter of polygons and the area of circles; choose and use appropriate methods, including formulas, to find the areas of rectangles, parallelograms, and triangles, and the volume of a prism; define *pi* as the ratio of a circle's circumference to its diameter.
34	**Patterns, Functions, and Algebra Goal 1:** Extend, describe, and create numeric patterns; describe rules for patterns and use them to solve problems; write rules for functions involving the four basic arithmetic operations; represent functions using words, symbols, tables, and graphs and use those representations to solve problems.

Assessment Masters

Contents

Progress Check

Unit 1 . . . . **154**
Unit 2 . . . . **158**
Unit 3 . . . . **164**
Unit 4 . . . . **170**
Unit 5 . . . . **175**
Unit 6 . . . . **180**
Unit 7 . . . . **185**
Unit 8 . . . . **190**
Unit 9 . . . . **194**
Unit 10 . . . . **199**
Unit 11 . . . . **205**
Unit 12 . . . . **210**
Progress Check Answers Unit 1 . . . **216**
Progress Check Answers Unit 2 . . . **217**
Progress Check Answers Unit 3 . . . **218**
Progress Check Answers Unit 4 . . . **219**
Progress Check Answers Unit 5 . . . **220**
Progress Check Answers Unit 6 . . . **221**
Progress Check Answers Unit 7 . . . **222**
Progress Check Answers Unit 8 . . . **223**
Progress Check Answers Unit 9 . . . **224**
Progress Check Answers Unit 10 . . **225**
Progress Check Answers Unit 11 . . **226**
Progress Check Answers Unit 12 . . **227**
Beginning-of-Year Assessment. . . **227A**
Mid-Year Assessment **228**
End-of-Year Assessment **234**
Beginning-of-Year, Mid-Year, and
End-of-Year
Assessment Answers **242**

Class Checklists and Individual Profiles of Progress

Unit 1 . . . . **246**
Unit 2 . . . . **250**
Unit 3 . . . . **254**
Unit 4 . . . . **258**
Unit 5 . . . . **262**
Unit 6 . . . . **266**
Unit 7 . . . . **270**
Unit 8 . . . . **274**
Unit 9 . . . . **278**
Unit 10 . . . . **282**
Unit 11 . . . . **286**
Unit 12 . . . . **290**
Quarter 1 . . . . **294**
Quarter 2 . . . . **296**
Quarter 3 . . . . **298**
Quarter 4 . . . . **300**

General Masters
(students' masters in italics)

Individual Profile of Progress **302**
Class Checklist **303**
Evaluating My Math Class **304**
My Math Class **305**
Weekly Math Log **306**
Math Log **307**
Number-Story Math Log **308**
Sample Math Work **309**
Discussion of My Math Work **310**
Exit Slip **311**
Parent Reflections **312**

LESSON 1·10

Self Assessment

Think about each skill listed below. Assess your progress by checking the most appropriate box.

Skills	I can do this on my own and explain how to do it.	I can do this on my own.	I can do this if I get help or look at an example.
1. Use prime factorization.			
2. Convert between exponential, repeated factor, and standard notation.			
3. Find and identify prime and composite numbers.			
4. Solve extended multiplication facts.			
5. Use divisibility tests to find factors and divisors.			
6. Read and write whole numbers through billions and decimals through thousandths.			
7. Factor numbers.			

LESSON 1·10 — Written Assessment

Progress Check 1

Part A

1. Mr. Martin has 24 tulip bulbs. He wants to plant them in a rectangular array consisting of at least 2 rows with at least 2 tulips in each row. On the grid at the right, draw three possible arrays.

2. List all the factors of 24.

    _____

    _____

3. Is 24 a prime or a composite number?

    _____

    How can you tell?

    _____

    _____

4. Circle the factors in Problem 2 that are prime numbers.

5. Suppose you are playing *Factor Captor* on the number grid at the right. The crossed-out numbers have already been picked. Which number would you choose next?

    _____

    Why? _____

    _____

    _____

✗	2	✗	4	✗
6	✗	8	9	10
11	12	13	14	15
16	17	18	19	20
✗	22	✗	24	✗
26	27	28	✗	30

Written Assessment *continued*

6. At the right is a calendar for a month. Use the following clues to figure out the date that Bret Harte School won its last basketball game.

   ◆ The date is not an even number.

   ◆ The date is not a square number.

   ◆ The date is not a prime number.

   ◆ The date is a multiple of 5.

S	M	T	W	T	F	S
	1	2	3	4	5	6
7	8	9	10	11	12	13
14	15	16	17	18	19	20
21	22	23	24	25	26	27
28	29	30	31			

On which day did the school win its last basketball game? _____

7. **a.** Write an 8-digit number that has
   3 in the ones place,
   7 in the hundred-thousands place,
   8 in the thousands place,
   5 in the hundredths place,
   and 0 in all other places.

   b. Write this numeral in words.

   _____

   _____

   _____

   __ __ __ , __ __ __ . __ __

Part B

8. Write the prime factorization for 24. _____

9. Write the prime factorization of 24 using exponents. _____

10. Fill in the missing numbers.

   a. $7^2 =$ _____

   b. $9^2 =$ _____

   c. $36 =$ _____^{2}

   d. $5^2 =$ _____

   e. $10^2 =$ _____

   f. $8 * 8 =$ _____^{2}

11. Name a number between 200 and 300 that is divisible by 3 but not by 2. _____

12. Name a number between 200 and 300 that is divisible by 2, 3, and 5. _____

Open Response

Divisibility

The Sandyville School 5th graders were doing a play. There was a big dance scene with dancers in rows.

Use these hints to figure out how many dancers there were.

- There were 35 fifth graders in the school, but they did not all dance.

- When the dancers rehearsed in rows of 2, one dancer was left to dance alone.

- When the dancers rehearsed in rows of 3, one dancer was left to dance alone.

- When the dancers rehearsed in rows of 4, one dancer was left to dance alone.

- When the dancers rehearsed in rows of 5, finally every dancer was in a row!

How many dancers could have been in the dance scene?

Explain how you got your answer.

LESSON 2·11   Self Assessment

Think about each skill listed below. Assess your own progress by checking the most appropriate box.

Skills	I can do this on my own and explain how to do this.	I can do this on my own.	I can do this if I get help or look at an example.
1. Add and subtract whole numbers and decimals.			
2. Convert between U.S. customary units of length.			
3. Identify the place value of digits.			
4. Multiply whole numbers and decimals.			
5. Make reasonable estimates.			
6. Write and solve number sentences.			
7. Describe probabilities using words or phrases.			
8. Write numbers in expanded notation.			
9. Find the landmarks for a data set.			

LESSON 2·11 | Written Assessment

Progress
Check 2

Part A

Solve at least one problem using the partial-sums addition method and at least one problem using the trade-first subtraction method. Use any method you want to solve the rest of the problems. Show your work.

1. $734 + 893 =$ _____

2. $24.7 + 103.9 =$ _____

3. _____ $= 58.2 + 76.08$

4. $692 - 348 =$ _____

5. $150.4 - 63.7 =$ _____

6. _____ $= 28.3 - 13.71$

LESSON 2·11   **Written Assessment** *continued*

7. Students were studying a map of New Zealand. The map legend stated that 1 inch = 400 miles. They measured the distance between two cities. It was $1\frac{1}{2}$ inches. About how many miles apart were the two cities?

_____

Fill in the blanks.

8. Demetrius walked 1,500 feet to the corner store in the rain. He wanted his friend to feel sorry for him. He said, "I just walked _____ inches to the store. And that was just one way!" His friend said, "That's not very far. It's only _____ yards."

9. Write the number that has
6 in the ones place,
4 in the thousands place,
7 in the ten-thousands place,
2 in the tenths place,
and 5 in all of the remaining places. ____ ____, ____ ____ ____ . ____ ____ ____

Solve the following problems using a paper-and-pencil algorithm. Show your work.

10.   28
     × 46

11.   365
     × 47

12. Choose one of the problems above, and explain why making a magnitude estimate of the answer before solving the problem is helpful.

_____

_____

_____

_____

_____

LESSON 2·11 | **Written Assessment** *continued*

For Problems 13 and 14, make a magnitude estimate. Circle the appropriate box. Then solve each problem using the algorithm of your choice. Show your work.

13. 6.4 * 8.3 = _____

10s	100s	1,000s	10,000s

14. 12.2 * 1.56 = _____

10s	100s	1,000s	10,000s

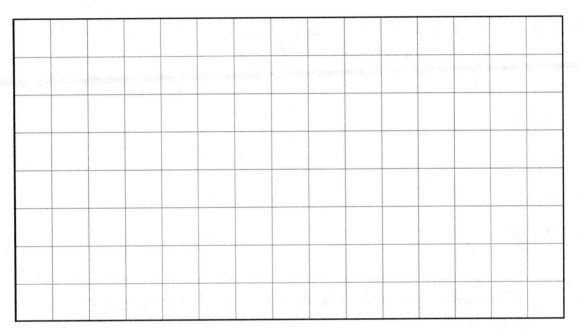

Fill in the blank with the phrase from the word bank that describes the chance the event will happen.

Word Bank

certain	very likely	likely	50-50 chance	unlikely	very unlikely	impossible

15. a. A 10% chance of rain _____

b. Tossing a coin which lands heads up _____

c. A $\frac{3}{4}$ chance of having pizza for dinner _____

d. Landing on red on a spinner that has
25% each of blue, red, yellow, and green _____

Part B

Write the following in expanded notation.

16. 37 = _____

17. 465.3 = _____

18. Elise had the following scores on her spelling tests: 78, 84, 94, 98, 62, 96, 89, 94, and 92. Find the following landmarks for this set of data.

    a. Maximum: _____

    b. Minimum: _____

    c. Range: _____

    d. Mode: _____

    e. Median: _____

19. Caitlin's great-grandmother was born in 1919. Her family had a big party for her on her 75th birthday. There were 52 family members at the party. In what year did they have the party?

    a. List the numbers needed to solve the problem. _____

    b. Describe what you need to find. _____

    c. Open sentence: _____

    d. Solution: _____

    e. Answer: _____

LESSON 2·11 | Open Response

Fund Raising

Two fifth grade classes raised money for their local animal shelters.

There are **20** students in Class A. Each student raised $12.

There are **26** students in Class B. **Each student** in Class B raised 1.5 times as much as each student in Class A.

1. How much money was raised altogether in both classrooms?
Show your work and explain your answer.

2. The money raised went to two shelters. One shelter received twice as much as the other. How much money did each shelter receive?
Show your work and explain your answer.

LESSON 3·11   **Self Assessment**   Progress Check 3

Think about each skill listed below. Assess your own progress by checking the most appropriate box.

Skills	I can do this on my own and explain how to do this.	I can do this on my own.	I can do this if I get help or look at an example.
1. Identify place value digits in numbers to billions.			
2. Identify right, straight, reflex, obtuse, and acute angles.			
3. Use a protractor to measure angles.			
4. Identify and draw right, isosceles, equilateral, and scalene triangles.			
5. Determine angle measures based on relationships between angles.			
6. Identify and compare properties of polygons.			
7. Make patterns that tessellate.			

Written Assessment

**Progress
Check 3**

Part A

Measure each angle below with a protractor. Then choose a word from the list to
name each angle type: acute, obtuse, adjacent, right.

1.

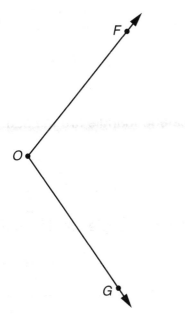

2.

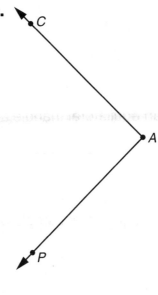

3.

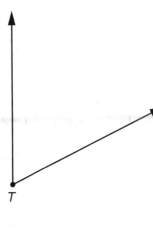

m∠FOG = _____

m∠CAP = _____

m∠T = _____

_____ angle

_____ angle

_____ angle

4. a. What is a reflex angle?

_____

_____

_____

b. Draw and label a reflex angle.

5. Write the number that has
4 in the ones place,
a digit in the hundred-thousands place that is
twice the digit in the ones place,
the smallest odd digit in the millions place,
7 in the tenths place, and
0 in all other places.

____,____ ____ ____,____ ____ ____.____ ____

LESSON 3·11 | **Written Assessment** *continued*

Use your Geometry Template to do the following:

6. Draw an equilateral triangle.

7. Draw an isosceles triangle that is not equilateral.

8. Draw a scalene triangle.

9. List at least one way in which an equilateral triangle and a scalene triangle are the same.

_____

_____

10. List at least one way in which an equilateral triangle and a scalene triangle are different.

_____

_____

_____

For each polygon below, fill in the ovals next to all true statements.

11.

○ This polygon is a quadrangle.
○ At least two sides are parallel.
   At least two angles are congruent.
○ This is a regular polygon.
○ At least one angle is acute.

12.

○ This polygon is a quadrangle.
○ At least two sides are parallel.
○ At least one angle is acute.
○ At least two angles are congruent.
○ This is a regular polygon.

LESSON 3·11 | **Written Assessment** *continued*

Part B

Find the missing angle measure without using your protractor.

13.

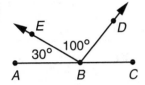

$\overline{ABC}$ is a straight line.

m∠DBC = _____

14.

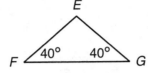

m∠E = _____

15.

Each angle of the regular hexagons at point *H* has a measure of _____ .

16. Name two adjacent angles in Problem 13.

_____

_____

17. a. At the right, use a straightedge to draw a pair of adjacent angles. Make one of the angles obtuse. Use letters to name the angles.

b. Tell which angle is obtuse.

∠ _____

c. Without using your protractor, estimate the measure of each angle to the nearest 10°.

m∠ _____ is about _____ °.   m∠ _____ is about _____ °.

LESSON 3·11 | **Written Assessment** *continued*

18. Use the table below to answer the questions.

Regional Populations 1850–2000				
Region	**1850**	**1900**	**1950**	**2000**
Northeast	8,627,000	21,047,000	39,478,000	52,107,000
South	8,983,000	24,524,000	47,197,000	97,614,000
Midwest	5,404,000	26,333,000	44,461,000	63,502,000
West	179,000	4,309,000	20,190,000	61,412,000

a. Which region had the smallest population in 1950? _____

b. Which had the smallest population 50 years later? _____

c. Which region had the greatest increase in population from 1850 to 2000?

_____ What was the increase? _____

19. Use the pattern-block shapes on your Geometry Template to draw a pattern that tessellates. (The pattern-block shapes are marked PB.)

20. Explain why your pattern is a tessellation.

_____

_____

LESSON 3·11 | **Open Response**

Adding Angles

Nate and Sam played 5 rounds of *Angle Tangle.* Nate drew the following types of angles for Sam:

> 1 reflex angle, 1 right angle, 2 acute angles, and 1 obtuse angle.

Both Nate and Sam were very good at estimating the measures of angles. Their total scores for the game were so close that the boys decided on another way to choose the winner.

They decided to add the measures of their 5 angles, and the one who had the greatest sum would win.

Sam's angles totaled 500°.

What could the measures of his 5 angles be? Show or explain how you found your answers.

Reflex angle: _____ °

Right angle: _____ °

Acute angle 1: _____ °

Acute angle 2: _____ °

Obtuse angle: _____ °

LESSON 4·8 — Self Assessment

Progress Check 4

Think about each skill listed below. Assess your own progress by checking the most appropriate box.

Skills	I can do this on my own and explain how to do it.	I can do this on my own.	I can do this if I get help or look at an example.
1. Find multiples, and use them to rename numbers.			
2. Know and use multiplication facts, related division facts, and extended facts.			
3. Divide using a friendly number strategy with the partial-quotients algorithm.			
4. Divide using an "at least...not more than strategy" with the partial-quotients algorithm.			
5. Make magnitude estimates to correctly place the decimal point in quotients.			
6. Measure and draw line segments to the nearest $\frac{1}{2}$ inch.			
7. Estimate distances using a map scale.			
8. Write an open number sentence for number stories.			
9. Determine what to do with a remainder.			

LESSON 4·8

Written Assessment

Progress Check 4

Part A

Use the map to answer the questions.

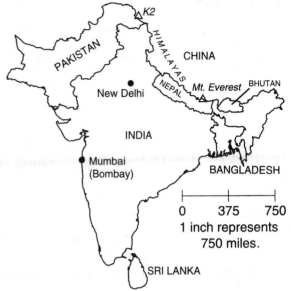

1. Estimate the distance from New Delhi to Mumbai (Bombay).

   Map distance: _____

   Real distance: _____

2. Estimate the distance from Mumbai (Bombay) to Mt. Everest.

   Map distance: _____

   Real distance: _____

3. About how many miles from the northern tip of Sri Lanka is K2? _____

Use a friendly number strategy to solve these problems mentally.

4. 84 divided by 6 equals _____.

   _____
   (friendly parts for 84)

5. 104 divided by 8 equals _____.

   _____
   (friendly parts for 104)

Solve.

6. $3\overline{)141}$ _____

   Check: _____

7. $624 \div 8 =$ _____

   Check: _____

LESSON 4·8 | Written Assessment continued

Make a magnitude estimate. Circle the appropriate box.

8. $59.4 \div 3$ How I estimated: _____

0.1s	1s	10s	100s

9. $6.428 / 4$ How I estimated: _____

0.1s	1s	10s	100s

In Problems 10 and 11:

◆ Find the value of x in the first number sentence.

◆ Use this value to complete the second number sentence.

10. $x = 100 - 95$ $x^2 =$ _____

11. $x = \frac{1}{2}$ of a dozen $30 * x =$ _____

12. Write an open number sentence you can use to solve the number story below. Then solve the number story.

Four friends rented a car. The total rental cost was $150, including tax. The friends split the cost evenly. How much did each friend contribute?

Number sentence: _____

Solution: _____

Solve. Show your work for Problems 13–18 on a computation grid.

13. $126 / 6 =$ _____   **14.** $9 *$ _____ $= 243$

Part B

15. $703 \div 14 \rightarrow$ _____   **16.** $482 \div 34 \rightarrow$ _____

Circle your magnitude estimate. Then solve.

17. $5\overline{)88.5}$ _____

0.1s	1s	10s	100s

18. $14\overline{)2.94}$ _____

0.1s	1s	10s	100s

In Problems 19 and 20, write an open sentence to represent the number story and use a division algorithm to solve the problem. Then decide what to do about the remainder and tell why you chose what to do.

19. Tammy has 130 photographs. She can tape 8 photos onto each page of her photo album. How many pages will she need to tape all her photos in the album?

Number sentence: _____

Solution: _____ pages

What does the remainder represent? _____

_____

Circle what you did with the remainder.

Ignored it   Reported it as a fraction or decimal   Rounded the answer up

20. For a relay race, the gym teacher divided the class into 4 teams with an equal number of students on each team. There were 30 students in the class. Extra students didn't race. How many members were on each team?

Number sentence: _____

Solution: _____ members

What does the remainder represent? _____

_____

Circle what you did with the remainder.

Ignored it   Reported it as a fraction or decimal   Rounded the answer up

LESSON 4·8 — Open Response

Missing Digits

Find digits A and B in the number below so that the following conditions are true. Show all of your work.

◆ The 5-digit number must be divisible by 4.

◆ The 5-digit number must be divisible by 9.

◆ Digit A cannot be the same as Digit B.

1 2 A 3 B

Explain the steps you followed to solve the problem.

LESSON 6·11 | **Written Assessment** | Progress Check 6

Part A

Fill in the ovals to match the words to their definitions.

1. Median

- ◯ smallest value
- ◯ largest value
- ◯ most frequent value
- ◯ middle value

2. Maximum

- ◯ smallest value
- ◯ largest value
- ◯ most frequent value
- ◯ middle value

3. Mode

- ◯ smallest value
- ◯ largest value
- ◯ most frequent value
- ◯ middle value

4. Minimum

- ◯ smallest value
- ◯ largest value
- ◯ most frequent value
- ◯ middle value

5. Sonia asked seven girls in her fifth-grade class how many CDs they own. Here are the results of her survey: 2   0   6   5   7   5   1

a. What was the median number of CDs owned? _____

b. Sonia concluded: *The typical fifth grader owns about 5 CDs.*

Do you agree with her conclusion? Explain. _____

c. Describe two ways Sonia could improve her survey. _____

_____

6. $\frac{4}{5} + \frac{2}{5} =$ _____

7. $1 - \frac{3}{4} =$ _____

8. $\frac{5}{8} - \frac{3}{8} =$ _____

9. $\frac{9}{16} + \frac{2}{8} =$ _____

10.
$$\begin{array}{r} \frac{7}{8} \\ -\frac{1}{2} \\ \hline \end{array}$$

11.
$$\begin{array}{r} \frac{2}{3} \\ +\frac{2}{5} \\ \hline \end{array}$$

12.
$$\begin{array}{r} \frac{5}{6} \\ -\frac{3}{8} \\ \hline \end{array}$$

13.
$$\begin{array}{r} \frac{2}{3} \\ +\frac{3}{4} \\ \hline \end{array}$$

14. Circle the fraction pair represented by the drawing below.

$\frac{2}{15}$ and $\frac{3}{5}$ $\frac{5}{3}$ and $\frac{9}{5}$ $\frac{2}{3}$ and $\frac{3}{4}$ $\frac{4}{15}$ and $\frac{2}{15}$

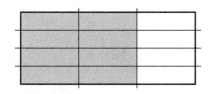
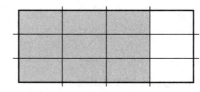

Written Assessment *continued*

15. Write a pair of fractions with common denominators for the
pictures in Problem 14.

_____   _____

16. David was writing a report on sleep and dreams. He gave a survey to the
21 students in his class. The following were three of the questions:

A. About how many hours do you sleep each night?

B. About how many dreams do you remember having in an average week?

C. What time do you usually get up on a school day?

The graphs below show the answers to two of these questions. Match the questions
with their graphs. (Write A, B, or C under each graph.)

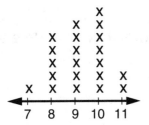

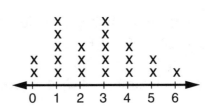

_____   _____

Part B

17. Circle each stem-and-leaf plot with a median of 24. Put an X through each stem-and-
leaf plot with a mode of 28. (There may be more than one.)

Stems (10s)	Leaves (1s)
1	3 4 7
2	0 2 4 4 4 4 8
3	0

Stems (10s)	Leaves (1s)
1	5 6 7
2	3 3 4 8 8 8 9
3	0

Stems (10s)	Leaves (1s)
1	8 9
2	3 4 8 8 8 9 9
3	0 1

18. Martha's class made these estimates for the number of jellybeans in a jar:

128, 126, 135, 139, 132, 130, 145, 147, 155, 120,
191, 135, 145, 135, 137, 158

a. Explain the mistake in the stem-and-leaf plot
for the jellybean estimates.

_____

_____

_____

Stems (100s and 10s)	Leaves (1s)
12	8 6 0
13	5 9 2 0 7
14	5 7
15	5 8
19	1

b. Correct the stem-and-leaf plot at the right.

Written Assessment *continued*

19. **a.** Use your ruler to draw a line segment that is $2\frac{3}{8}$ in. long.

b. If you erased $\frac{3}{4}$ inch from this line segment, how long would it be? _____

c. If you drew a line segment twice as long as the original line segment, how long would it be? _____

20. One survey reported favorite types of books for fifth graders. The results of the survey were as follows:

adventure books: 38%

mystery books: 30%

comedies: 22%

other: 10%

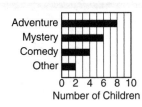

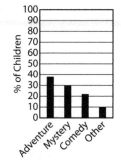

a. Circle the bar graph that best represents the survey results.

b. If 100 students answered the survey, how many of them chose adventures? _____

c. If 10 students answered the survey, how many of them chose other? _____

d. If 50 students answered the survey, how many of them chose mysteries? _____

e. If you were trying to decide what kinds of books to buy for the library in your town, how many fifth graders would you interview? _____

Explain why you chose that number. _____

21. Explain how you would use the multiplication rule to find common denominators for the fraction pair you circled in Problem 14.

_____

_____

22. Explain one way to rename $\frac{3}{5}$ as a percent without using a calculator.

_____

_____

LESSON 6·11 | **Open Response**

Mean Age

Imagine a family of six people. Pretend you are one of the 6 people in the family.

The **average age** of this family is **24 years.**

1. List the ages of all six people in the family. Describe the relationship each of the imaginary family members has to you—for example, my mom, my little sister, etc.

2. Explain how you used the mean to find the ages of the family members.

LESSON 7·12   Self Assessment

Think about each skill listed below. Assess your own progress by checking the most appropriate box.

Skills	I can do this on my own and explain how to do it.	I can do this on my own.	I can do this if I get help or look at an example.
1. Read and understand numbers written in scientific notation.			
2. Understand and use powers of 10.			
3. Understand and use exponential notation.			
4. Order and compare positive and negative numbers.			
5. Tell whether a number sentence is true or false.			
6. Understand and use parentheses in number sentences.			
7. Add and subtract positive and negative numbers.			
8. Understand and use order of operations.			

LESSON 7·12 | **Written Assessment** | Progress Check 7

Part A

Write >, <, or =.

1. −4 _____ 3

2. −12 _____ −10

3. 37 _____ −42

4. 10^2 _____ −200

5. $-\frac{3}{8}$ _____ −1

6. 9^2 _____ 6^3

7. −3 + (−3) _____ −6

8. 7 _____ −1 − (−10)

9. 24 / 3 _____ 6 − (−7)

10. Some of the expressions below are not number sentences. Cross them out. Then circle the number sentences that are true.

14 + (−25) > −50	$6^2 = 2^6$	11 * 11 * 11 = 33^3
2 * 10^3	−21 − (−39) = 60	38 < 7^2 − (−20)
$\frac{3}{4} + \frac{3}{4} > 1$	19	−5 = 20 + (−25)

11. Draw a line from each story to the number model that matches.

a. Jada baked 4 trays of cookies with one dozen on each tray. She and her brother ate 6 of the cookies while they were still warm.

    4 * 12 − 6

    6 * 12 − 4

b. Otis baked 4 trays of cookies. He started with one dozen on each tray. Then his mom removed 6 cookies from each tray to send to Otis's grandmother.

    6 * (12 − 4)

    4 * (12 − 6)

Insert parentheses when necessary to make the number sentences true. (Because of the rules for order of operations, some of the problems might not need parentheses.)

12. 9 + 2 * 5 = 19

13. 12 + 8 ÷ 2 = 16

14. −8 + 43 ÷ 5 = 7

15. 12 + 4 ÷ 8 = $12\frac{1}{2}$

16. −3 + 5 * 2 − (−6) = 16

17. 4^2 + (−3) − (−5) * 2 = 20

LESSON 7·12 | **Written Assessment** *continued*

Solve. You may use your ⊞ and ⊟ counters or your slide rule to help you.

18. $6 + (-8) =$ _____

19. $(-9) + (-6) =$ _____

20. $16 + (-5) =$ _____

21. $(-7) + 13 =$ _____

22. $(-14) - 3 =$ _____

23. $(-8) - (-5) =$ _____

24. $6 -$ _____ $= 17$

25. $17 - 20 =$ _____

26. Kerri is playing a game. She is 8 points "in the hole." (She has −8 points.)

a. She gets 12 points on her next turn. What is her score now? _____

b. If she loses 12 points instead, what will her score be? _____

Part B

Use your ⊞ and ⊟ counters.

27. Draw a picture that shows an account with a balance of −$6.

28. Draw a picture that shows a balance of $8, using exactly 10 counters.

29. What is your balance if you have the same number of ⊞ and ⊟ counters? _____

There are 15 ⊞ and 10 ⊟ counters in a container.

30. What is the balance in the container? _____

31. How many ⊟ counters do you
need to add to get a negative balance? _____

32. What will be the new balance if you
remove 6 ⊟ counters from the original balance? _____

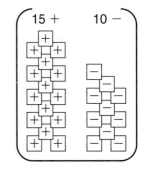

33. What will be the new balance if you

a. remove 7 ⊟ counters from the original balance? _____

b. add 3 ⊟ counters to the original balance? _____

LESSON 7·12 **Written Assessment** *continued*

34. Write each number in standard notation and in number-and-word notation.

Number	Standard Notation	Number-and-Word Notation
10^5		
10^9		
$6 * 10^7$		
$3.2 * 10^6$		

35. Use the graph to answer the questions.

a. How many kilometers did Jean travel in the first hour of the trip? _____

b. How far did Jean travel in all? _____

36. Use the following data to make a line graph.

Jean's Trip

Distance (km) vs. Time of Day

Word Study Test	1	2	3	4	5
Number of Correct Answers (out of 20)	15	10	20	15	5

LESSON 7·12 | Open Response

Operations in the Klasies Caves

Recently, archaeologists were studying cave art near the Klasies River in South Africa. They discovered what looked like number sentences on the wall of a cave. The numbers were written with the same digits as ours, but the symbols showed that the operations were different. Several number sentences are listed below. Use these samples to relate our operations symbols with the symbols from the cave.

$$(78 \; \bullet \; 3 \; \curlyvee \; 18) \; \blacktriangleright \; 2 = 64$$

$$(10 \; \blacklozenge \; 5) \; \bullet \; 3 = 5$$

$$90 \; \blacklozenge \; 6 = 4 \; \oslash \; (24 \; \curlyvee \; 16) \; \oslash \; 3$$

List what operation each Klasies River symbol represents. Explain how you figured out the symbols. Show all of your work.

Try This

Write a true number sentence using all of the symbols at least once.

Self Assessment

Think about each skill listed below. Assess your own progress by checking the most appropriate box.

Skills	I can do this on my own and explain how to do it.	I can do this on my own.	I can do this if I get help or look at an example.
1. Convert among fractions, decimals, and percents.			
2. Find common denominators.			
3. Order and compare fractions.			
4. Use an algorithm to subtract mixed numbers with like denominators.			
5. Use an algorithm to add mixed numbers.			
6. Convert between fractions and mixed or whole numbers.			
7. Find a percent of a number.			
8. Use an algorithm to multiply fractions and mixed numbers.			
9. Divide fractions.			

LESSON 8·13 | **Written Assessment** | Progress Check 8

Part A

Write each fraction as a decimal and a percent.

1. $\frac{7}{10}$ _____, _____

2. $\frac{8}{25}$ _____, _____

3. What is a common denominator for $\frac{1}{4}$ and $\frac{4}{7}$? _____

4. Explain how you found the common denominator in Problem 3.

_____

_____

5. Is $\frac{13}{25}$ greater than or less than $\frac{1}{2}$? _____

6. Explain how you decided on your answer for Problem 5.

_____

_____

7. a. Use your ruler to draw a line segment $2\frac{1}{4}$ inches long.

b. If you erased $\frac{3}{4}$ inch from this line segment,
how long would the new line segment be? _____ in.

Add or subtract. Write your answer in simplest form.

8. $\frac{5}{8} + \frac{3}{4} =$ _____

9. $\begin{array}{r} \frac{1}{1} \\ -\ \frac{2}{3} \\ \hline \end{array}$

10. $\begin{array}{r} \frac{5}{8} \\ -\ \frac{1}{2} \\ \hline \end{array}$

11. $\begin{array}{r} \frac{3}{4} \\ +\ 1\frac{1}{2} \\ \hline \end{array}$

12. $3\frac{3}{7} - 1\frac{6}{7} =$ _____

13. $3\frac{1}{3} + 1\frac{7}{8} =$ _____

14. $2\frac{1}{5} - 1\frac{4}{5} =$ _____

Fill in the missing number.

15. $3\frac{5}{8} = 2\frac{\square}{8}$

16. $5\frac{2}{6} = \square\frac{8}{6}$

17. $3\frac{1}{7} = 2\frac{\square}{7}$

18. $6\frac{5}{9} = \square\frac{14}{9}$

LESSON 8·13 Written Assessment *continued*

19. Fill in the oval next to possible common denominators for each fraction pair. (There may be more than one correct answer.)

a. $\frac{1}{3}$ and $\frac{4}{9}$

   ◯ 3
   ◯ 6
   ◯ 9
   ◯ 12

b. $\frac{3}{4}$ and $\frac{5}{6}$

   ◯ 4
   ◯ 6
   ◯ 12
   ◯ 24

c. $\frac{5}{8}$ and $\frac{2}{3}$

   ◯ 3
   ◯ 8
   ◯ 12
   ◯ 24

d. $\frac{3}{12}$ and $\frac{2}{5}$

   ◯ 5
   ◯ 7
   ◯ 30
   ◯ 60

20. List the eight fractions from Problem 19 in order from smallest to largest.

_____ _____ _____ _____ _____ _____ _____ _____

smallest   largest

Part B

21. If you draw a line segment twice as long as a $2\frac{1}{4}$-inch line segment, how long would the new line segment be? (Circle one.)

    $4\frac{6}{16}$ in. $4\frac{2}{4}$ in. $4\frac{3}{8}$ in. $4\frac{3}{16}$ in.

22. Bobbie measured the growth of her corn plant every week. One Friday, it was $3\frac{7}{8}$ inches tall. The following Friday, it was $6\frac{3}{8}$ inches tall. How much had it grown in one week? _____ in.

23. Explain how you found your answer for Problem 22.

_____

_____

24. How many minutes are in $\frac{1}{3}$ of an hour? _____ min

25. Mary Lou baked 36 cupcakes for the bake sale. If 75% of them had chocolate frosting, how many cupcakes had chocolate frosting? _____ cupcakes

Multiply or divide. Write your answer in simplest form. Draw a picture on the back to help you solve the problems if necessary.

26. $\frac{3}{8} * \frac{4}{5} =$ _____   **27.** $3\frac{1}{5} * 4\frac{5}{8} =$ _____   **28.** $\frac{1}{2} \div 6 =$ _____   **29.** $5 \div \frac{1}{4} =$ _____

LESSON 8·13 | Open Response

Writing Egyptian Fractions

A fifth grade class was doing research about fractions. They've found that the ancient Egyptians wrote all of their fractions as a sum of unit fractions where **no unit fraction is repeated.**

For example, you cannot write $\frac{3}{4} = \frac{1}{4} + \frac{1}{4} + \frac{1}{4}$. One way to write it would be: $\frac{1}{2} + \frac{1}{4}$.

An algorithm for finding a unit fraction expression for any fraction is the Greedy Method. To use the Greedy Method on fraction X:

Start with the largest unit fraction less than fraction X. Then continue in the same manner to represent the remaining value.

Example: Represent $\frac{7}{8}$ as a sum of unit fractions.

Step 1: $\frac{7}{8} = \frac{1}{2} + \frac{3}{8}$ $\frac{1}{2}$ is the largest unit fraction $< \frac{7}{8}$

Step 2: $\frac{7}{8} = \frac{1}{2} + \frac{1}{4} + \frac{1}{8}$ $\frac{1}{4}$ is the largest unit fraction $< \frac{3}{8}$

1. Represent $\frac{9}{10}$ as a sum of unit fractions. Show all of your work. Explain your thinking.

2. Represent $\frac{9}{10}$ as a sum of unit fractions in a different way. Show all of your steps.

LESSON 9·11   Self Assessment

Think about each skill listed below. Assess your own progress by checking the most appropriate box.

Skills	I can do this on my own and explain how to do it.	I can do this on my own.	I can do this if I get help or look at an example.
1. Identify and plot ordered pairs on a one-quadrant and four-quadrant coordinate grid.			
2. Understand the concept of area of a figure.			
3. Use a formula to find the area of rectangles, triangles, and parallelograms.			
4. Identify the base and height of triangles and parallelograms.			
5. Understand the concept of volume of a figure.			
6. Use a formula to find the volume of prisms.			

Written Assessment

Part A

Use the grid at the right for Problems 1–4.

1. **a.** Plot and label the following points:

    A: (1,1)   *B:* (2,3)   *C:* (5,3)   *D:* (4,1)

  b. Draw line segments to connect the points
    as follows:

    A to *B, B* to *C, C* to *D,* and *D* to *A.*

  c. Describe the figure you have drawn.

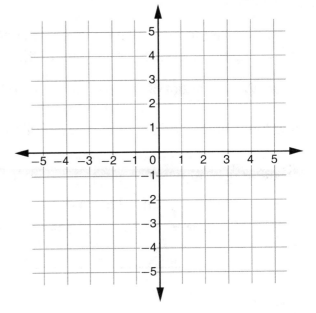

_____

_____

_____

_____

2. Plot points on the grid to make a reflection of the figure. Begin with the
reflection of point *A* at (1, −1).

3. Record the points you used below.

Point	Original Figure	Reflected Figure
A	(1,1)	(_____ , _____)
B	(2,3)	(_____ , _____)
C	(5,3)	(_____ , _____)
D	(4,1)	(_____ , _____)

4. Describe a rule for changing the points from the original figure to get the
reflected figure.

_____

_____

_____

LESSON 9·11 | **Written Assessment** *continued*

5. Jim wants to build a fence around his rectangular garden. The garden is 15 feet by 5 feet.

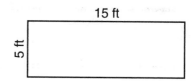

15 ft

5 ft

    a. In order to build a fence, does Jim need to find the area or the perimeter of the garden? _____

    b. What amount of fence does he need? _____
                                                                 (unit)

Find the area of the figures below. Use the formulas to help you.

> Area of rectangle = length of base * height: $A = b * h$
> Area of parallelogram = length of base * height: $A = b * h$
> Area of triangle = $\frac{1}{2}$ * length of base * height: $A = \frac{1}{2} * b * h$

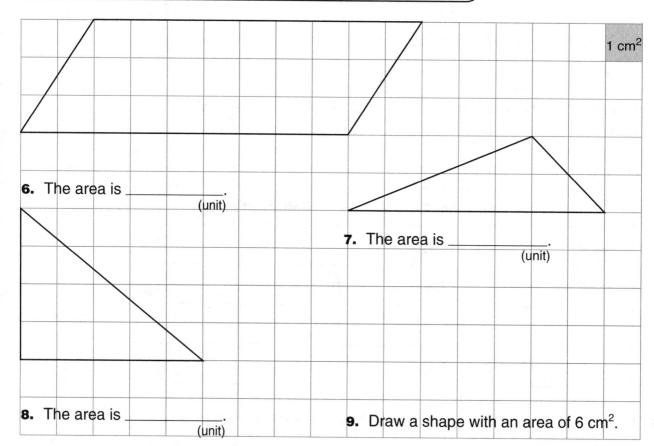

1 cm²

6. The area is _____. (unit)

7. The area is _____. (unit)

8. The area is _____. (unit)

9. Draw a shape with an area of 6 cm².

10. Label the base and height on the figures in Problems 6–9.

11. Explain what the area of a figure is. _____

_____

LESSON 9·11 Written Assessment *continued*

12. What ordered number pair names Point *A* in the coordinate grid at the right? _____

13. Plot and label a Point *C* in the grid so that triangle *ABC* has an area of 4 cm². What ordered number pair names Point *C*?

_____

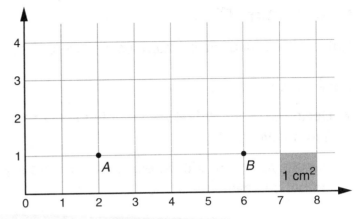

The prism at the right is made up of centimeter cubes.

14. What is the area of the base of the prism? _____
(unit)

15. What is the height of the prism? _____
(unit)

16. What is the volume of the prism? _____
(unit)

17. a. If you kept the area of the base the same and changed the height so that the volume tripled, what would the new volume be?

_____
(unit)

b. What would the new height be? _____
(unit)

Part B

Find the volume of the prisms below.

18.

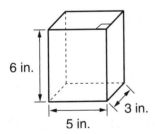

6 in.

5 in.

3 in.

Volume: _____
(unit)

19.

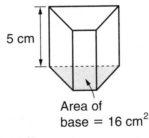

5 cm

Area of base = 16 cm²

Volume: _____
(unit)

20.

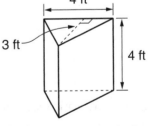

4 ft

3 ft

4 ft

Volume: _____
(unit)

21. The rectangular prism at the right has a volume of 120 in³.

What is its height? _____
(unit)

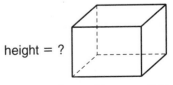

height = ?

Area of base = 24 in²

22. Explain how you can find the volume of any prism.

_____

LESSON 9·11 | **Open Response**

Countertop Tiles

Rafael is covering two countertops with tiles. The tiles are three inches by six inches.

For each countertop:

◆ Decide whether Rafael will be able to cover the entire surface with whole tiles (no gaps and no overlaps).

◆ Record your work with labeled pictures, and explain in words why the countertop can or cannot be covered with the tiles.

1. Countertop A: 15 inches by 18 inches

2. Countertop B: 9 inches by 9 inches

3. Based on your work, what rule could be used to determine whether or not a countertop can be covered with three-inch-by-six-inch tiles without having to draw a plan?

LESSON 10·10   Self Assessment

Think about each skill listed below. Assess your own progress by checking the most appropriate box.

Skills	I can do this on my own and explain how to do it.	I can do this on my own.	I can do this if I get help or look at an example.
1. Write algebraic expressions to represent situations.			
2. Solve one-step pan-balance problems.			
3. Interpret mystery line plots and graphs.			
4. Distinguish between circumference and area of a circle.			
5. Use formulas to find circumference and area of a circle.			
6. Solve two-step pan-balance problems.			
7. Represent rate problems as formulas.			

LESSON 10·10 — Written Assessment

Progress Check 10

Part A

Marge earns *D* dollars per hour.

1. Tom earns $5 per hour more than Marge. How much does he earn per hour? (Circle the answer.)

$$5 * D \qquad D - 5 \qquad D + 5 \qquad D + D$$

2. Marge's aunt earns twice as much per hour as Marge. How much does she earn per hour? (Circle the answer.)

$$2 * D \qquad 2 + D \qquad D - 2 \qquad \frac{1}{2} * D$$

3. Write an expression that shows how much Marge earns in 40 hours.

_____

Solve the pan-balance problems below.

4. One apple weighs

as much as _____ marbles.

5. One block weighs

as much as _____ marbles.

6. One ball weighs

as much as _____ blocks.

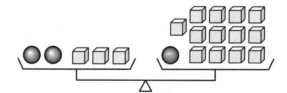

7. Shawna wrote an equation but covered one number.

15 + 7 = □ + 12. What is the covered number? _____

LESSON 10·10   Written Assessment *continued*

8. Mrs. Griffin surveyed her class by asking three questions. The class made the line plots below to show the results for each question.

Write the number of the line plot next to the question it represents.

◆ How many complete months are there until your next birthday?   Plot _____

◆ How many years old is the oldest child living at your house?   Plot _____

◆ How many books did you read last summer?   Plot _____

Plot #1

```
                X   X                   X   X   X
        X   X   X               X       X   X   X   X   X
X   X   X   X               X   X       X   X   X   X   X
0   1   2   3   4   5   6   7   8   9  10  11
```

Plot #2

```
    X       X
    X   X   X
    X   X   X                   X
    X   X   X       X       X   X
X   X   X   X       X       X   X               X                           X
0   1   2   3   4   5   6   7   8   9  10  11  12  13  14  15 16  17  18  19  20
```

Plot #3

```
        X
        X
        X
        X
        X       X                   X
        X       X       X           X
        X       X       X           X       X       X
        X       X       X           X       X       X                   X
    10  11  12  13  14  15  16  17  18  19  20
```

LESSON 10·10 | **Written Assessment** *continued*

To solve each of the following problems, would you need to find the circumference, perimeter, or area? (Circle the answer.)

9. Mario ran around a circular track 20 times.
How far did he run?   circumference   area

10. Mr. Li is planting tomatoes in his garden.
He wants one plant for every 2 square feet.
How many plants should he buy?   perimeter   area

11. Jill is building a fence around her swimming pool.
How many feet of fencing should she buy?   perimeter   area

Part B

> Circumference of a circle $= \pi * \text{diameter}$
>
> Area of a circle $= \pi * \text{radius}^2$

Complete each of the following sentences, rounding each answer to the nearest centimeter. Use the π key on your calculator or use 3.14 as an approximation for π.

12. The diameter is about _____ cm.

13. The radius is about _____ cm.

14. The circumference is about _____ cm.

15. The area is about _____ cm^2.

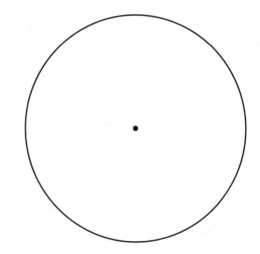

LESSON 10·10 | **Written Assessment** *continued*

16. Pete set up a pan balance. He found that 2 calculators balance 16 marbles. He then used the pan balance to find that 5 marbles balance 3 marbles and 10 paper clips. Fill in the blanks below.

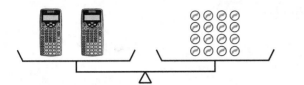 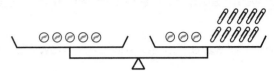

a. One calculator weighs as much as _____ paper clips.

b. One calculator weighs as much as _____ marbles.

17. The copy machine in the school office can make 40 copies per minute. This is given below as a rule.

Complete the table. Then graph the data in the table.

Rule: Number of copies = 40 * number of minutes

Time (min)	Number of Copies
1	
	80
3	
	100
4½	
	220

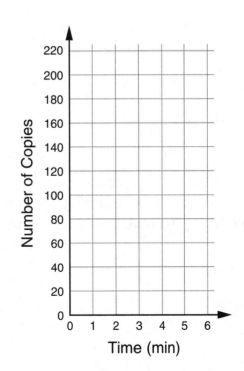

18. Ms. Southern needs to make 150 copies.

About how long will this take? _____

Open Response

An Age Puzzle

Renee is twice as old as Dana.
Four years ago, Renee was three times as old as Dana.

1. How old are Renee and Dana now? Show your work.

2. Explain what you did to solve the problem.

3. Write an algebraic expression to tell how old Renee is if Dana is *d* years old.
Explain how you figured out your expression.

LESSON 11·8   Self Assessment

Think about each skill listed below. Assess your own progress by checking the most appropriate box.

Skills	I can do this on my own and explain how to do it.	I can do this on my own.	I can do this if I get help or look at an example.
1. Use formulas to find the volume of prisms and cylinders.			
2. Use formulas to find the area of polygons and circles.			
3. Find the surface area of prisms.			
4. Explain how to find the surface area of cylinders.			
5. Explain the relationship between the volume of pyramids and prisms and the volume of cones and cylinders.			
6. Describe capacity and how to calculate it.			

LESSON 11·8 | **Written Assessment** | Progress Check 11

Part A

Complete each sentence with one of the following names of the geometric solids:

pyramid   cone   rectangular prism   cylinder

1. I have exactly two bases and no vertices. I am a _____.

2. All of my faces are triangular. I am a _____.

3. I have one base and one curved surface. I am a _____.

4. I have a pair of bases and exactly eight vertices. I am a _____.

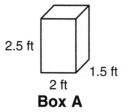

2.5 ft
1.5 ft
2 ft
Box A

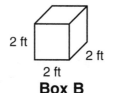

2 ft
2 ft
2 ft
Box B

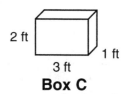

2 ft
1 ft
3 ft
Box C

5. Which of the boxes above has the greatest volume? _____

Explain how you know. _____

_____

_____

_____

_____

6. The rectangular prism at the right has a volume
of 120 cubic inches.

What is the area of the base? _____

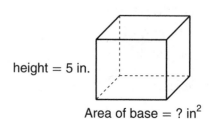

height = 5 in.

Area of base = ? in^2

LESSON 11·8 | **Written Assessment** *continued*

Area of rectangle: $A = l * w$	**Circumference of a circle:** $C = \pi * d$
Volume of rectangular prism:	**Area of circle:** $A = \pi * r^2$
$\quad V = l * w * h$	**Volume of cylinder:** $V = \pi * r^2 * h$

7. What is the radius of the circle at the right? _____

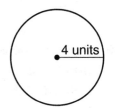
4 units

8. What is the diameter of the circle? _____

9. What is the circumference? _____

10. What is the area of the base of the cylinder at the right? _____

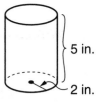
5 in.
2 in.

11. What is the volume of the cylinder? _____

The prism at the right is made of centimeter cubes.

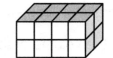

12. What is the area of the base of the prism? _____

13. What is the height of the prism? _____

14. What is the volume of the prism? _____

15. If you kept the base the same, but tripled the
volume of this prism, what would the height be? _____

16. Write a number sentence to show how you solved Problem 15. _____

Part B

17. a. What is the surface area of the prism in Problem 12? _____

b. Explain how you found the surface area.

_____

_____

_____

_____

LESSON 11·8 | **Written Assessment** *continued*

18. What information do you need to figure out how many square inches of paint you would use if you painted the entire cylinder on page 207 (top, bottom, and sides)?

_____

_____

19. If you place a cone inside of the cylinder in Problem 11 on page 207, and the cone is an exact fit (that is, the apex of the cone touches the bottom of the cylinder, and the base of the cone fits exactly at the top of the cylinder), what would the volume of the cone be? _____

Write a number sentence to show how you found your answer.

_____

20. The pyramid at the right has the same height as the prism in Problem 6 on page 206.

What is the volume of the pyramid? _____

Write a number sentence to show how you found your answer.

_____

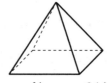

Area of base = 24 in²

Min's fish are sick, and she wants to add medicine to the tank. The instructions suggest adding one drop of medicine for every 4 L of water. The base of the fish tank measures 40 cm by 25 cm. The tank is filled with water to a height of about 20 cm.

Reminder: 1 L = 1,000 cm³

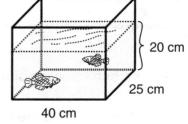

20 cm

25 cm

40 cm

21. How many drops of medicine should Min add to her tank? _____

22. Explain what you did to find the answer.

_____

_____

LESSON 11·8

Open Response

A Treasure Hunt

The intrepid explorer Cindy Rella went to the Amazon basin in search of the lost treasure of the Waorani Indians.

Traps had been set to guard the treasure. Cindy fell through a trap door into a 9-foot high rectangular room that measured 4 feet wide by 6 feet long.

Suddenly, the room began to fill with water but stopped when it was 3 feet deep. Cindy sighed with relief, but her relief didn't last long.

The two 4-foot wide walls of the room began to move, making the room smaller and causing the water level to rise. Every 10 minutes, the walls were 1 foot closer together.

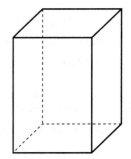

1. Label the rectangular prism with the dimensions of the original room.

2. Figure out how much time will pass before the water lifts Cindy to the trapdoor exit in the ceiling of the room.

   Show your work and explain how you found your answer.

LESSON 12·9 | Self Assessment

Think about each skill listed below. Assess your own progress by checking the most appropriate box.

Skills	I can do this on my own and explain how to do it.	I can do this on my own.	I can do this if I get help or look at an example.
1. Find all the factors of a number.			
2. Find the prime factorization of a number.			
3. Find the greatest common factor of two numbers.			
4. Find the least common multiple of two numbers.			
5. Solve rate and ratio number stories.			
6. Use the Multiplication Counting Principle to solve problems.			
7. Use tree diagrams to solve problems.			

LESSON 12·9 | **Written Assessment**

Progress Check 12

Part A

For each number below, draw a factor tree and write the prime factorization.

1.   60

2.   84

60 = _____

84 = _____

3. What prime factors do 60 and 84 have in common? _____

4. What is the greatest common factor of 60 and 84? _____

Explain how you found it. _____

_____

_____

5. What is the least common multiple of 60 and 84? _____

Explain how you found it. _____

_____

_____

_____

Rewrite each fraction pair with a common denominator.

6. $\frac{3}{8}$ and $\frac{5}{12}$ _____ and _____

7. $\frac{6}{7}$ and $\frac{5}{10}$ _____ and _____

8. Explain how you found the answer to Problem 6.

_____

_____

_____

LESSON 12·9 | **Written Assessment** *continued*

9. Sven bought a large pizza. He wants to cut the pizza so that it can be shared equally by 2 people, 3 people, 4 people, 6 people, or 8 people. Into how many slices should Sven cut the pizza? _____
(unit)

10. There are 30 students in Linda's class. Two-thirds of her class rides to school on the school bus. The other students walk to school. How many students walk to school? _____
(unit)

11. Matt was playing *Name That Number.* Of the 5 cards he turned over, 60% were black. How many black cards were there? _____
(unit)

12. Three out of 7 cars parked on one street were red. If there were 28 cars, how many cars were red? _____
(unit)

13. What is the ratio of cars that were not red to total cars in Problem 12? _____

Explain how you found your answer. _____

_____

_____

Solve each number story. Record the number model and the solution.

14. Susan rode her bike $4\frac{4}{5}$ miles on Thursday. She rode her bike $2\frac{1}{2}$ times that far on Friday. How far did she ride her bike on Friday?

a. Open number model: _____

b. Solution: _____

15. At a bank, Maggie exchanged a $5 bill for $5 in quarters. How many quarters did she get?

a. Open number model: _____

b. Solution: _____

LESSON 12·9 | **Written Assessment** *continued*

Part B

16. Darin rolls a 6-sided die and then flips a coin.

How many different ways can the die roll and coin toss turn out?

a. Use the Multiplication Counting Principle to answer. _____ different ways

b. Draw a tree diagram to show all the possible ways.
Suggestion: Use the letters H and T to represent HEADS and TAILS.

c. Which method do you think is easier for finding the number of

possible results? _____

d. Explain your answer. _____

_____

_____

17. In Problem 16, what is the probability that Darin…

a. rolls a 5 and the coin lands on HEADS? _____

b. rolls an even number and the coin lands on TAILS? _____

c. rolls a prime number? _____

d. tosses the coin so that it lands on HEADS? _____

LESSON 12·9 | **Written Assessment** *continued*

Write a number model for each problem. Then solve the problem.

18. Rosalyn's family was driving from home to her aunt's house. After going 48 miles, they were $\frac{3}{4}$ of the way there. How far from home was her aunt's house?

Number model: _____   Answer: _____ miles

19. In Doreen's first basketball game, she made a basket 9 times out of 15 attempts. She made the same ratio of baskets out of 25 attempts in the second game. How many baskets did she make in her 25 attempts?

Number model: _____   Answer: _____ baskets

20. Explain how you found your answer to Problem 19.

_____

_____

_____

_____

_____

21. Marcus's heart beats 11 times in 10 seconds. At this rate, about how many times would it beat in 1 minute?   _____ times

22. Carlo was buying tickets for his family at the school fair. He got 7 tickets for each dollar. He received a total of 224 tickets. How much did he spend on tickets?   _____

LESSON 12·9 | **Open Response**

Counting Cars

Use the statements below to figure out how many trips the Rock Island Ferry made.

◆ The Rock Island Ferry took 64 cars and trucks across the Rock Island River one Saturday.
◆ The total ratio of cars to trucks for the day was 5 to 3.
◆ The ferry carries 6 cars and 4 trucks when it is full.
◆ It was full on every trip except for the last trip of the day.

How many trips did the ferry make?

Show all of your work and describe, in words, the steps you followed to solve the problem.

LESSON 1·10 **Written Assessment**

Progress Check 1

Part A

1. Mr. Martin has 24 tulip bulbs. He wants to plant them in a rectangular array consisting of at least 2 rows with at least 2 tulips in each row. On the grid at the right, draw three possible arrays.

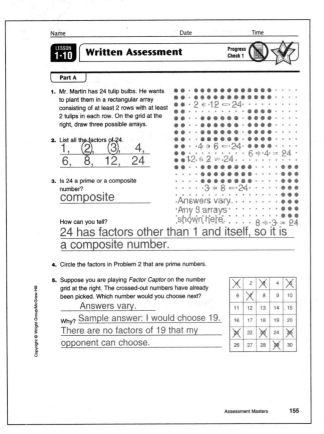

2 ∗ 12 ⇐ 24
4 ∗ 6 ⇐ 24   6 ∗ 4 ⇒ 24
12 ∗ 2 = 24
3 ∗ 8 = 24
Answers vary.
Any 3 arrays
shown here.   8 ∗ 3 = 24

2. List all the factors of 24.

1, ②, ③, 4,
6, 8, 12, 24

3. Is 24 a prime or a composite number?

composite

How can you tell?

24 has factors other than 1 and itself, so it is a composite number.

4. Circle the factors in Problem 2 that are prime numbers.

5. Suppose you are playing *Factor Captor* on the number grid at the right. The crossed-out numbers have already been picked. Which number would you choose next?

Answers vary.

Why? Sample answer: I would choose 19. There are no factors of 19 that my opponent can choose.

✗	2	✗	4	✗
6	✗	8	9	10
11	12	13	14	15
16	17	18	19	20
✗	22	✗	24	✗
26	27	28	✗	30

Assessment Masters   **155**

LESSON 1·10 **Written Assessment** *continued*

6. At the right is a calendar for a month. Use the following clues to figure out the date that Bret Harte School won its last basketball game.

♦ The date is not an even number.
♦ The date is not a square number.
♦ The date is not a prime number.
♦ The date is a multiple of 5.

S	M	T	W	T	F	S
	1	2	3	4	5	6
7	8	9	10	11	12	13
14	15	16	17	18	19	20
21	22	23	24	25	26	27
28	29	30	31			

On which day did the school win its last basketball game? The 15th

7. a. Write an 8-digit number that has
3 in the ones place,
7 in the hundred-thousands place,
8 in the thousands place,
5 in the hundredths place,
and 0 in all other places.

7 0 8 0 0 3 0 5

b. Write this numeral in words.

Seven hundred eight thousand three and five hundredths

Part B

8. Write the prime factorization for 24. 2 ∗ 2 ∗ 2 ∗ 3

9. Write the prime factorization of 24 using exponents. 2^3 ∗ 3

10. Fill in the missing numbers.

a. $7^2 =$ 49   b. $9^2 =$ 81   c. 36 = 6^2

d. $5^2 =$ 25   e. $10^2 =$ 100   f. 8 ∗ 8 = 8^2

11. Name a number between 200 and 300 that is divisible by 3 but not by 2.
Sample answers: 231, 285

12. Name a number between 200 and 300 that is divisible by 2, 3, and 5.
Sample answers: 210, 240, 270

156   *Assessment Handbook*

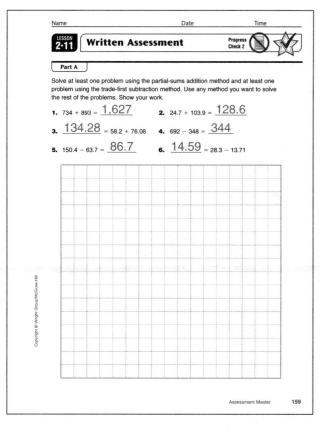

LESSON 2·11 Written Assessment   Progress Check 2

Part A

Solve at least one problem using the partial-sums addition method and at least one problem using the trade-first subtraction method. Use any method you want to solve the rest of the problems. Show your work.

1. 734 + 893 = _1,627_   **2.** 24.7 + 103.9 = _128.6_

3. _134.28_ = 58.2 + 76.08   **4.** 692 − 348 = _344_

5. 150.4 − 63.7 = _86.7_   **6.** _14.59_ = 28.3 − 13.71

Assessment Master   159

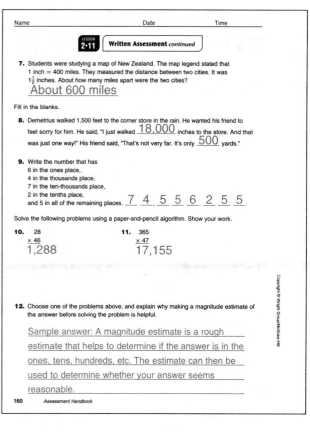

LESSON 2·11 Written Assessment *continued*

7. Students were studying a map of New Zealand. The map legend stated that 1 inch = 400 miles. They measured the distance between two cities. It was $1\frac{1}{2}$ inches. About how many miles apart were the two cities?
About 600 miles

Fill in the blanks.

8. Demetrius walked 1,500 feet to the corner store in the rain. He wanted his friend to feel sorry for him. He said, "I just walked _18,000_ inches to the store. And that was just one way!" His friend said, "That's not very far. It's only _500_ yards."

9. Write the number that has
6 in the ones place,
4 in the thousands place,
7 in the ten-thousands place,
2 in the tenths place,
and 5 in all of the remaining places. _7 4 5 5 6 . 2 5 5_

Solve the following problems using a paper-and-pencil algorithm. Show your work.

10. 28   **11.** 365
      × 46   × 47
    _1,288_   _17,155_

12. Choose one of the problems above, and explain why making a magnitude estimate of the answer before solving the problem is helpful.

Sample answer: A magnitude estimate is a rough
estimate that helps to determine if the answer is in the
ones, tens, hundreds, etc. The estimate can then be
used to determine whether your answer seems
reasonable.

160   Assessment Handbook

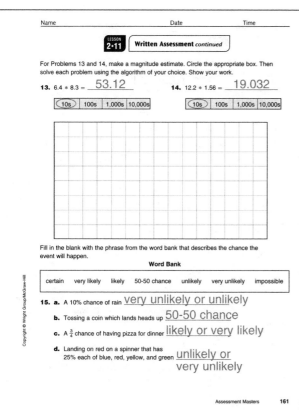

LESSON 2·11 Written Assessment *continued*

For Problems 13 and 14, make a magnitude estimate. Circle the appropriate box. Then solve each problem using the algorithm of your choice. Show your work.

13. 6.4 * 8.3 = _53.12_   **14.** 12.2 * 1.56 = _19.032_

| (10s) | 100s | 1,000s | 10,000s | | (10s) | 100s | 1,000s | 10,000s |

Fill in the blank with the phrase from the word bank that describes the chance the event will happen.

Word Bank

| certain | very likely | likely | 50-50 chance | unlikely | very unlikely | impossible |

15. a. A 10% chance of rain _very unlikely or unlikely_

b. Tossing a coin which lands heads up _50-50 chance_

c. A $\frac{3}{4}$ chance of having pizza for dinner _likely or very likely_

d. Landing on red on a spinner that has 25% each of blue, red, yellow, and green _unlikely or very unlikely_

Assessment Masters   161

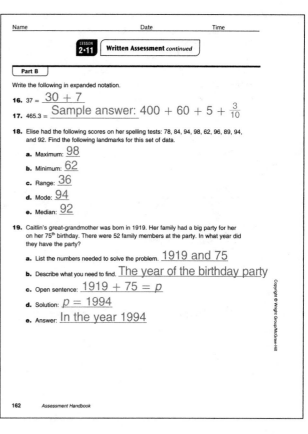

LESSON 2·11 Written Assessment *continued*

Part B

Write the following in expanded notation.

16. 37 = _30 + 7_

17. 465.3 = _Sample answer: 400 + 60 + 5 + $\frac{3}{10}$_

18. Elise had the following scores on her spelling tests: 78, 84, 94, 98, 62, 96, 89, 94, and 92. Find the following landmarks for this set of data.

a. Maximum: _98_

b. Minimum: _62_

c. Range: _36_

d. Mode: _94_

e. Median: _92_

19. Caitlin's great-grandmother was born in 1919. Her family had a big party for her on her 75th birthday. There were 52 family members at the party. In what year did they have the party?

a. List the numbers needed to solve the problem. _1919 and 75_

b. Describe what you need to find. _The year of the birthday party_

c. Open sentence: _1919 + 75 = p_

d. Solution: _p = 1994_

e. Answer: _In the year 1994_

162   Assessment Handbook

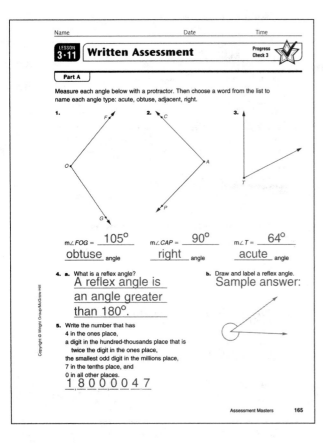

Name _____ Date _____ Time _____

LESSON 3·11 | **Written Assessment** Progress Check 3

Part A

Measure each angle below with a protractor. Then choose a word from the list to name each angle type: acute, obtuse, adjacent, right.

1.

2.

3.

m∠FOG = __105°__
__obtuse__ angle

m∠CAP = __90°__
__right__ angle

m∠T = __64°__
__acute__ angle

4. **a.** What is a reflex angle?
__A reflex angle is__
__an angle greater__
__than 180°.__

b. Draw and label a reflex angle.
__Sample answer:__

5. Write the number that has
4 in the ones place,
a digit in the hundred-thousands place that is
   twice the digit in the ones place,
the smallest odd digit in the millions place,
7 in the tenths place, and
0 in all other places.
__1,8 0 0 0 0 4 7__

Assessment Masters 165

Name _____ Date _____ Time _____

LESSON 3·11 | **Written Assessment** *continued*

Use your Geometry Template to do the following:

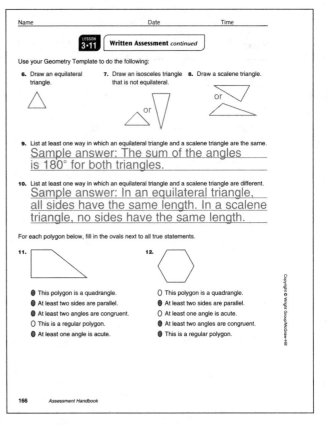

6. Draw an equilateral triangle.

7. Draw an isosceles triangle that is not equilateral.

8. Draw a scalene triangle.

9. List at least one way in which an equilateral triangle and a scalene triangle are the same.
__Sample answer: The sum of the angles__
__is 180° for both triangles.__

10. List at least one way in which an equilateral triangle and a scalene triangle are different.
__Sample answer: In an equilateral triangle,__
__all sides have the same length. In a scalene__
__triangle, no sides have the same length.__

For each polygon below, fill in the ovals next to all true statements.

11.

12.

- ● This polygon is a quadrangle.
- ● At least two sides are parallel.
- ● At least two angles are congruent.
- ○ This is a regular polygon.
- ● At least one angle is acute.

- ○ This polygon is a quadrangle.
- ● At least two sides are parallel.
- ○ At least one angle is acute.
- ● At least two angles are congruent.
- ● This is a regular polygon.

166 *Assessment Handbook*

Name _____ Date _____ Time _____

LESSON 3·11 | **Written Assessment** *continued*

Part B

Find the missing angle measure without using your protractor.

13.

14.

15.

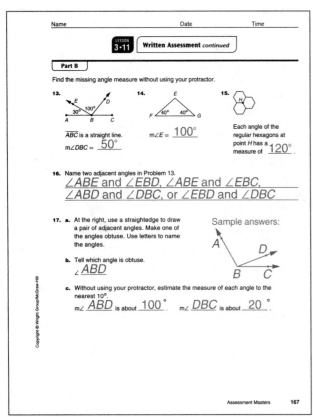

$\overline{ABC}$ is a straight line.
m∠DBC = __50°__

m∠E = __100°__

Each angle of the regular hexagons at point *H* has a measure of __120°__.

16. Name two adjacent angles in Problem 13.
__∠ABE and ∠EBD, ∠ABE and ∠EBC,__
__∠ABD and ∠DBC, or ∠EBD and ∠DBC__

17. **a.** At the right, use a straightedge to draw a pair of adjacent angles. Make one of the angles obtuse. Use letters to name the angles.

Sample answers:

b. Tell which angle is obtuse.
__∠ABD__

c. Without using your protractor, estimate the measure of each angle to the nearest 10°.
m∠ __ABD__ is about __100__°. m∠ __DBC__ is about __20__°.

Assessment Masters 167

Name _____ Date _____ Time _____

LESSON 3·11 | **Written Assessment** *continued*

18. Use the table below to answer the questions.

Regional Populations 1850–2000				
Region	**1850**	**1900**	**1950**	**2000**
Northeast	8,627,000	21,047,000	39,478,000	52,107,000
South	8,983,000	24,524,000	47,197,000	97,614,000
Midwest	5,404,000	26,333,000	44,461,000	63,502,000
West	179,000	4,309,000	20,190,000	61,412,000

a. Which region had the smallest population in 1950? __West__

b. Which had the smallest population 50 years later? __Northeast__

c. Which region had the greatest increase in population from 1850 to 2000?
__South__ What was the increase? __88,631,000__

19. Use the pattern-block shapes on your Geometry Template to draw a pattern that tessellates. (The pattern-block shapes are marked PB.)

Sample answers:

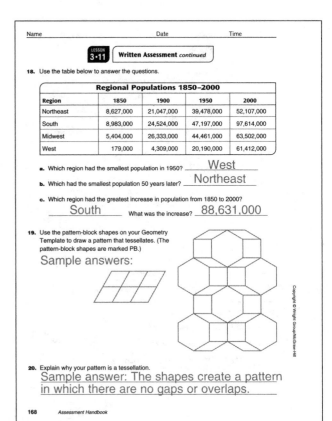

20. Explain why your pattern is a tessellation.
__Sample answer: The shapes create a pattern__
__in which there are no gaps or overlaps.__

168 *Assessment Handbook*

LESSON 4·8 | Written Assessment

Progress Check 4

Part A

Use the map to answer the questions.

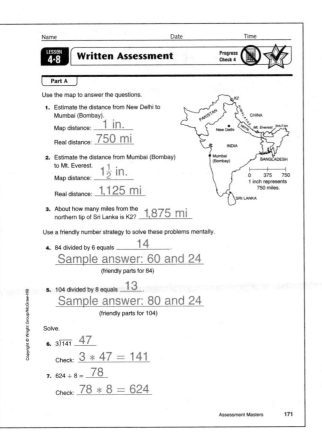

1. Estimate the distance from New Delhi to Mumbai (Bombay).

   Map distance: __1 in.__

   Real distance: __750 mi__

2. Estimate the distance from Mumbai (Bombay) to Mt. Everest.

   Map distance: __$1\frac{1}{2}$ in.__

   Real distance: __1,125 mi__

3. About how many miles from the northern tip of Sri Lanka is K2? __1,875 mi__

Use a friendly number strategy to solve these problems mentally.

4. 84 divided by 6 equals __14__.

   Sample answer: 60 and 24
   (friendly parts for 84)

5. 104 divided by 8 equals __13__.

   Sample answer: 80 and 24
   (friendly parts for 104)

Solve.

6. 3)141 __47__

   Check: $3 * 47 = 141$

7. $624 ÷ 8 =$ __78__

   Check: $78 * 8 = 624$

LESSON 4·8 | Written Assessment continued

Make a magnitude estimate. Circle the appropriate box.

8. $59.4 ÷ 3$ How I estimated: __$60 ÷ 3 = 20$__

   0.1s   1s   (10s)   100s

9. $6.428 / 4$ How I estimated: __$6 ÷ 4 = 1.5$__

   0.1s   (1s)   10s   100s

In Problems 10 and 11:

♦ Find the value of x in the first number sentence.

♦ Use this value to complete the second number sentence.

10. $x = 100 - 95$ $x^2 =$ __25__

11. $x = \frac{1}{2}$ of a dozen $30 * x =$ __180__

12. Write an open number sentence you can use to solve the number story below. Then solve the number story.

    Four friends rented a car. The total rental cost was $150, including tax. The friends split the cost evenly. How much did each friend contribute?

    Number sentence: __$150 ÷ 4 = c$, or $4 * c = 150$__

    Solution: __$37.50__

Solve. Show your work for Problems 13–18 on a computation grid.

13. $126 / 6 =$ __21__   14. $9 *$ __27__ $= 243$

Part B

15. $703 ÷ 14 →$ __50 R3__   16. $482 ÷ 34 →$ __14 R6__

LESSON 4·8 | Written Assessment continued

Circle your magnitude estimate. Then solve.

17. 5)88.5 __17.7__   0.1s   1s   (10s)   100s

18. 14)2.94 __0.21__   (0.1s)   1s   10s   100s

In Problems 19 and 20, write an open sentence to represent the number story and use a division algorithm to solve the problem. Then decide what to do about the remainder and tell why you chose what to do.

19. Tammy has 130 photographs. She can tape 8 photos onto each page of her photo album. How many pages will she need to tape all her photos in the album?

    Number sentence: __$130 ÷ 8 = p$, or $8 * p = 130$__

    Solution: __17__ pages

    What does the remainder represent? __The 2 photographs remaining after 16 pages have been completely filled__

    Circle what you did with the remainder.

    Ignored it   Reported it as a fraction or decimal   (Rounded the answer up)

20. For a relay race, the gym teacher divided the class into 4 teams with an equal number of students on each team. There were 30 students in the class. Extra students didn't race. How many members were on each team?

    Number sentence: __$30 ÷ 4 = t$, or $4 * t = 30$__

    Solution: __7__ members

    What does the remainder represent? __The 2 extra students who did not race__

    Circle what you did with the remainder.

    (Ignored it)   Reported it as a fraction or decimal   Rounded the answer up

LESSON 5·13 Written Assessment *Progress Check 5*

Part A

Write three equivalent fractions for each fraction below. Sample answers:

1. $\frac{3}{7}$ $\frac{6}{14}, \frac{9}{21}, \frac{30}{70}$ 2. $\frac{6}{9}$ $\frac{2}{3}, \frac{12}{18}, \frac{18}{27}$

3. $\frac{9}{10}$ $\frac{18}{20}, \frac{27}{30}, \frac{90}{100}$

Fill in the oval next to each equivalent fraction or mixed number. (*Hint:* There may be more than one correct answer.)

4. $\frac{12}{5}$
- ○ 3
- ○ $2\frac{4}{5}$
- ● $1\frac{7}{5}$
- ● $2\frac{2}{5}$

5. $\frac{18}{8}$
- ○ 2
- ● $2\frac{1}{4}$
- ○ $3\frac{1}{8}$
- ○ $2\frac{2}{8}$

6. $3\frac{4}{9}$
- ○ $\frac{7}{9}$
- ● $\frac{31}{9}$
- ○ $\frac{15}{9}$
- ○ $\frac{34}{9}$

7. $5\frac{7}{3}$
- ○ $\frac{35}{3}$
- ○ $\frac{12}{3}$
- ○ $\frac{15}{3}$
- ● $\frac{22}{3}$

Write the mixed number and fraction for each diagram below. In each diagram, the square is worth 1.

Whole
square

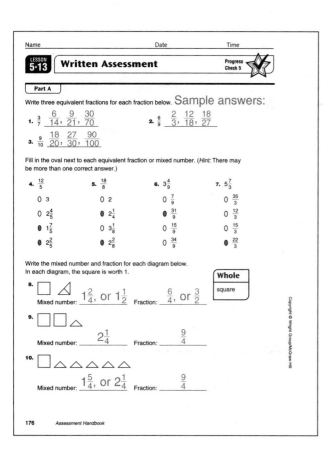

8. Mixed number: $1\frac{2}{4}$, or $1\frac{1}{2}$ Fraction: $\frac{6}{4}$, or $\frac{3}{2}$

9. Mixed number: $2\frac{1}{4}$ Fraction: $\frac{9}{4}$

10. Mixed number: $1\frac{5}{4}$, or $2\frac{1}{4}$ Fraction: $\frac{9}{4}$

LESSON 5·13 Written Assessment *continued*

Use fraction sticks to add the fractions.

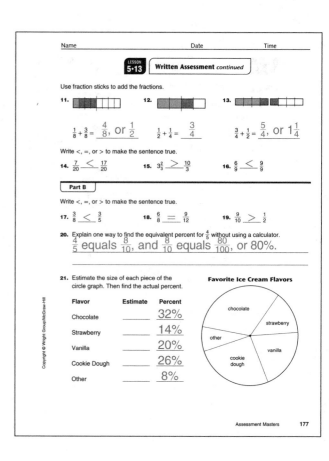

11. $\frac{1}{8} + \frac{3}{8} = \frac{4}{8}$, or $\frac{1}{2}$

12. $\frac{1}{2} + \frac{1}{4} = \frac{3}{4}$

13. $\frac{3}{4} + \frac{1}{2} = \frac{5}{4}$, or $1\frac{1}{4}$

Write <, =, or > to make the sentence true.

14. $\frac{7}{20} < \frac{17}{20}$ 15. $3\frac{2}{3} > \frac{10}{3}$ 16. $\frac{6}{9} < \frac{9}{9}$

Part B

Write <, =, or > to make the sentence true.

17. $\frac{3}{8} < \frac{3}{5}$ 18. $\frac{6}{8} = \frac{9}{12}$ 19. $\frac{9}{10} > \frac{1}{2}$

20. Explain one way to find the equivalent percent for $\frac{4}{5}$ without using a calculator.
$\frac{4}{5}$ equals $\frac{8}{10}$, and $\frac{8}{10}$ equals $\frac{80}{100}$, or 80%.

21. Estimate the size of each piece of the circle graph. Then find the actual percent.

Favorite Ice Cream Flavors

Flavor	Estimate	Percent
Chocolate	_____	32%
Strawberry	_____	14%
Vanilla	_____	20%
Cookie Dough	_____	26%
Other	_____	8%

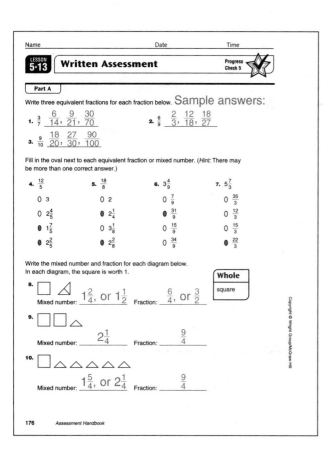

LESSON 5·13 Written Assessment *continued*

22. Why is it helpful to make an estimate before finding the size of a piece of a circle graph?
Answers vary.

A survey reported favorite types of books for fifth graders. The results of the survey were as follows:

38% Adventure books   30% Mystery books   22% Humor books   10% Other

23. Make and label a circle graph for this data below. Use your Percent Circle.

Favorite Books

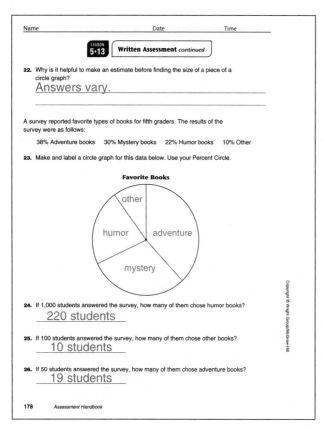

24. If 1,000 students answered the survey, how many of them chose humor books?
220 students

25. If 100 students answered the survey, how many of them chose other books?
10 students

26. If 50 students answered the survey, how many of them chose adventure books?
19 students

LESSON 6·11 Written Assessment

Progress Check 6

Part A

Fill in the ovals to match the words to their definitions.

1. Median
- ○ smallest value
- ○ largest value
- ○ most frequent value
- ● middle value

2. Maximum
- ○ smallest value
- ● largest value
- ○ most frequent value
- ○ middle value

3. Mode
- ○ smallest value
- ○ largest value
- ● most frequent value
- ○ middle value

4. Minimum
- ● smallest value
- ○ largest value
- ○ most frequent value
- ○ middle value

5. Sonia asked seven girls in her fifth-grade class how many CDs they own. Here are the results of her survey: 2 0 6 5 7 5 1

a. What was the median number of CDs owned? __5 CDs__

b. Sonia concluded: *The typical fifth grader owns about 5 CDs.*

Do you agree with her conclusion? Explain. Answers vary.

c. Describe two ways Sonia could improve her survey. Sample answers: Ask more students. Ask boys and girls.

6. $\frac{4}{5} + \frac{2}{5} = \frac{6}{5}$, or $1\frac{1}{5}$

7. $1 - \frac{3}{4} = \frac{1}{4}$

8. $\frac{5}{8} - \frac{3}{8} = \frac{2}{8}$, or $\frac{1}{4}$

9. $\frac{9}{16} + \frac{2}{8} = \frac{13}{16}$

10.
$$\frac{7}{8}$$
$$-\frac{1}{2}$$
$$\frac{3}{8}$$

11.
$$\frac{2}{3}$$
$$+\frac{2}{5}$$
$$\frac{16}{15}, \text{ or } 1\frac{1}{15}$$

12.
$$\frac{5}{6}$$
$$-\frac{3}{8}$$
$$\frac{11}{24}$$

13.
$$\frac{2}{3}$$
$$+\frac{3}{4}$$
$$\frac{17}{12}, \text{ or } 1\frac{5}{12}$$

14. Circle the fraction pair represented by the drawing below.

$\frac{2}{15}$ and $\frac{3}{5}$ $\frac{5}{3}$ and $\frac{9}{5}$ ($\frac{2}{3}$ and $\frac{3}{4}$) $\frac{4}{15}$ and $\frac{2}{15}$

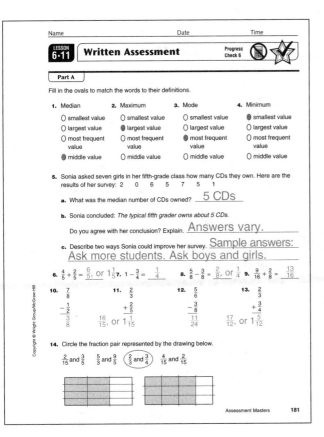

Assessment Masters   181

LESSON 6·11 Written Assessment *continued*

15. Write a pair of fractions with common denominators for the pictures in Problem 14. $\frac{8}{12}$ $\frac{9}{12}$

16. David was writing a report on sleep and dreams. He gave a survey to the 21 students in his class. The following were three of the questions:

A. About how many hours do you sleep each night?

B. About how many dreams do you remember having in an average week?

C. What time do you usually get up on a school day?

The graphs below show the answers to two of these questions. Match the questions with their graphs. (Write A, B, or C under each graph.)

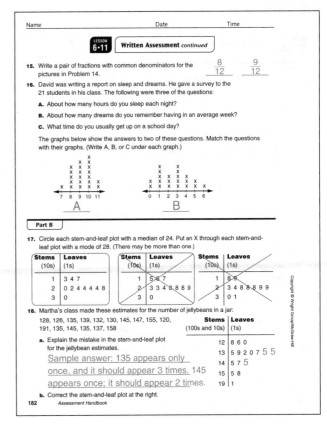

A   B

Part B

17. Circle each stem-and-leaf plot with a median of 24. Put an X through each stem-and-leaf plot with a mode of 28. (There may be more than one.)

Stems (10s)	Leaves (1s)
1	3 4 7
2	0 2 4 4 4 4 8
3	0

Stems (10s)	Leaves (1s)
1	5 6 7
2	3 3 4 8 8 8 9
3	0

Stems (10s)	Leaves (1s)
1	8 9
2	3 4 8 8 8 9 9
3	0 1

18. Martha's class made these estimates for the number of jellybeans in a jar:

128, 126, 135, 139, 132, 130, 145, 147, 155, 120, 191, 135, 145, 135, 137, 158

a. Explain the mistake in the stem-and-leaf plot for the jellybean estimates.
Sample answer: 135 appears only once, and it should appear 3 times. 145 appears once; it should appear 2 times.

Stems (100s and 10s)	Leaves (1s)
12	8 6 0
13	5 9 2 0 7 5 5
14	5 7 5
15	5 8
19	1

b. Correct the stem-and-leaf plot at the right.

182   *Assessment Handbook*

LESSON 6·11 Written Assessment *continued*

19. a. Use your ruler to draw a line segment that is $2\frac{3}{8}$ in. long.

_____

b. If you erased $\frac{3}{4}$ inch from this line segment, how long would it be? $1\frac{5}{8}$ in.

c. If you drew a line segment twice as long as the original line segment, how long would it be? $4\frac{6}{8}$ in., or $4\frac{3}{4}$ in.

20. One survey reported favorite types of books for fifth graders. The results of the survey were as follows:

adventure books: 38%
mystery books: 30%
comedies: 22%
other: 10%

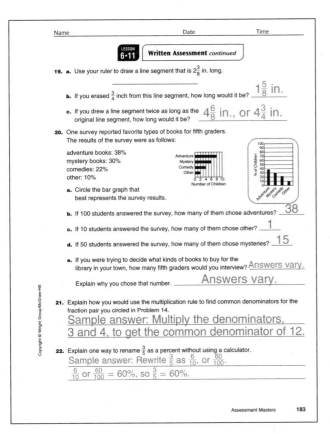

a. Circle the bar graph that best represents the survey results.

b. If 100 students answered the survey, how many of them chose adventures? __38__

c. If 10 students answered the survey, how many of them chose other? __1__

d. If 50 students answered the survey, how many of them chose mysteries? __15__

e. If you were trying to decide what kinds of books to buy for the library in your town, how many fifth graders would you interview? Answers vary.

Explain why you chose that number. Answers vary.

21. Explain how you would use the multiplication rule to find common denominators for the fraction pair you circled in Problem 14.
Sample answer: Multiply the denominators, 3 and 4, to get the common denominator of 12.

22. Explain one way to rename $\frac{3}{5}$ as a percent without using a calculator.
Sample answer: Rewrite $\frac{3}{5}$ as $\frac{6}{10}$, or $\frac{60}{100}$.
$\frac{6}{10}$ or $\frac{60}{100} = 60\%$, so $\frac{3}{5} = 60\%$.

Assessment Masters   183

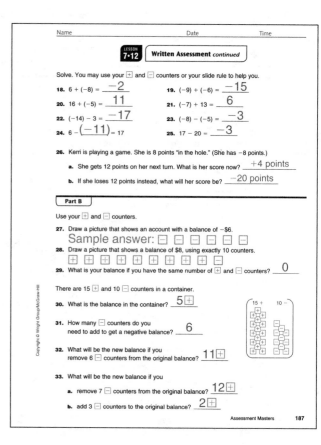

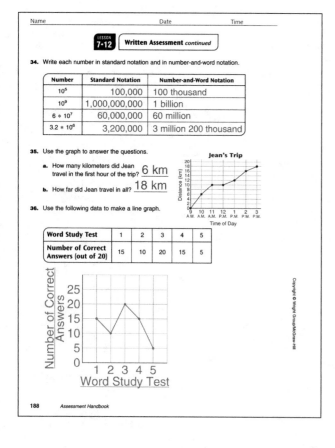

Page 186 (Part A)

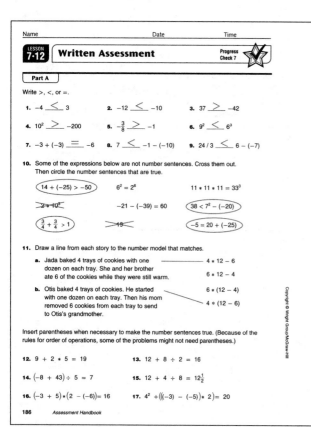

Name _____ Date _____ Time _____

LESSON 7·12 | **Written Assessment** | Progress Check 7

Part A

Write >, <, or =.

1. −4 $\leq$ 3
2. −12 $\leq$ −10
3. 37 $>$ −42
4. 10^2 $>$ −200
5. $-\frac{3}{8}$ $>$ −1
6. 9^2 $\leq$ 6^3
7. −3 + (−3) $=$ −6
8. 7 $\leq$ −1 − (−10)
9. 24 / 3 $\leq$ 6 − (−7)

10. Some of the expressions below are not number sentences. Cross them out. Then circle the number sentences that are true.

(14 + (−25) > −50) $6^2 = 2^6$ 11 * 11 * 11 = 33^3

~~2 * 10²~~   −21 − (−39) = 60   (38 < 7^2 − (−20))

($\frac{3}{4} + \frac{3}{4}$ > 1)   ~~19~~   (−5 = 20 + (−25))

11. Draw a line from each story to the number model that matches.

 a. Jada baked 4 trays of cookies with one dozen on each tray. She and her brother ate 6 of the cookies while they were still warm. — 4 * 12 − 6

 6 * 12 − 4

 b. Otis baked 4 trays of cookies. He started with one dozen on each tray. Then his mom removed 6 cookies from each tray to send to Otis's grandmother. 6 * (12 − 4)

 4 * (12 − 6)

Insert parentheses when necessary to make the number sentences true. (Because of the rules for order of operations, some of the problems might not need parentheses.)

12. 9 + 2 * 5 = 19
13. 12 + 8 ÷ 2 = 16
14. (−8 + 43) ÷ 5 = 7
15. 12 + 4 ÷ 8 = $12\frac{1}{2}$
16. (−3 + 5) * (2 − (−6)) = 16
17. 4^2 + (((−3) − (−5)) * 2) = 20

186   Assessment Handbook

Copyright © Wright Group/McGraw-Hill

Page 187 (continued)

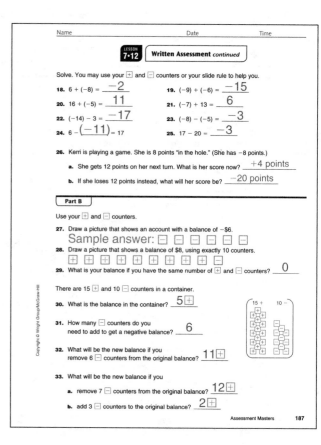

Name _____ Date _____ Time _____

LESSON 7·12 | **Written Assessment** continued

Solve. You may use your ⊞ and ⊟ counters or your slide rule to help you.

18. 6 + (−8) = −2
19. (−9) + (−6) = −15
20. 16 + (−5) = 11
21. (−7) + 13 = 6
22. (−14) − 3 = −17
23. (−8) − (−5) = −3
24. 6 − (−11) = 17
25. 17 − 20 = −3

26. Kerri is playing a game. She is 8 points "in the hole." (She has −8 points.)

 a. She gets 12 points on her next turn. What is her score now? +4 points

 b. If she loses 12 points instead, what will her score be? −20 points

Part B

Use your ⊞ and ⊟ counters.

27. Draw a picture that shows an account with a balance of −$6.

 Sample answer: ⊟ ⊟ ⊟ ⊟ ⊟ ⊟

28. Draw a picture that shows a balance of $8, using exactly 10 counters.

 ⊞ ⊞ ⊞ ⊞ ⊞ ⊞ ⊞ ⊞ ⊞ ⊟

29. What is your balance if you have the same number of ⊞ and ⊟ counters? 0

There are 15 ⊞ and 10 ⊟ counters in a container.

30. What is the balance in the container? 5⊞

31. How many ⊟ counters do you need to add to get a negative balance? 6

32. What will be the new balance if you remove 6 ⊟ counters from the original balance? 11⊞

33. What will be the new balance if you

 a. remove 7 ⊟ counters from the original balance? 12⊞

 b. add 3 ⊟ counters to the original balance? 2⊞

Assessment Masters   187

Copyright © Wright Group/McGraw-Hill

Page 188 (continued)

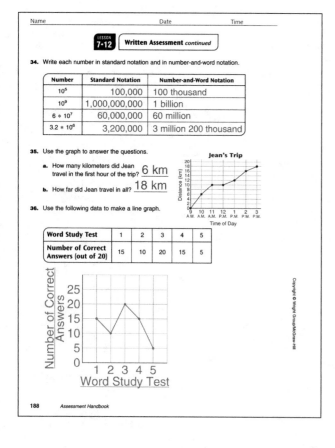

Name _____ Date _____ Time _____

LESSON 7·12 | **Written Assessment** continued

34. Write each number in standard notation and in number-and-word notation.

Number	Standard Notation	Number-and-Word Notation
10^5	100,000	100 thousand
10^9	1,000,000,000	1 billion
$6 * 10^7$	60,000,000	60 million
$3.2 * 10^6$	3,200,000	3 million 200 thousand

35. Use the graph to answer the questions.

 a. How many kilometers did Jean travel in the first hour of the trip? 6 km

 b. How far did Jean travel in all? 18 km

 Jean's Trip

36. Use the following data to make a line graph.

Word Study Test	1	2	3	4	5
Number of Correct Answers (out of 20)	15	10	20	15	5

188   Assessment Handbook

Copyright © Wright Group/McGraw-Hill

222   Assessment Handbook

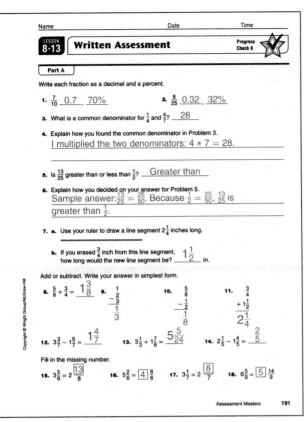

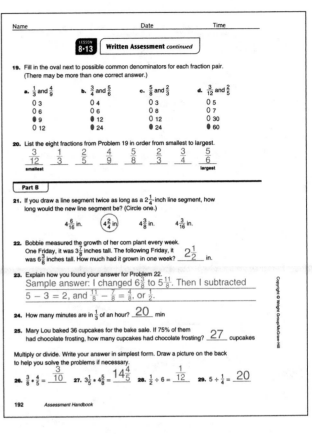

LESSON 9·11 **Written Assessment**   Progress Check 9

Part A

Use the grid at the right for Problems 1–4.

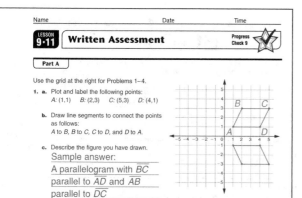

1. a. Plot and label the following points:
   A: (1,1)   B: (2,3)   C: (5,3)   D: (4,1)

   b. Draw line segments to connect the points as follows:
   A to B, B to C, C to D, and D to A.

   c. Describe the figure you have drawn.
   Sample answer:
   A parallelogram with $\overline{BC}$ parallel to $\overline{AD}$ and $\overline{AB}$ parallel to $\overline{DC}$

2. Plot points on the grid to make a reflection of the figure. Begin with the reflection of point A at (1,−1).

3. Record the points you used below.

Point	Original Figure	Reflected Figure
A	(1,1)	(1 , −1)
B	(2,3)	(2 , −3)
C	(5,3)	(5 , −3)
D	(4,1)	(4 , −1)

4. Describe a rule for changing the points from the original figure to get the reflected figure.
Sample answer: Change the second number in each number pair to its opposite.

LESSON 9·11 **Written Assessment** *continued*

5. Jim wants to build a fence around his rectangular garden. The garden is 15 feet by 5 feet.

   15 ft / 5 ft

   a. In order to build a fence, does Jim need to find the area or the perimeter of the garden? __perimeter__

   b. What amount of fence does he need? __40 feet__ (unit)

Find the area of the figures below. Use the formulas to help you.

| Area of rectangle = length of base * height: $A = b * h$ |
| Area of parallelogram = length of base * height: $A = b * h$ |
| Area of triangle = $\frac{1}{2}$ * length of base * height: $A = \frac{1}{2} * b * h$ |

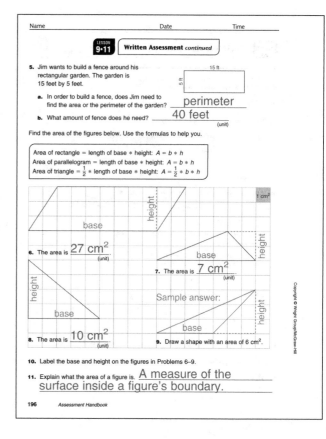

6. The area is __27 cm²__ (unit)

7. The area is __7 cm²__ (unit)

Sample answer:

8. The area is __10 cm²__ (unit)

9. Draw a shape with an area of 6 cm².

10. Label the base and height on the figures in Problems 6–9.

11. Explain what the area of a figure is. A measure of the surface inside a figure's boundary.

LESSON 9·11 **Written Assessment** *continued*

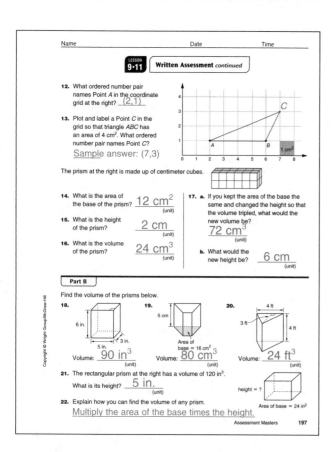

12. What ordered number pair names Point A in the coordinate grid at the right? __(2,1)__

13. Plot and label a Point C in the grid so that triangle ABC has an area of 4 cm². What ordered number pair names Point C?
Sample answer: (7,3)

The prism at the right is made up of centimeter cubes.

14. What is the area of the base of the prism? __12 cm²__ (unit)

15. What is the height of the prism? __2 cm__ (unit)

16. What is the volume of the prism? __24 cm³__ (unit)

17. a. If you kept the area of the base the same and changed the height so that the volume tripled, what would the new volume be? __72 cm³__ (unit)

   b. What would the new height be? __6 cm__ (unit)

Part B

Find the volume of the prisms below.

18. 6 in. / 5 in. / 3 in.
Volume: __90 in³__ (unit)

19. 5 cm / Area of base = 16 cm²
Volume: __80 cm³__ (unit)

20. 4 ft / 3 ft / 4 ft
Volume: __24 ft³__ (unit)

21. The rectangular prism at the right has a volume of 120 in³. What is its height? __5 in.__ (unit)
height = ? / Area of base = 24 in²

22. Explain how you can find the volume of any prism.
Multiply the area of the base times the height.

LESSON 10·10 | **Written Assessment** | Progress Check 10

Part A

Marge earns *D* dollars per hour.

1. Tom earns $5 per hour more than Marge. How much does he earn per hour? (Circle the answer.)

$5 * D$ $D - 5$ (($D + 5$)) $D + D$

2. Marge's aunt earns twice as much per hour as Marge. How much does she earn per hour? (Circle the answer.)

(($2 * D$)) $2 + D$ $D - 2$ $\frac{1}{2} * D$

3. Write an expression that shows how much Marge earns in 40 hours.

$40 * D$, or $40D$

Solve the pan-balance problems below.

4. One apple weighs as much as __12__ marbles.

5. One block weighs as much as __4__ marbles.

6. One ball weighs as much as __10__ blocks.

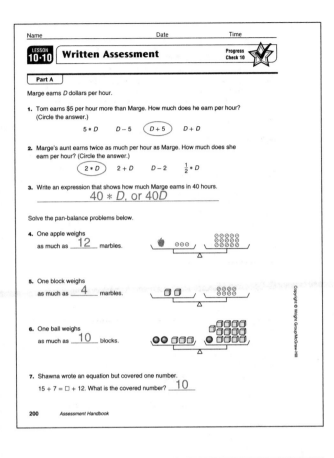

7. Shawna wrote an equation but covered one number.

$15 + 7 = \Box + 12$. What is the covered number? __10__

LESSON 10·10 | **Written Assessment** *continued*

8. Mrs. Griffin surveyed her class by asking three questions. The class made the line plots below to show the results for each question.

Write the number of the line plot next to the question it represents.

♦ How many complete months are there until your next birthday?   Plot __#1__
♦ How many years old is the oldest child living at your house?   Plot __#3__
♦ How many books did you read last summer?   Plot __#2__

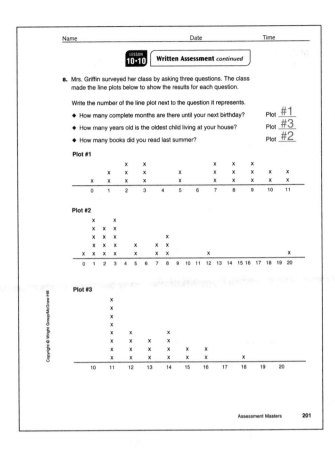

LESSON 10·10 | **Written Assessment** *continued*

To solve each of the following problems, would you need to find the circumference, perimeter, or area? (Circle the answer.)

9. Mario ran around a circular track 20 times. How far did he run?   ((circumference))   area

10. Mr. Li is planting tomatoes in his garden. He wants one plant for every 2 square feet. How many plants should he buy?   perimeter   ((area))

11. Jill is building a fence around her swimming pool. How many feet of fencing should she buy?   ((perimeter))   area

Part B

> Circumference of a circle = π * diameter
> Area of a circle = π * radius²

Complete each of the following sentences, rounding each answer to the nearest centimeter. Use the π key on your calculator or use 3.14 as an approximation for π.

12. The diameter is about __6__ cm.

13. The radius is about __3__ cm.

14. The circumference is about __19__ cm.

15. The area is about __28__ cm².

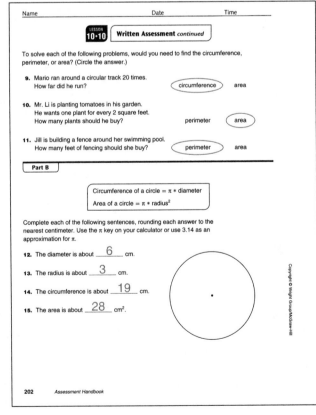

LESSON 10·10 | **Written Assessment** *continued*

16. Pete set up a pan balance. He found that 2 calculators balance 16 marbles. He then used the pan balance to find that 5 marbles balance 3 marbles and 10 paper clips. Fill in the blanks below.

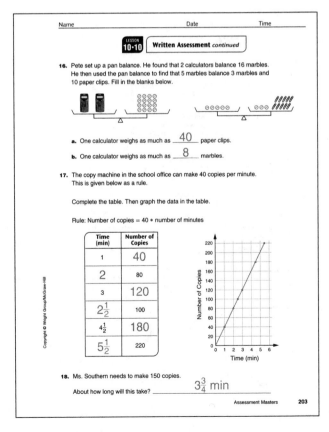

a. One calculator weighs as much as __40__ paper clips.

b. One calculator weighs as much as __8__ marbles.

17. The copy machine in the school office can make 40 copies per minute. This is given below as a rule.

Complete the table. Then graph the data in the table.

Rule: Number of copies = 40 * number of minutes

Time (min)	Number of Copies
1	40
2	80
3	120
$2\frac{1}{2}$	100
$4\frac{1}{2}$	180
$5\frac{1}{2}$	220

18. Ms. Southern needs to make 150 copies. About how long will this take? __$3\frac{3}{4}$ min__

Name   Date   Time

LESSON 11·8 Written Assessment

Progress Check 11

Part A

Complete each sentence with one of the following names of the geometric solids:

pyramid   cone   rectangular prism   cylinder

1. I have exactly two bases and no vertices. I am a ___cylinder___

2. All of my faces are triangular. I am a ___pyramid___

3. I have one base and one curved surface. I am a ___cone___

4. I have a pair of bases and exactly eight vertices. I am a <u>rectangular prism</u>

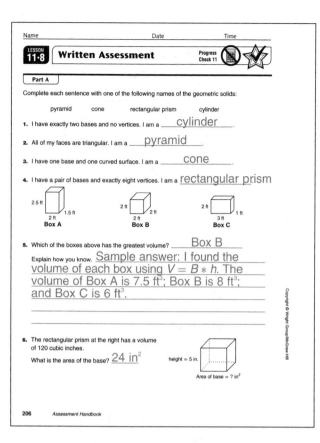

Box A   **Box B**   **Box C**

5. Which of the boxes above has the greatest volume? ___Box B___

Explain how you know. Sample answer: I found the volume of each box using $V = B * h$. The volume of Box A is 7.5 ft³; Box B is 8 ft³; and Box C is 6 ft³.

6. The rectangular prism at the right has a volume of 120 cubic inches.

What is the area of the base? ___24 in²___

height = 5 in.

Area of base = ? in²

Name   Date   Time

LESSON 11·8 Written Assessment *continued*

Area of rectangle: $A = l * w$	Circumference of a circle: $C = \pi * d$
Volume of rectangular prism: $V = l * w * h$	Area of circle: $A = \pi * r^2$
	Volume of cylinder: $V = \pi * r^2 * h$

7. What is the radius of the circle at the right? 4 units

8. What is the diameter of the circle? 8 units

9. What is the circumference? 25.13 units

4 units

10. What is the area of the base of the cylinder at the right? 12.57 in²

11. What is the volume of the cylinder? 62.83 in³

5 in.

2 in.

The prism at the right is made of centimeter cubes.

12. What is the area of the base of the prism? 8 cm²

13. What is the height of the prism? 2 cm

14. What is the volume of the prism? 16 cm³

15. If you kept the base the same, but tripled the volume of this prism, what would the height be? 6 cm

16. Write a number sentence to show how you solved Problem 15. $h = (16 * 3) / 8$

Part B

17. **a.** What is the surface area of the prism in Problem 12? 40 cm²

    b. Explain how you found the surface area.

    I found the area of the top and doubled it, $8 * 2 = 16$; the area of the side and doubled it, $4 * 2 = 8$; and the area of the front and doubled it, $8 * 2 = 16$. Then I added all of the areas together, $16 + 8 + 16 = 40$ cm².

Name   Date   Time

LESSON 11·8 Written Assessment *continued*

18. What information do you need to figure out how many square inches of paint you would use if you painted the entire cylinder on page 207 (top, bottom, and sides)?

The area of the base, the circumference of the base, and the height

19. If you place a cone inside of the cylinder in Problem 11 on page 207, and the cone is an exact fit (that is, the apex of the cone touches the bottom of the cylinder, and the base of the cone fits exactly at the top of the cylinder), what would the volume of the cone be? 20.94 in³

Write a number sentence to show how you found your answer.

$\frac{1}{3} * 62.83 = 20.94$ in³, or $62.83 \div 3 = 20.94$ in³

20. The pyramid at the right has the same height as the prism in Problem 6 on page 206.

What is the volume of the pyramid? 40 in³

Area of base = 24 in²

Write a number sentence to show how you found your answer.

$V = \frac{1}{3} * 24 * 5$, or $V = \frac{120}{3}$

Min's fish are sick, and she wants to add medicine to the tank. The instructions suggest adding one drop of medicine for every 4 L of water. The base of the fish tank measures 40 cm by 25 cm. The tank is filled with water to a height of about 20 cm.

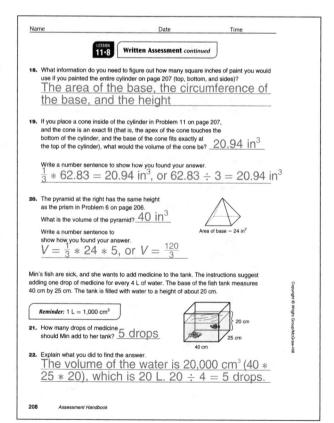

Reminder: 1 L = 1,000 cm³

20 cm

25 cm

40 cm

21. How many drops of medicine should Min add to her tank? 5 drops

22. Explain what you did to find the answer.

The volume of the water is 20,000 cm³ ($40 * 25 * 20$), which is 20 L. $20 \div 4 = 5$ drops.

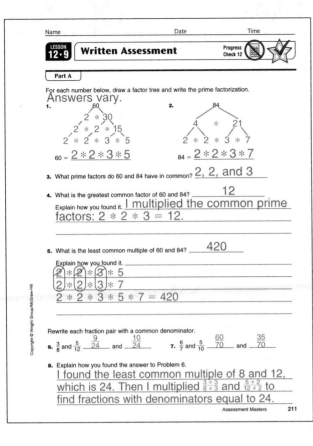

LESSON 12·9 | **Written Assessment** | Progress Check 12

Part A

For each number below, draw a factor tree and write the prime factorization.

Answers vary.

1. 60
2. 84

$60 = 2 * 2 * 3 * 5$ $84 = 2 * 2 * 3 * 7$

3. What prime factors do 60 and 84 have in common? 2, 2, and 3

4. What is the greatest common factor of 60 and 84? 12
Explain how you found it. I multiplied the common prime factors: $2 * 2 * 3 = 12$.

5. What is the least common multiple of 60 and 84? 420
Explain how you found it.
$(2) * (2) * (3) * 5$
$(2) * (2) * (3) * 7$
$2 * 2 * 3 * 5 * 7 = 420$

Rewrite each fraction pair with a common denominator.

6. $\frac{3}{8}$ and $\frac{5}{12}$ $\frac{9}{24}$ and $\frac{10}{24}$ 7. $\frac{6}{7}$ and $\frac{5}{10}$ $\frac{60}{70}$ and $\frac{35}{70}$

8. Explain how you found the answer to Problem 6.
I found the least common multiple of 8 and 12, which is 24. Then I multiplied $\frac{3*3}{8*3}$ and $\frac{5*2}{12*2}$ to find fractions with denominators equal to 24.

LESSON 12·9 | **Written Assessment** continued

9. Sven bought a large pizza. He wants to cut the pizza so that it can be shared equally by 2 people, 3 people, 4 people, 6 people, or 8 people. Into how many slices should Sven cut the pizza?   24 slices (unit)

10. There are 30 students in Linda's class. Two-thirds of her class rides to school on the school bus. The other students walk to school. How many students walk to school?   10 students (unit)

11. Matt was playing *Name That Number*. Of the 5 cards he turned over, 60% were black. How many black cards were there?   3 cards (unit)

12. Three out of 7 cars parked on one street were red. If there were 28 cars, how many cars were red?   12 cars (unit)

13. What is the ratio of cars that were not red to total cars in Problem 12? $\frac{16}{28}$ or $\frac{4}{7}$
Explain how you found your answer. Since 12 out of 28 cars were red, and $28 - 12 = 16$, then 16 cars were not red.

Solve each number story. Record the number model and the solution.

14. Susan rode her bike $4\frac{4}{5}$ miles on Thursday. She rode her bike $2\frac{1}{2}$ times that far on Friday. How far did she ride her bike on Friday?
   a. Open number model: $4\frac{4}{5} * 2\frac{1}{2} = m$
   b. Solution: 12 miles

15. At a bank, Maggie exchanged a $5 bill for $5 in quarters. How many quarters did she get?
   a. Open number model: $5 \div \frac{1}{4} = q$
   b. Solution: 20 quarters

LESSON 12·9 | **Written Assessment** continued

Part B

16. Darin rolls a 6-sided die and then flips a coin.

How many different ways can the die roll and coin toss turn out?

   a. Use the Multiplication Counting Principle to answer.   12 different ways

   b. Draw a tree diagram to show all the possible ways.
   Suggestion: Use the letters H and T to represent HEADS and TAILS.

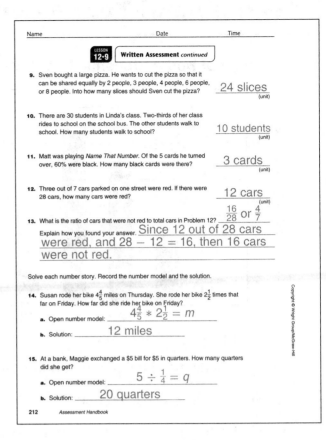

die: 1   2   3   4   5   6
coin: H T H T H T H T H T H T

   c. Which method do you think is easier for finding the number of possible results? Answers vary.

   d. Explain your answer. Answers vary.

17. In Problem 16, what is the probability that Darin…
   a. rolls a 5 and the coin lands on HEADS? $\frac{1}{12}$
   b. rolls an even number and the coin lands on TAILS? $\frac{3}{12}$, or $\frac{1}{4}$
   c. rolls a prime number? $\frac{6}{12}$, $\frac{3}{6}$, or $\frac{1}{2}$
   d. tosses the coin so that it lands on HEADS? $\frac{6}{12}$, or $\frac{1}{2}$

LESSON 12·9 | **Written Assessment** continued

Write a number model for each problem. Then solve the problem.

18. Rosalyn's family was driving from home to her aunt's house. After going 48 miles, they were $\frac{3}{4}$ of the way there. How far from home was her aunt's house?
   Number model: $\frac{3}{4} = \frac{48}{\square}$ Answer: 64 miles

19. In Doreen's first basketball game, she made a basket 9 times out of 15 attempts. She made the same ratio of baskets out of 25 attempts in the second game. How many baskets did she make in her 25 attempts?
   Number model: $\frac{9}{15} = \frac{\square}{25}$ Answer: 15 baskets

20. Explain how you found your answer to Problem 19.
$\frac{9}{15} = \frac{3}{5}$. So the number model can be written as $\frac{3}{5} = \frac{\square}{25} \rightarrow \frac{3*5}{5*5} = \frac{15}{25}$. 9 out of 15 is the same ratio as 15 out of 25. She made 15 baskets.

21. Marcus's heart beats 11 times in 10 seconds. At this rate, about how many times would it beat in 1 minute?   66 times

22. Carlo was buying tickets for his family at the school fair. He got 7 tickets for each dollar. He received a total of 224 tickets. How much did he spend on tickets? $32

Beginning-of-Year Assessment

1.   **Number of Hours Students Slept Last Night**

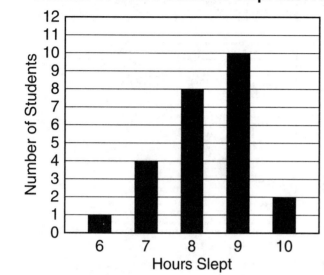

a. What is the median number of hours slept? _____

b. What is the mode of the hours slept? _____

c. What is the minimum number of hours slept? _____

d. What is the maximum number of hours slept? _____

e. What is the range of hours slept? _____

2. Solve the problems below. Show your work.

   a.   3,441   **b.**   2,502

        + 2,389   − 1,379

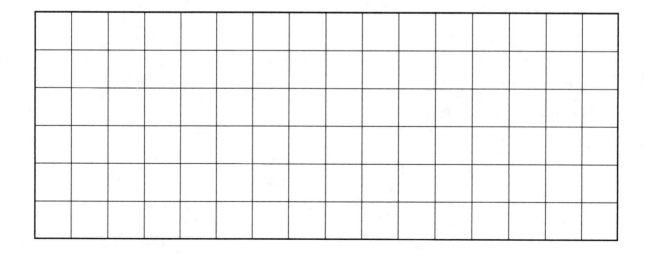

Beginning-of-Year Assessment *continued*

3. Fill in the blanks.

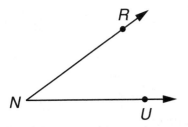

a. Is ∠RNU acute or obtuse? _____

b. Estimate the measure of the angle.

∠RNU measures about _____.

4. Fill in the blanks.

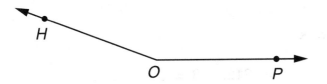

a. Is ∠HOP acute or obtuse? _____

b. Estimate the measure of the angle.

∠HOP measures about _____.

5. Solve the problems below. Show your work.

a. $65 * 43 =$ _____

b. _____ $= 96 * 84$

c. _____ $= 581 / 7$

d. $734 / 8 =$ _____

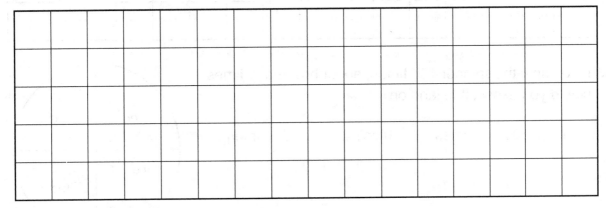

Beginning-of-Year Assessment *continued*

6. Name and describe each geometric solid pictured below.

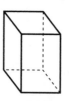

Name of Shape: _____

Description: _____

_____

_____

_____

_____

Name of Shape: _____

Description: _____

_____

_____

_____

_____

7. Solve the problems below. Show your work.

a. $6.5 * 8.9 =$ _____

b. $312.4 / 8 =$ _____

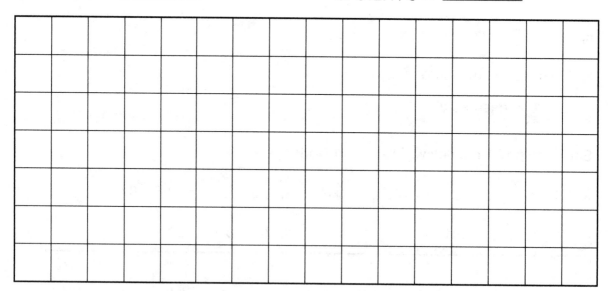

8. If you spin the spinner 100 times, about how many times would you expect it to land on

red? _____ times   blue? _____ times

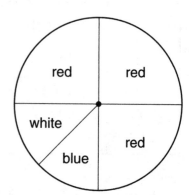

Beginning-of-Year Assessment *continued*

9. **a.** What do you think is a good estimate for 123 * 28?

_____

b. How did you get your estimate?

_____

_____

c. Are there better estimates than yours? Why or why not?

_____

10. **a.** What do you think is a good estimate for 4.5 * 6.9?

_____

b. How did you get your estimate?

_____

_____

c. Are there better estimates than yours? Why or why not?

_____

11. Use your ruler. Measure the line segment to the nearest $\frac{1}{4}$ inch.

_____

_____ inch

12. Mrs. Porter's class recorded the number of books read by her students for
1 week. Below are the results:
Number of books read in 1 week: 2, 3, 5, 6, 3, 3, 4, 5, 2, 2, 2, 3, 4, 3, 3

a. What is the median number of books read in 1 week? _____

b. What is the mode? _____

c. What is the minimum number of books read in 1 week? _____

d. What is the maximum number of books read in 1 week? _____

e. What is the range of books read in 1 week? _____

LESSON 6·11

Mid-Year Assessment

1. Solve. Show your work.

    a. $5,609 + 9,732 =$ _____   **b.** $58,391 + 12,029 =$ _____

    c. $6,230 - 941 =$ _____   **d.** $17,491 - 5,802 =$ _____

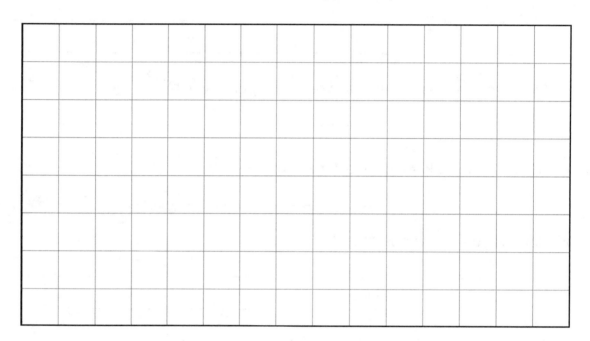

2. Complete.

    a. _____ $* 9 = 360$ **b.** $720 \div$ _____ $= 9$

    c. $70 =$ _____ $\div 9$ **d.** $420 = 6 *$ _____

3. Write the following numbers in standard notation:

    a. Two hundred eighty-five thousand, fifty-three _____

    b. Four million, nine hundred three thousand, six hundred eighteen _____

4. Write the value of the digit written in **bold**.

    a. 2,5**6**7,091 _____   **b.** 509,8**4**3 _____

    c. 3,0**0**2,495 _____   **d.** 4**5**,809 _____

LESSON 6·11   **Mid-Year Assessment** *continued*

5. The scale on McKenna's map is 1 inch = 150 miles. The distance from her house to her grandmother's house on the map is 3 inches. What is the

distance in miles to her grandmother's house? _____ miles

Explain how you found your answer.

_____

_____

_____

6. Use your protractor. Measure each angle below. Record your answer to the nearest degree.

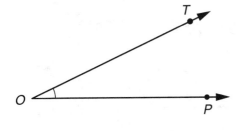

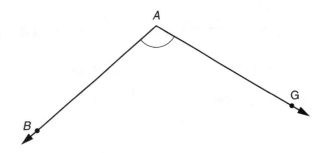

  a. ∠*TOP* measures about _____ .   **b.** ∠*BAG* measures about _____ .

  c. ∠*TOP* is an _____   **d.** ∠*BAG* is an _____
     (acute or obtuse) angle.   (acute or obtuse) angle.

LESSON 6·11   **Mid-Year Assessment** *continued*

7. Find the perimeter of the rectangle.

2 cm

4.5 cm

perimeter = _____

Explain how you found your answer.

_____

_____

_____

_____

8. A figure is partially hidden. Which one of the following polygons might it be?

⬭ square   ⬭ rhombus

⬭ rectangle   ⬭ triangle

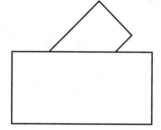

9. What is the measure of angle *T*? _____

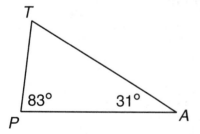

83°   31°

T

P   *A*

LESSON 6·11   **Mid-Year Assessment** *continued*

10. Solve.

    a. $7.6 + 9.43 =$ _____   **b.** $83.6 + 4.736 =$ _____

    c. $30.4 - 27.603 =$ _____   **d.** $80.34 - 5.176 =$ _____

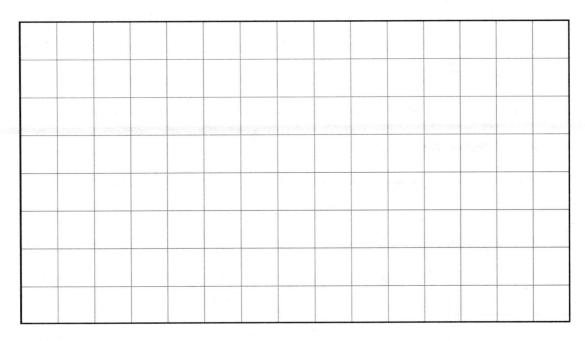

11. Use your protractor to draw $\angle ABC$ that measures $172°$.

LESSON 6·11 | **Mid-Year Assessment** *continued*

12. a. Draw a reflex angle. Label it *RUN*.

b. Define a reflex angle.

_____

c. Use your protractor. Measure ∠*RUN*.

m ∠*RUN* = _____

13. Solve.

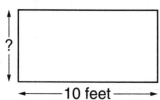

Jenny planted a rectangular garden. It is 10 feet long and its perimeter is 30 feet. What is the width of the garden? _____

Explain how you found your answer.

_____

_____

_____

_____

14. Write a number model to describe the array.

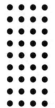

Number model: _____

LESSON 6·11

Mid-Year Assessment *continued*

15. Use the data in the table to make a line graph. Label the graph and give it a title.

Samantha's Scores for the 50-Fact Test	
Week	**Score**
1	23
2	28
3	34
4	29
5	39
6	40
7	38
8	42
9	44
10	49

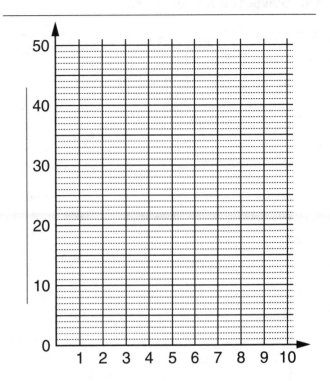

16. In the number 5.089,

  a. what is the digit in the hundredths place? _____

  b. what is the digit in the tenths place? _____

  c. what is the digit in the thousandths place? _____

17. Complete.

  a. 60 * _____ = 480   **b.** 420 ÷ _____ = 7

  c. _____ = 30 * 90   **d.** _____ ÷ 70 = 300

  e. 8,100 ÷ 900 = _____   **f.** 49,000 = _____ * 70

LESSON 6·11

Mid-Year Assessment *continued*

18. Solve. Show your work.

a. 498 + 1,604 + 3,946 = _____

b. 76,500 + 7,650 + 765 = _____

c. 3,107 – 498 = _____

d. 42,300 – 9,892 = _____

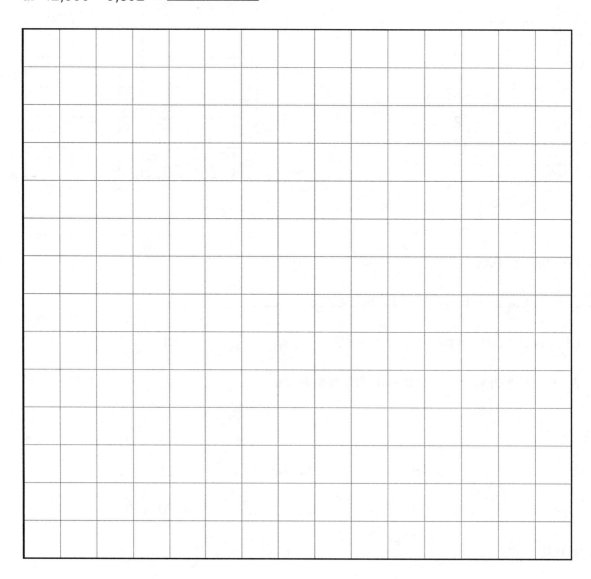

LESSON 6·11

Mid-Year Assessment *continued*

19. Solve. Show your work.

a. 64.72 + 8.35 = _____

b. 16.37 + 53.82 = _____

c. 12.68 – 9.9 = _____

d. 97.34 – 68.55 = _____

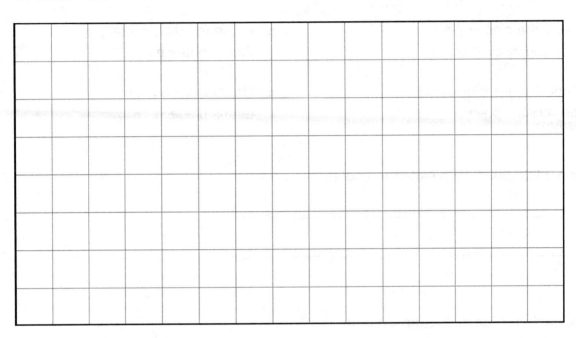

20. a. Write thirty-seven and five hundred four thousandths in

standard notation. _____

b. Circle the digit in the tenths place.

c. Underline the digit in the thousandths place.

LESSON 12·9 **End-of-Year Assessment**

1. **a.** Write five hundred forty-six million, three hundred nine thousand, forty-one in standard notation.

   _____

   b. Circle the digit in the ten-thousands place.

   c. Underline the digit in the ten-millions place.

2. **a.** Write five and three hundred eighty-seven thousandths in standard notation.

   _____

   b. Circle the digit in the thousandths place.

   c. Underline the digit in the tenths place.

3. Write 3,980,300.045 in expanded notation.

   _____

   _____

4. Write each fraction in its simplest form.

   a. $\dfrac{28}{3} = $ _____

   b. $4\dfrac{18}{24} = $ _____

   c. $11\dfrac{54}{72} = $ _____

5. Find the missing number.

   a. $\dfrac{1}{5} = \dfrac{19}{x}$ $x = $ _____

   b. $\dfrac{8}{20} = \dfrac{s}{10}$ $s = $ _____

   c. $\dfrac{n}{120} = \dfrac{3}{4}$ $n = $ _____

   d. $\dfrac{36}{m} = \dfrac{4}{7}$ $m = $ _____

6. Write the prime factorization for 72. _____

LESSON 12·9 **End-of-Year Assessment** *continued*

7. Mr. Hernandez's fifth grade students measured their heights to the nearest centimeter. Use the data in the table to create a bar graph below. Label the parts of the graph.

Height (cm)	Number of Students
135	1
137	2
145	4
147	3
148	1
150	5
152	2
157	1
165	1

a.

_____

_____

Use the data above to find the following landmarks.

b. Median: _____

c. Mode: _____

d. Mean (rounded to the nearest cm): _____

e. What would happen to the median if two students were added to the class data and both measured 146 centimeters?

_____

8. Add or subtract.

a. $-5 + (-5) =$ _____ **b.** $8 - (-20) =$ _____ **c.** $10 + (-3) =$ _____

LESSON 12·9 | **End-of-Year Assessment** *continued*

9. Draw a line to match each sentence to the name of the correct geometric solid.

   a. I have 6 congruent square faces.   square pyramid

   b. I have a square base, and all of my
   other faces are triangles.   cube

   c. I have 2 congruent triangular bases,
   and all of my other faces are rectangles.   cone

   d. I have a special vertex called an apex
   and a curved surface.   triangular prism

10. **a.** Each square in the grid below has an area of
    1 square centimeter. What is the area of triangle *END*? _____ cm²

    b. Draw a rectangle that has an area of 12 cm².

    c. What is the perimeter of this rectangle? _____ cm

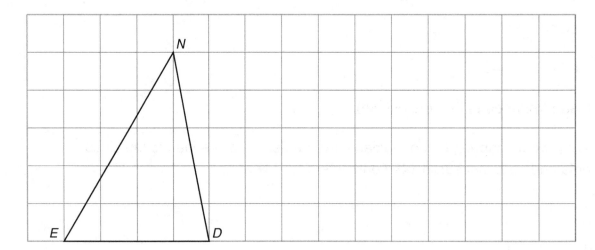

11. Insert parentheses to make the number sentences true.

    a. $210 \div 6 * 2 + 5 = 5$ **b.** $144 = 18 - 12 + 42 * 3$

12. Add or subtract.

    a. $6\frac{1}{8} - \frac{3}{4} =$ _____   **b.** $3\frac{1}{5} + 4\frac{3}{4} =$ _____

LESSON 12·9 **End-of-Year Assessment** *continued*

13. What is the volume of the prism to the right?

_____
(unit)

3 in.

4 in.   2 in.

Volume of a prism: $V = B * h$ or $V = l * w * h$

Solve. Write your answers in simplest form.

14. a. $\dfrac{7}{8} * \dfrac{14}{16} =$ _____

b. $12\dfrac{3}{5} * \dfrac{5}{6} =$ _____

c. $4\dfrac{2}{7} * 3\dfrac{1}{6} =$ _____

15. a. $10 \div \dfrac{1}{3} =$ _____

b. $\dfrac{1}{8} \div 2 =$ _____

c. $\dfrac{1}{2} \div \dfrac{5}{6} =$ _____

16. Fill in the blanks.

a. $36 * 42 = 42 *$ _____

b. $815 + 934 =$ _____ $+ 815$

c. $34 *$ _____ $= 34$

d. _____ $+ 0 = 45$

e. $8 * 527 = ($ _____ $* 500) + (8 *$ _____ $) + (8 *$ _____ $)$

17. Jean combined $\dfrac{1}{3}$ cup of corn flour with $\dfrac{3}{4}$ cup of white flour.

Is the total amount of flour more or less than 1 cup? _____

Explain. _____

_____

_____

18. The scale on Dominique's map is 1 cm = 70 mi. The distance
on the map from the train station in his hometown to his cousin's
house is 5.5 cm. How many miles is it to his cousin's house? _____

(unit)

LESSON 12·9 **End-of-Year Assessment** *continued*

19. a. Use the data in the table to make and label a circle graph. Use your Percent Circle.

Eye Colors of Ms. Brooke's Fifth Grade Class
10% green
25% blue
60% brown
5% hazel

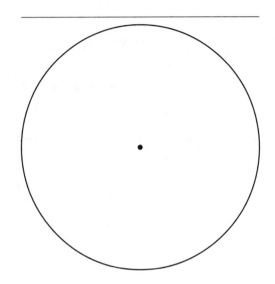

b. If there are 40 students in Ms. Brooke's class, how many students have hazel eyes?

_____

20. Write the following in order from least to greatest.

$-\dfrac{1}{2}$ 0.5   0.036 -0.33 $\dfrac{2}{5}$ -45 $2\dfrac{1}{3}$

_____, _____, _____, _____, _____, _____, _____
least   greatest

21. Complete the table.

Standard Notation	Exponential Notation	Repeated-Factor Notation
	3^6	
1,000		
		$9*9*9$

22. Jimmy got 52 hits in his last 100 times at bat. Use probability terms to describe the chance of him getting a hit the next time at bat.

_____

_____

LESSON 12·9 | **End-of-Year Assessment** *continued*

23. Solve. Show your work.

a. 7.34 * 45 = _____

b. 9.7 * 67.2 = _____

c. 7,835 ÷ 12 = _____

d. 806.3 ÷ 5 = _____

24. The probability of landing on the shaded sectors of the spinner is 25% or $\frac{1}{4}$, the probability of landing on white is $\frac{1}{12}$. What is the probability of landing on the striped sectors of the spinner?

_____

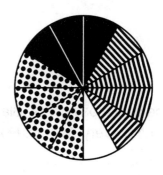

25. Complete the following statements.

a. 1 meter = _____cm

b. 137 cm = _____mm

c. 4.5 m = _____mm

d. 9,300 mm = _____m

e. 36 ft = _____yd

f. 48 in. = _____ft

26. Use order of operations to tell whether each number sentence is true or false.

a. 0 = (−5 + 3) * 2 _____

b. 40 − 15 / 5 + 2 = 39 _____

LESSON 12·9 | **End-of-Year Assessment** *continued*

27. Complete.

a. _____ * 9,000 = 27,000

b. 3,200,000 = 80 * _____

c. 560,000 ÷ _____ = 7

d. _____ ÷ 300 = 7,000

28. Solve. Show your work.

a. 14.95 + 7.064 = _____

b. 24.71 + 569.809 = _____

c. 76.9 – 46.170 = _____

d. 7.083 – 0.79 = _____

29. During the basketball game, Blaire shot the ball 28 times. She made 3 out of every 7 shots. How many baskets did she make? _____

30. Mark the following points on the ruler.

A: $\frac{3}{8}$ in. B: $2\frac{5}{8}$ in. C: $1\frac{3}{4}$ in. D: $1\frac{1}{2}$ in. E: $1\frac{7}{8}$ in.

INCHES

31. Use what you know about angle measure to record the missing angle measurements in the figure below.

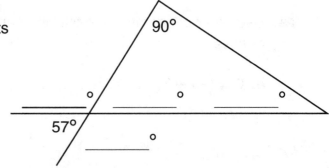

90°

57°

LESSON 12·9

End-of-Year Assessment *continued*

Use the grid at the right for Problems 32a–32d.

32. **a.** Plot the following points: (5,–1), (5,–3), (3,–3), (1,–1)

b. Draw line segments to connect the points to make a polygon.

c. Plot new points on the grid to make a translation of the polygon.

d. Are the two polygons you made congruent?

_____

How do you know?

_____

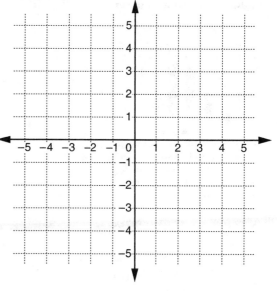

| **Circumference of circle:** $C = \pi * d$ | **Area of a circle:** $A = \pi * r^2$ |

33. Use the circle at the right to calculate the following: Use 3.14 as an approximation for *pi*.

a. Diameter: _____

b. Radius: _____

c. Circumference: _____

d. Area: _____

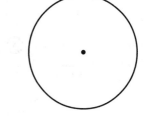

34. Complete the table. Then graph the data in the table.
Rule: Number of words = minutes * 46 words

Time (min)	Number of Words
1	
4	184
3	
	92
	115

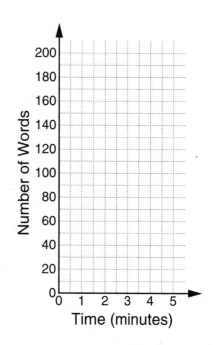

Beginning-of-Year Assessment

1. Number of Hours Students Slept Last Night

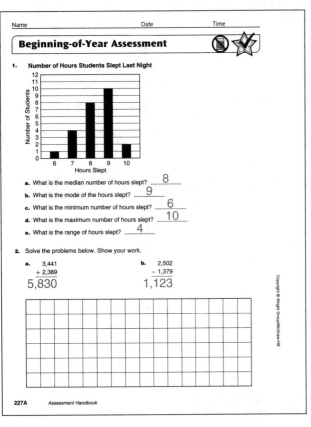

a. What is the median number of hours slept? ___8___

b. What is the mode of the hours slept? ___9___

c. What is the minimum number of hours slept? ___6___

d. What is the maximum number of hours slept? ___10___

e. What is the range of hours slept? ___4___

2. Solve the problems below. Show your work.

a. 3,441
    + 2,389
    ___5,830___

b. 2,502
    − 1,379
    ___1,123___

Beginning-of-Year Assessment *continued*

3. Fill in the blanks.

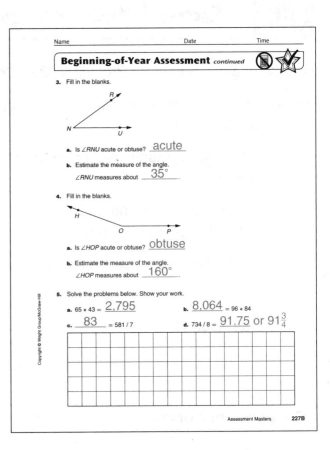

a. Is ∠RNU acute or obtuse? ___acute___

b. Estimate the measure of the angle.
∠RNU measures about ___35°___.

4. Fill in the blanks.

a. Is ∠HOP acute or obtuse? ___obtuse___

b. Estimate the measure of the angle.
∠HOP measures about ___160°___.

5. Solve the problems below. Show your work.

a. $65 * 43 = $ ___2,795___

b. ___8,064___ $= 96 * 84$

c. ___83___ $= 581 / 7$

d. $734 / 8 = $ ___91.75 or $91\frac{3}{4}$___

Beginning-of-Year Assessment *continued*

6. Name and describe each geometric solid pictured below.

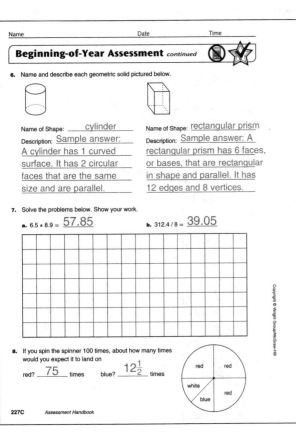

Name of Shape: ___cylinder___
Description: Sample answer: A cylinder has 1 curved surface. It has 2 circular faces that are the same size and are parallel.

Name of Shape: rectangular prism
Description: Sample answer: A rectangular prism has 6 faces, or bases, that are rectangular in shape and parallel. It has 12 edges and 8 vertices.

7. Solve the problems below. Show your work.

a. $6.5 * 8.9 = $ ___57.85___

b. $312.4 / 8 = $ ___39.05___

8. If you spin the spinner 100 times, about how many times would you expect it to land on

red? ___75___ times   blue? ___$12\frac{1}{2}$___ times

Beginning-of-Year Assessment *continued*

9. a. What do you think is a good estimate for $123 * 28$?
There are no incorrect answers. Sample answer: 3,000

b. How did you get your estimate?
Sample answer: I know that 123 is close to 100 and 28 is close to 30 so I multiplied 100 and 30 to get 3,000.

c. Are there better estimates than yours? Why or why not?
Answers vary.

10. a. What do you think is a good estimate for $4.5 * 6.9$?
There are no incorrect answers. Sample answer: 35

b. How did you get your estimate?
Sample answer: I know that 4.5 is close to 5 and 6.9 is close to 7 so I multiplied 5 and 7 to get 35.

c. Are there better estimates than yours? Why or why not?
Answers vary.

11. Use your ruler. Measure the line segment to the nearest $\frac{1}{4}$ inch.

___$4\frac{3}{4}$___ inch

12. Mrs. Porter's class recorded the number of books read by her students for 1 week. Below are the results:
Number of books read in 1 week: 2, 3, 5, 6, 3, 3, 4, 5, 2, 2, 2, 3, 4, 3, 3

a. What is the median number of books read in 1 week? ___3___

b. What is the mode? ___3___

c. What is the minimum number of books read in 1 week? ___2___

d. What is the maximum number of books read in 1 week? ___6___

e. What is the range of books read in 1 week? ___4___

LESSON 6·11 Mid-Year Assessment

1. Solve. Show your work.

a. 5,609 + 9,732 = __15,341__   b. 58,391 + 12,029 = __70,420__

c. 6,230 – 941 = __5,289__   d. 17,491 – 5,802 = __11,689__

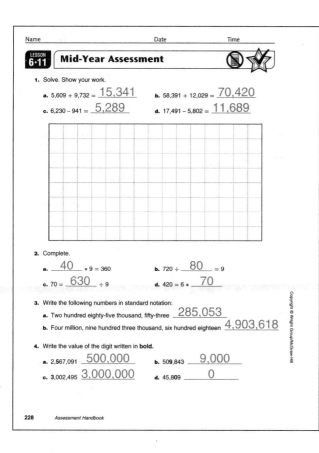

2. Complete.

a. __40__ * 9 = 360   b. 720 ÷ __80__ = 9

c. 70 = __630__ ÷ 9   d. 420 = 6 * __70__

3. Write the following numbers in standard notation:

a. Two hundred eighty-five thousand, fifty-three __285,053__

b. Four million, nine hundred three thousand, six hundred eighteen __4,903,618__

4. Write the value of the digit written in **bold**.

a. 2,5**6**7,091 __500,000__   b. 50**9**,843 __9,000__

c. **3**,002,495 __3,000,000__   d. 45,80**9** __0__

LESSON 6·11 Mid-Year Assessment *continued*

5. The scale on McKenna's map is 1 inch = 150 miles. The distance from her house to her grandmother's house on the map is 3 inches. What is the distance in miles to her grandmother's house? __450__ miles

Explain how you found your answer.

Sample answer: 1 inch equals 150 miles, and I want to find the distance for 3 inches, so I multiplied 150 by 3 and got 450 miles.

6. Use your protractor. Measure each angle below. Record your answer to the nearest degree.

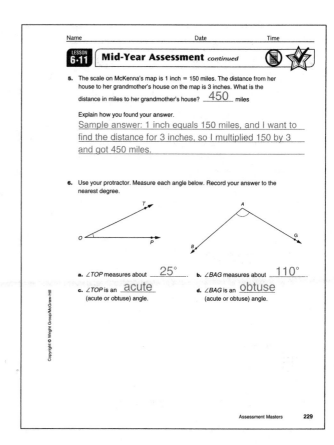

a. ∠TOP measures about __25°__   b. ∠BAG measures about __110°__

c. ∠TOP is an __acute__ (acute or obtuse) angle.   d. ∠BAG is an __obtuse__ (acute or obtuse) angle.

LESSON 6·11 Mid-Year Assessment *continued*

7. Find the perimeter of the rectangle.

2 cm

4.5 cm

perimeter = __13 cm__

Explain how you found your answer.

Sample answer: Opposite sides of a rectangle have equal length. So, there are two sides with length 2 cm and two sides with length 4.5 cm. The perimeter is 2 cm + 2 cm + 4.5 cm + 4.5 cm = 13 cm.

8. A figure is partially hidden. Which one of the following polygons might it be?

○ square ○ rhombus
⬭ rectangle ○ triangle

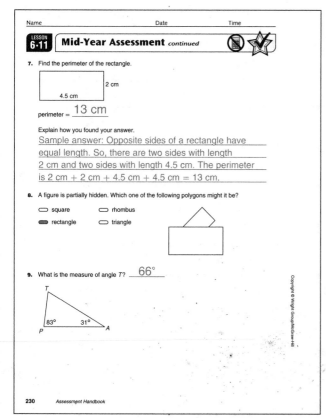

9. What is the measure of angle T? __66°__

83° 31°

LESSON 6·11 Mid-Year Assessment *continued*

10. Solve.

a. 7.6 + 9.43 = __17.03__   b. 83.6 + 4.736 = __88.336__

c. 30.4 – 27.603 = __2.797__   d. 80.34 – 5.176 = __75.164__

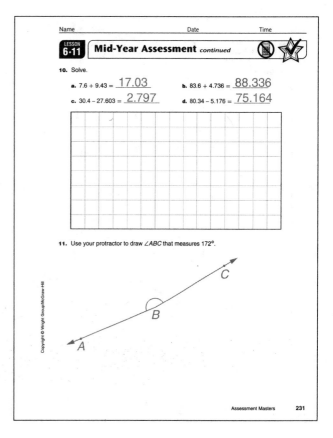

11. Use your protractor to draw ∠ABC that measures 172°.

LESSON 6·11 Mid-Year Assessment *continued*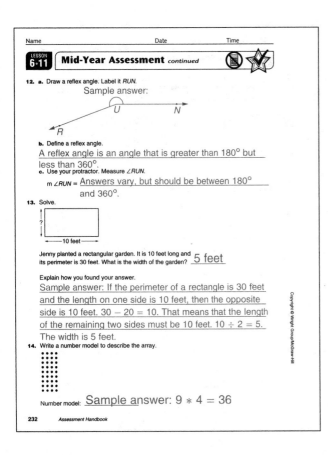

12. a. Draw a reflex angle. Label it *RUN*.

Sample answer:

b. Define a reflex angle.

A reflex angle is an angle that is greater than 180° but less than 360°.

c. Use your protractor. Measure ∠*RUN*.

m ∠*RUN* = Answers vary, but should be between 180° and 360°.

13. Solve.

Jenny planted a rectangular garden. It is 10 feet long and its perimeter is 30 feet. What is the width of the garden? **5 feet**

Explain how you found your answer.

Sample answer: If the perimeter of a rectangle is 30 feet and the length on one side is 10 feet, then the opposite side is 10 feet. 30 − 20 = 10. That means that the length of the remaining two sides must be 10 feet. 10 ÷ 2 = 5. The width is 5 feet.

14. Write a number model to describe the array.

Number model: Sample answer: 9 ∗ 4 = 36

LESSON 6·11 Mid-Year Assessment *continued*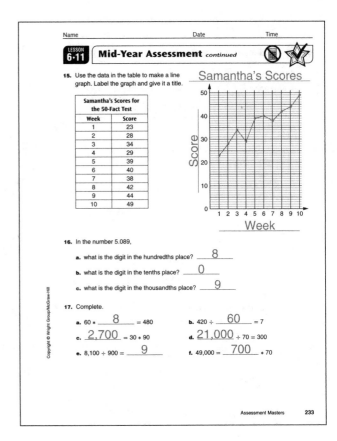

15. Use the data in the table to make a line graph. Label the graph and give it a title.

Samantha's Scores for the 50-Fact Test	
Week	**Score**
1	23
2	28
3	34
4	29
5	39
6	40
7	38
8	42
9	44
10	49

16. In the number 5.089,

a. what is the digit in the hundredths place? **8**

b. what is the digit in the tenths place? **0**

c. what is the digit in the thousandths place? **9**

17. Complete.

a. 60 ∗ **8** = 480   **b.** 420 ÷ **60** = 7

c. **2,700** = 30 ∗ 90   **d.** **21,000** ÷ 70 = 300

e. 8,100 ÷ 900 = **9**   **f.** 49,000 = **700** ∗ 70

LESSON 6·11 Mid-Year Assessment *continued*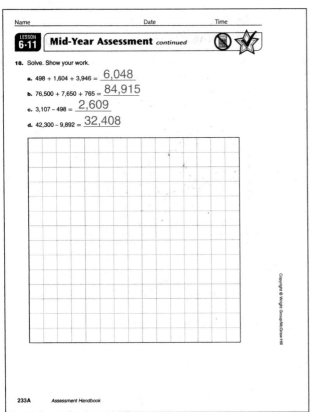

18. Solve. Show your work.

a. 498 + 1,604 + 3,946 = **6,048**

b. 76,500 + 7,650 + 765 = **84,915**

c. 3,107 − 498 = **2,609**

d. 42,300 − 9,892 = **32,408**

LESSON 6·11 Mid-Year Assessment *continued*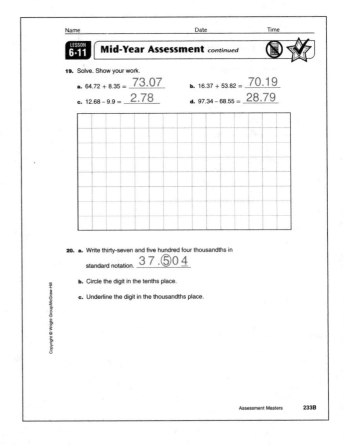

19. Solve. Show your work.

a. 64.72 + 8.35 = **73.07**   **b.** 16.37 + 53.82 = **70.19**

c. 12.68 − 9.9 = **2.78**   **d.** 97.34 − 68.55 = **28.79**

20. a. Write thirty-seven and five hundred four thousandths in standard notation. **37.504**

b. Circle the digit in the tenths place.

c. Underline the digit in the thousandths place.

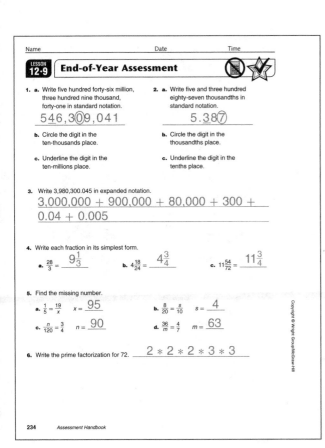

LESSON 12·9 End-of-Year Assessment

1. a. Write five hundred forty-six million, three hundred nine thousand, forty-one in standard notation.

546,3⟨0⟩9,041

b. Circle the digit in the ten-thousands place.

c. Underline the digit in the ten-millions place.

2. a. Write five and three hundred eighty-seven thousandths in standard notation.

5.38⟨7⟩

b. Circle the digit in the thousandths place.

c. Underline the digit in the tenths place.

3. Write 3,980,300.045 in expanded notation.

3,000,000 + 900,000 + 80,000 + 300 + 0.04 + 0.005

4. Write each fraction in its simplest form.

a. $\frac{28}{3} =$ $9\frac{1}{3}$ **b.** $4\frac{18}{24} =$ $4\frac{3}{4}$ **c.** $11\frac{54}{72} =$ $11\frac{3}{4}$

5. Find the missing number.

a. $\frac{1}{5} = \frac{19}{x}$ $x =$ 95   **b.** $\frac{8}{20} = \frac{s}{10}$ $s =$ 4

c. $\frac{n}{120} = \frac{3}{4}$ $n =$ 90   **d.** $\frac{36}{m} = \frac{4}{7}$ $m =$ 63

6. Write the prime factorization for 72. $2 * 2 * 2 * 3 * 3$

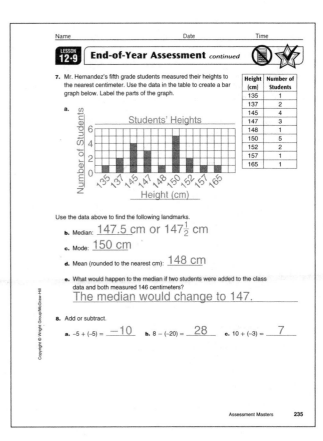

LESSON 12·9 End-of-Year Assessment *continued*

7. Mr. Hernandez's fifth grade students measured their heights to the nearest centimeter. Use the data in the table to create a bar graph below. Label the parts of the graph.

Height (cm)	Number of Students
135	1
137	2
145	4
147	3
148	1
150	5
152	2
157	1
165	1

a.

Students' Heights — bar graph, Number of Students vs Height (cm)

Use the data above to find the following landmarks.

b. Median: 147.5 cm or $147\frac{1}{2}$ cm

c. Mode: 150 cm

d. Mean (rounded to the nearest cm): 148 cm

e. What would happen to the median if two students were added to the class data and both measured 146 centimeters?

The median would change to 147.

8. Add or subtract.

a. $-5 + (-5) =$ −10   **b.** $8 - (-20) =$ 28   **c.** $10 + (-3) =$ 7

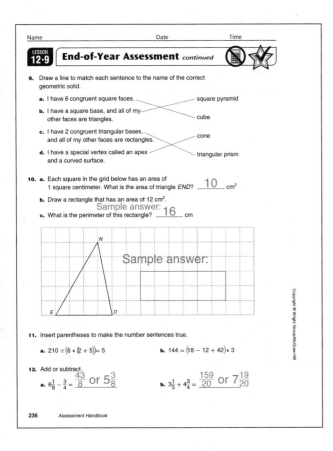

LESSON 12·9 End-of-Year Assessment *continued*

9. Draw a line to match each sentence to the name of the correct geometric solid.

a. I have 6 congruent square faces.   square pyramid

b. I have a square base, and all of my other faces are triangles.   cube

c. I have 2 congruent triangular bases, and all of my other faces are rectangles.   cone

d. I have a special vertex called an apex and a curved surface.   triangular prism

10. a. Each square in the grid below has an area of 1 square centimeter. What is the area of triangle *END*?   10 cm²

b. Draw a rectangle that has an area of 12 cm². Sample answer:

c. What is the perimeter of this rectangle?   16 cm

Sample answer: (grid with triangle *N*, *E*, *D* and rectangle)

11. Insert parentheses to make the number sentences true.

a. $210 \div (6 * (2 + 5)) = 5$ **b.** $144 = (18 - 12 + 42) * 3$

12. Add or subtract.

a. $6\frac{1}{8} - \frac{3}{4} =$ $\frac{43}{8}$ or $5\frac{3}{8}$ **b.** $3\frac{1}{5} + 4\frac{3}{4} =$ $\frac{159}{20}$ or $7\frac{19}{20}$

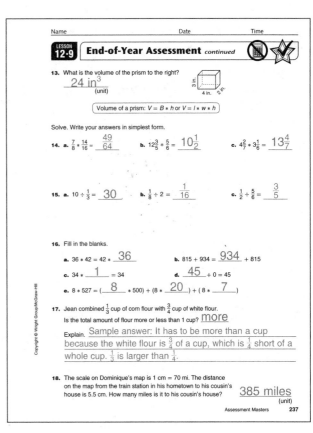

LESSON 12·9 End-of-Year Assessment *continued*

13. What is the volume of the prism to the right?   24 in³ (unit)

(prism: 3 in, 4 in, 2 in)

Volume of a prism: $V = B * h$ or $V = l * w * h$

Solve. Write your answers in simplest form.

14. a. $\frac{7}{8} * \frac{14}{16} =$ $\frac{49}{64}$ **b.** $12\frac{3}{5} * \frac{5}{6} =$ $10\frac{1}{2}$ **c.** $4\frac{2}{7} * 3\frac{1}{6} =$ $13\frac{4}{7}$

15. a. $10 \div \frac{1}{3} =$ 30   **b.** $\frac{1}{8} \div 2 =$ $\frac{1}{16}$ **c.** $\frac{1}{2} \div \frac{5}{6} =$ $\frac{3}{5}$

16. Fill in the blanks.

a. $36 * 42 = 42 *$ 36   **b.** $815 + 934 =$ 934 $+ 815$

c. $34 *$ 1 $= 34$ **d.** 45 $+ 0 = 45$

e. $8 * 527 = ($ 8 $* 500) + (8 *$ 20 $) + (8 *$ 7 $)$

17. Jean combined $\frac{1}{3}$ cup of corn flour with $\frac{3}{4}$ cup of white flour. Is the total amount of flour more or less than 1 cup? more

Explain. Sample answer: It has to be more than a cup because the white flour is $\frac{3}{4}$ of a cup, which is $\frac{1}{4}$ short of a whole cup. $\frac{1}{3}$ is larger than $\frac{1}{4}$.

18. The scale on Dominique's map is 1 cm = 70 mi. The distance on the map from the train station in his hometown to his cousin's house is 5.5 cm. How many miles is it to his cousin's house?   385 miles (unit)

LESSON 12·9   **End-of-Year Assessment** *continued*

19. a. Use the data in the table to make and label a circle graph. Use your Percent Circle.

Eye Colors of Ms. Brooke's Fifth Grade Class
10% green
25% blue
60% brown
5% hazel

Eye Colors

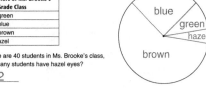

blue
green
hazel
brown

b. If there are 40 students in Ms. Brooke's class, how many students have hazel eyes?

2

20. Write the following in order from least to greatest.

$-\frac{1}{2}$ 0.5   0.036 -0.33 $\frac{2}{5}$ -45 $2\frac{1}{3}$

$\underset{\text{least}}{-45}$ $-\frac{1}{2}$ -0.33 0.036 $\frac{2}{5}$ 0.5 $\underset{\text{greatest}}{2\frac{1}{3}}$

21. Complete the table.

Standard Notation	Exponential Notation	Repeated-Factor Notation
729	3^6	3*3*3*3*3*3
1,000	10^3	10*10*10
729	9^3	9*9*9

22. Jimmy got 52 hits in his last 100 times at bat. Use probability terms to describe the chance of him getting a hit the next time at bat.

Sample answer: Jimmy's chance of getting a hit is about a 50-50 chance

---

LESSON 12·9   **End-of-Year Assessment** *continued*

23. Solve. Show your work.

a. 7.34 * 45 = 330.3   **b.** 9.7 * 67.2 = 651.84

c. 7,835 ÷ 12 = 652 R11 or 652.91$\overline{6}$ or $652\frac{11}{12}$ **d.** 806.3 ÷ 5 = 161.26

24. The probability of landing on the shaded sectors of the spinner is 25% or $\frac{1}{4}$, the probability of landing on white is $\frac{1}{12}$. What is the probability of landing on the striped sectors of the spinner?

$\frac{4}{12}$ or $\frac{1}{3}$

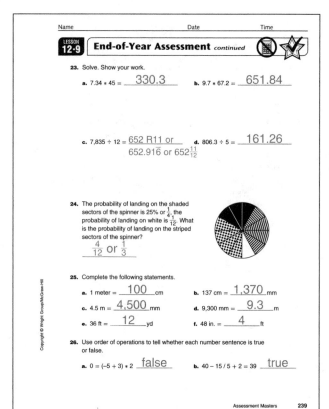

25. Complete the following statements.

a. 1 meter = 100 cm   **b.** 137 cm = 1,370 mm

c. 4.5 m = 4,500 mm   **d.** 9,300 mm = 9.3 m

e. 36 ft = 12 yd   **f.** 48 in. = 4 ft

26. Use order of operations to tell whether each number sentence is true or false.

a. 0 = (−5 + 3) * 2   false   **b.** 40 − 15 / 5 + 2 = 39   true

---

LESSON 12·9   **End-of-Year Assessment** *continued*

27. Complete.

a. 3 * 9,000 = 27,000   **b.** 3,200,000 = 80 * 40,000

c. 560,000 ÷ 80,000 = 7   **d.** 2,100,000 ÷ 300 = 7,000

28. Solve. Show your work.

a. 14.95 + 7.064 = 22.014   **b.** 24.71 + 569.809 = 594.519

c. 76.9 − 46.170 = 30.73   **d.** 7.083 − 0.79 = 6.293

29. During the basketball game, Blaire shot the ball 28 times. She made 3 out of every 7 shots. How many baskets did she make? 12

30. Mark the following points on the ruler.

A: $\frac{3}{8}$ in.   B: $2\frac{5}{8}$ in.   C: $1\frac{3}{4}$ in.   D: $1\frac{1}{2}$ in.   E: $1\frac{7}{8}$ in.

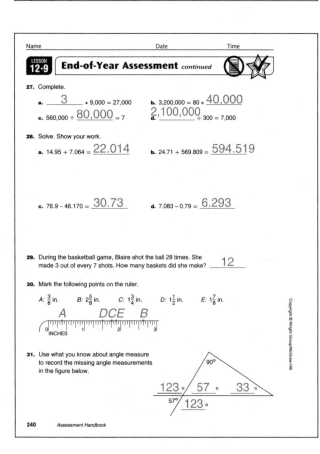

A   DCE   B
INCHES   1   2   3

31. Use what you know about angle measure to record the missing angle measurements in the figure below.

90°
123°   57°   33°
57°
123°

LESSON 12·9   **End-of-Year Assessment** *continued*

Use the grid at the right for Problems 32a–32d.

32. a. Plot the following points: (5,−1), (5,−3), (3,−3), (1,−1)

b. Draw line segments to connect the points to make a polygon.

c. Plot new points on the grid to make a translation of the polygon.

d. Are the two polygons you made congruent?

yes

How do you know?

Sample answer: The two trapezoids are congruent because they are the same shape and size.

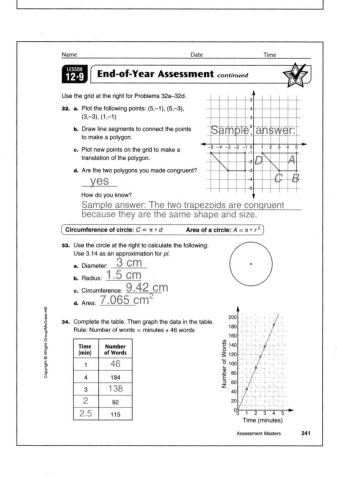

Sample answer:
D   A
C   B

Circumference of circle: $C = \pi * d$ Area of a circle: $A = \pi * r^2$

33. Use the circle at the right to calculate the following: Use 3.14 as an approximation for *pi*.

a. Diameter: 3 cm

b. Radius: 1.5 cm

c. Circumference: 9.42 cm

d. Area: 7.065 cm^2

34. Complete the table. Then graph the data in the table.
Rule: Number of words = minutes * 46 words

Time (min)	Number of Words
1	46
4	184
3	138
2	92
2.5	115

Number of Words
200 180 160 140 120 100 80 60 40 20 0
0 1 2 3 4 5
Time (minutes)

Name _____   Date _____

Lesson	Recognizing Student Achievement	A.P.*	Comments
1•1	**Identify place value.** [Number and Numeration Goal 1]		
1•2	**Build arrays and identify factors that describe arrays.** [Operations and Computation Goal 7]		
1•3	**Identify factor pairs.** [Number and Numeration Goal 3]		
1•4	**Identify prime numbers.** [Number and Numeration Goal 3]		
1•5	**Identify place value.** [Number and Numeration Goal 1]		
1•6	**Factor numbers in the form of arrays.** [Number and Numeration Goal 3]		
1•7	**Use exponential notation to write square numbers.** [Number and Numeration Goal 4]		
1•8	**Solve and compare multiplication fact extensions.** [Operations and Computation Goal 2]		
1•9	**Find factors of a number.** [Number and Numeration Goal 3]		

*Assess Progress:  = adequate progress    = not adequate progress   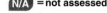 = not assessed

Individual Profile of Progress

_____   _____
Name   Date

Problem(s)	Progress Check 1	A.P.*	Comments
Oral/Slate Assessment			
1	**Identify numbers as prime or composite.** [Number and Numeration Goal 3]		
2	**Say if 345 and 282 are divisible by 2, 3, 5, 6, 9, 10.** [Number and Numeration Goal 3]		
3	**What is 7 squared? 5 squared? 8 squared? What number squared equals 16?** [Number and Numeration Goal 4]		
4	**What is the square root of 36? 81? 100? 144?** [Number and Numeration Goal 4]		
5	**Solve multiplication fact extensions.** [Operations and Computation Goal 2]		
Written Assessment Part A			
1	**Use arrays to model multiplication.** [Operations and Computation Goal 7]		
2, 5	**Factor numbers.** [Number and Numeration Goal 3]		
3, 4, 6	**Identify numbers as prime or composite.** [Number and Numeration Goal 3]		
7	**Write whole numbers and decimals and identify the value of digits.** [Number and Numeration Goal 1]		
Written Assessment Part B			
8	**Write the prime factorization of a number.** [Number and Numeration Goals 3 and 4]		
9	**Use exponents to write prime factorization.** [Number and Numeration Goal 4]		
10	**Rename numbers in exponential and standard notations.** [Number and Numeration Goals 3 and 4]		
11, 12	**Identify divisibility.** [Number and Numeration Goal 3]		

*__Assess Progress:__ **A** = adequate progress   **N** = not adequate progress   **N/A** = not assessed   **Formative Assessments**

Class Checklist:
Recognizing Student Achievement

Class _____

Date _____

Names	Identify place value. [Number and Numeration Goal 1] 1·1	Build arrays and identify factors that describe arrays. [Operations and Computation Goal 7] 1·2	Identify factor pairs. [Number and Numeration Goal 3] 1·3	Identify prime numbers. [Number and Numeration Goal 3] 1·4	Identify place value. [Number and Numeration Goal 1] 1·5	Factor numbers in the form of arrays. [Number and Numeration Goal 3] 1·6	Use exponential notation to write square numbers. [Number and Numeration Goal 4] 1·7	Solve and compare multiplication fact extensions. [Operations and Computation Goal 2] 1·8	Find factors of a number. [Number and Numeration Goal 3] 1·9
1.									
2.									
3.									
4.									
5.									
6.									
7.									
8.									
9.									
10.									
11.									
12.									
13.									
14.									
15.									
16.									
17.									
18.									
19.									
20.									
21.									
22.									
23.									
24.									
25.									

Assess Progress: 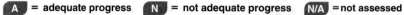 **A** = adequate progress **N** = not adequate progress **N/A** = not assessed

Go to *www.everydaymathonline.com* for digital checklists.

Class _____

Date _____

	Oral/Slate					Written Part A				Part B			
Names	1. Identify numbers as prime or composite. [Number and Numeration Goal 3]	2. Say if 345 and 282 are divisible by 2, 3, 5, 6, 9, 10. [Number and Numeration Goal 3]	3. What is 7 squared? 5 squared? 8 squared? What number squared equals 16? [Number and Numeration Goal 4]	4. What is the square root of 36? 81? 100? 144? [Number and Numeration Goal 4]	5. Solve multiplication fact extensions. [Operations and Computation Goal 2]	1. Use arrays to model multiplication. [Operations and Computation Goal 7]	2, 5. Factor numbers. [Number and Numeration Goal 3]	3, 4, 6. Identify numbers as prime or composite. [Number and Numeration Goal 3]	7. Write whole numbers and decimals and identify the value of digits. [Number and Numeration Goal 1]	8. Write the prime factorization of a number. [Number and Numeration Goals 3 and 4]	9. Use exponents to write prime factorization. [Number and Numeration Goal 4]	10. Rename numbers in exponential and standard notations. [Number and Numeration Goals 3 and 4]	11, 12. Identify divisibility. [Number and Numeration Goal 3]
1.													
2.													
3.													
4.													
5.													
6.													
7.													
8.													
9.													
10.													
11.													
12.													
13.													
14.													
15.													
16.													
17.													
18.													
19.													
20.													
21.													
22.													
23.													
24.													
25.													

Assess Progress: **A** = adequate progress   **N** = not adequate progress   **N/A** = not assessed   **Formative Assessments**

Individual Profile of Progress

Name _____   Date _____

Lesson	Recognizing Student Achievement	A.P.*	Comments
2•1	**Solve extended facts problems mentally.** [Operations and Computation Goal 2]		
2•2	**Solve multidigit addition problems.** [Operations and Computation Goal 1]		
2•3	**Use the trade-first method with multidigit subtraction problems.** [Operations and Computation Goal 1]		
2•4	**Write open number sentences to model given situations.** [Patterns, Functions, and Algebra Goal 2]		
2•5	**Compare decimals.** [Number and Numeration Goal 6]		
2•6	**Explain why the Probability Meter is labeled with fractions, decimals, and percents.** [Number and Numeration Goal 5]		
2•7	**Add and subtract whole numbers.** [Operations and Computation Goal 1]		
2•8	**Make reasonable magnitude estimates for multiplication problems based on number sentences.** [Operations and Computation Goal 6]		
2•9	**Explain how to solve multiplication problems.** [Operations and Computation Goal 3]		
2•10	**Know place value and compare large numbers.** [Number and Numeration Goals 1 and 6]		

*Assess Progress:  = adequate progress   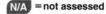 = not adequate progress    = not assessed

Individual Profile of Progress

Name _____   Date _____

Problem(s)	Progress Check 2	A.P.*	Comments
Oral/Slate Assessment			
1–3	**Make reasonable magnitude estimates.** [Operations and Computation Goal 6]		
4	**Identify the ten-thousands and hundred-thousands digits in 543,607.** [Number and Numeration Goal 1]		
5	**Identify the tenths and tens digits in 204.39.** [Number and Numeration Goal 1]		
Written Assessment Part A			
1–6	**Addition and subtraction of whole numbers and decimals.** [Operations and Computation Goal 1]		
7	**Use scaling to model multiplication and division.** [Operations and Computation Goal 7]		
8	**Convert between U.S. customary units of length.** [Measurement and Reference Frames Goal 3]		
9	**Identify place values of digits.** [Number and Numeration Goal 1]		
10, 11, 13, 14	**Multiply whole numbers and decimals.** [Operations and Computation Goal 3]		
12–14	**Make reasonable magnitude estimates.** [Operations and Computation Goal 6]		
15	**Describe given numerical probabilities using words or phrases.** [Data and Chance Goal 3]		
Written Assessment Part B			
16, 17	**Write numbers in expanded notation.** [Number and Numeration Goal 1]		
18	**Find landmarks for a data set.** [Data and Chance Goal 2]		
19	**Write and solve number sentences.** [Patterns, Functions, and Algebra Goal 3]		

*Assess Progress: **A** = adequate progress   **N** = not adequate progress   **N/A** = not assessed   **Formative Assessments**

Class Checklist:
Recognizing Student Achievement

Class _____

Date _____

Names	Solve extended facts problems mentally. [Operations and Computation Goal 2] 2·1	Solve multidigit addition problems. [Operations and Computation Goal 1] 2·2	Use the trade-first method with multidigit subtraction problems. [Operations and Computation Goal 1] 2·3	Write open number sentences to model given situations. [Patterns, Functions, and Algebra Goal 2] 2·4	Compare decimals. [Number and Numeration Goal 6] 2·5	Explain why the Probability Meter is labeled with fractions, decimals, and percents. [Number and Numeration Goal 5] 2·6	Add and subtract whole numbers. [Operations and Computation Goal 1] 2·7	Make reasonable magnitude estimates for multiplication problems based on number sentences. [Operations and Computation Goal 6] 2·8	Explain how to solve multiplication problems. [Operations and Computation Goal 3] 2·9	Know place value and compare large numbers. [Number and Numeration Goals 1 and 6] 2·10
1.										
2.										
3.										
4.										
5.										
6.										
7.										
8.										
9.										
10.										
11.										
12.										
13.										
14.										
15.										
16.										
17.										
18.										
19.										
20.										
21.										
22.										
23.										
24.										
25.										

Assess Progress:  = adequate progress  = not adequate progress 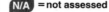 = not assessed

Go to *www.everydaymathonline.com* for digital checklists.

Class _____

Date _____

Names	Oral/Slate			Written — Part A								Written — Part B		
	1–3. Make reasonable magnitude estimates. [Operations and Computation Goal 6]	4. Identify the ten-thousands and hundred-thousands digits in 543,607. [Number and Numeration Goal 1]	5. Identify the tenths and tens digits in 204.39. [Number and Numeration Goal 1]	1–6. Addition and subtraction of whole numbers and decimals. [Operations and Computation Goal 1]	7. Use scaling to model multiplication and division. [Operations and Computation Goal 7]	8. Convert between U.S. customary units of length. [Measurement and Reference Frames Goal 3]	9. Identify place values of digits. [Number and Numeration Goal 1]	10, 11, 13, 14. Multiply whole numbers and decimals. [Operations and Computation Goal 3]	12–14. Make reasonable magnitude estimates. [Operations and Computation Goal 6]	15. Describe given numerical probabilities using words or phrases. [Data and Chance Goal 3]	16, 17. Write numbers in expanded notation. [Number and Numeration Goal 1]	18. Find landmarks for a data set. [Data and Chance Goal 2]	19. Write and solve number sentences. [Patterns, Functions, and Algebra Goal 3]
1.													
2.													
3.													
4.													
5.													
6.													
7.													
8.													
9.													
10.													
11.													
12.													
13.													
14.													
15.													
16.													
17.													
18.													
19.													
20.													
21.													
22.													
23.													
24.													
25.													

Assess Progress:  **A** = adequate progress **N** = not adequate progress **N/A** = not assessed **Formative Assessments**

Name _____   Date _____

Lesson	Recognizing Student Achievement	A.P.*	Comments
3•1	**Read and write large whole numbers.** [Number and Numeration Goal 1]		
3•2	**Add and subtract whole numbers and decimals.** [Operations and Computation Goal 1]		
3•3	**Use the relationship between circles and polygons to identify angle measures.** [Geometry Goal 1]		
3•4	**Use full-circle and half-circle protractors to measure angles.** [Measurement and Reference Frames Goal 1]		
3•5	**Solve extended multiplication facts mentally.** [Operations and Computation Goal 2]		
3•6	**Compare decimals.** [Number and Numeration Goal 6]		
3•7	**Use attributes to identify polygons.** [Geometry Goal 2]		
3•8	**Classify quadrangles.** [Geometry Goal 2]		
3•9	**Use the sum of angles in triangles to find the sums of angles in other polygons.** [Geometry Goal 1]		
3•10	**Make magnitude estimates for division problems.** [Operations and Computation Goal 6]		

*Assess Progress: **A** = adequate progress   **N** = not adequate progress   **N/A** = not assessed

Individual Profile of Progress

Name _____ Date _____

Problem(s)	Progress Check 3	A.P.*	Comments
Oral/Slate Assessment			
1	**Round numbers to the nearest ten, whole number, and tenth.** [Number and Numeration Goal 1]		
2	**Indicate whether a given number is divisible by the stated divisor or not.** [Number and Numeration Goal 3]		
3	**Circle and underline digits in indicated places.** [Number and Numeration Goal 1]		
4	**Complete multiplication problems.** [Operations and Computation Goal 2]		
Written Assessment Part A			
1–4	**Measure angles.** [Geometry Goal 1]		
1–4	**Identify types of angles.** [Geometry Goal 1]		
5	**Identify place value in numbers to billions.** [Number and Numeration Goal 1]		
6–8	**Draw types of triangles.** [Geometry Goal 2]		
9, 10	**Identify types of triangles and compare properties.** [Geometry Goal 2]		
11, 12	**Compare the properties of polygons.** [Geometry Goal 2]		
Written Assessment Part B			
13–15	**Determine angle measures based on relationships between angles.** [Geometry Goal 1]		
16, 17	**Identify types of angles.** [Geometry Goal 1]		
17	**Estimate the measure of angles without tools.** [Measurement and Reference Frames Goal 1]		
18	**Read a chart.** [Data and Chance Goal 2]		
19, 20	**Create and define tessellations.** [Geometry Goal 3]		

*Assess Progress: **A** = adequate progress   **N** = not adequate progress   **N/A** = not assessed   **Formative Assessments**

Unit 3

Class Checklist:
Recognizing Student Achievement

Class _____

Date _____

Names	3·1 Read and write large whole numbers. [Number and Numeration Goal 1]	3·2 Add and subtract whole numbers and decimals. [Operations and Computation Goal 1]	3·3 Use the relationship between circles and polygons to identify angle measures. [Geometry Goal 1]	3·4 Use full-circle and half-circle protractors to measure angles. [Measurement and Reference Frames Goal 1]	3·5 Solve extended multiplication facts mentally. [Operations and Computation Goal 2]	3·6 Compare decimals. [Number and Numeration Goal 6]	3·7 Use attributes to identify polygons. [Geometry Goal 2]	3·8 Classify quadrangles. [Geometry Goal 2]	3·9 Use the sum of angles in triangles to find the sums of angles in other polygons. [Geometry Goal 1]	3·10 Make magnitude estimates for division problems. [Operations and Computation Goal 6]
1.										
2.										
3.										
4.										
5.										
6.										
7.										
8.										
9.										
10.										
11.										
12.										
13.										
14.										
15.										
16.										
17.										
18.										
19.										
20.										
21.										
22.										
23.										
24.										
25.										

Assess Progress:  **A** = adequate progress **N** = not adequate progress **N/A** = not assessed

Go to *www.everydaymathonline.com* for digital checklists.

Class Checklist:
Progress Check 3

	Oral/Slate				Written Part A						Part B				
Names	1. Round numbers to the nearest ten, whole number, and tenth. [Number and Numeration Goal 1]	2. Indicate whether a given number is divisible by the stated divisor or not. [Number and Numeration Goal 3]	3. Circle and underline digits in indicated places. [Number and Numeration Goal 1]	4. Complete multiplication problems. [Operations and Computation Goal 2]	1–4. Measure angles. [Geometry Goal 1]	1–4. Identify types of angles. [Geometry Goal 1]	5. Identify place value in numbers to billions. [Number and Numeration Goal 1]	6–8. Draw types of triangles. [Geometry Goal 2]	9, 10. Identify types of triangles and compare properties. [Geometry Goal 2]	11, 12. Compare the properties of polygons. [Geometry Goal 2]	13–15. Determine angle measures based on relationships between angles. [Geometry Goal 1]	16, 17. Identify types of angles. [Geometry Goal 1]	17. Estimate the measure of angles without tools. [Measurement and Reference Frames Goal 1]	18. Read a chart. [Data and Chance Goal 2]	19, 20. Create and define tessellations. [Geometry Goal 3]
1.															
2.															
3.															
4.															
5.															
6.															
7.															
8.															
9.															
10.															
11.															
12.															
13.															
14.															
15.															
16.															
17.															
18.															
19.															
20.															
21.															
22.															
23.															
24.															
25.															

Assess Progress:  **A** = adequate progress **N** = not adequate progress **N/A** = not assessed **Formative Assessments**

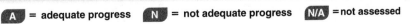

Go to *www.everydaymathonline.com* for digital checklists.

Unit 4

Individual Profile of Progress

Name _____ Date _____

Lesson	Recognizing Student Achievement	A.P.*	Comments
4•1	Use multiplication and division facts to solve division problems with 1-digit divisors. [Operations and Computation Goal 3]		
4•2	Use the partial-quotients algorithm to solve division problems. [Operations and Computation Goal 3]		
4•3	Identify place value in decimals. [Number and Numeration Goal 1]		
4•4	Write a number story. [Operations and Computation Goal 3]		
4•5	Make magnitude estimates for division problems. [Operations and Computation Goal 6]		
4•6	Interpret the remainder in division problems. [Operations and Computation Goal 3]		
4•7	Find the value of an algebraic expression. [Patterns, Functions, and Algebra Goal 2]		

*Assess Progress:  = adequate progress 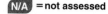 = not adequate progress 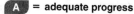 = not assessed

Individual Profile of Progress

Name _____   Date _____

Problem(s)	Progress Check 4	A.P.*	Comments
Oral/Slate Assessment			
1	**Determine how many 5s are in 35, what number times 7 equals 63, multiply 400 by 9, and so on.** [Operations and Computation Goal 2]		
2	**Determine whether 4,492 is divisible by 2, by 3, by 9, and so on.** [Number and Numeration Goal 3]		
3	**Solve multiplication problems involving fact extensions.** [Operations and Computation Goal 2]		
4	**Express remainders as whole numbers, fractions, and decimals.** [Operations and Computation Goal 3]		
Written Assessment Part A			
1–3	**Use a map scale to estimate distance.** [Operations and Computation Goal 7; Measurement and Reference Frames Goal 1]		
4, 5	**Use a friendly-number strategy to divide.** [Number and Numeration Goal 4; Operations and Computation Goals 2 and 3]		
6, 7, 13, 14	**Use the partial-quotients algorithm.** [Operations and Computation Goals 2 and 3]		
8, 9	**Make a magnitude estimate to place the decimal point.** [Operations and Computation Goal 6]		
10–12	**Write and solve number sentences.** [Patterns, Functions, and Algebra Goal 2]		
Written Assessment Part B			
15, 16	**Use the partial-quotients algorithm.** [Operations and Computation Goals 2 and 3]		
17, 18	**Divide decimals.** [Operations and Computation Goal 3]		
17, 18	**Make reasonable magnitude estimates.** [Operations and Computation Goal 6]		
19, 20	**Write number sentences that model number stories.** [Patterns, Functions, and Algebra Goal 2]		
19, 20	**Interpret remainders in a division problem.** [Operations and Computation Goal 3]		

*Assess Progress: **A** = adequate progress   **N** = not adequate progress   **N/A** = not assessed   **Formative Assessments**

Class Checklist:
Recognizing Student Achievement

Class _____

Date _____

Names	Use multiplication and division facts to solve division problems with 1-digit divisors. [Operations and Computation Goal 3]	Use the partial-quotients algorithm to solve division problems. [Operations and Computation Goal 3]	Identify place value in decimals. [Number and Numeration Goal 1]	Write a number story. [Operations and Computation Goal 3]	Make magnitude estimates for division problems. [Operations and Computation Goal 6]	Interpret the remainder in division problems. [Operations and Computation Goal 3]	Find the value of an algebraic expression. [Patterns, Functions, and Algebra Goal 2]
	4•1	4•2	4•3	4•4	4•5	4•6	4•7
1.							
2.							
3.							
4.							
5.							
6.							
7.							
8.							
9.							
10.							
11.							
12.							
13.							
14.							
15.							
16.							
17.							
18.							
19.							
20.							
21.							
22.							
23.							
24.							
25.							

Assess Progress: **A** = adequate progress   **N** = not adequate progress   **N/A** = not assessed

Go to *www.everydaymathonline.com* for digital checklists.

Class Checklist:
Progress Check 4

Class _____

Date _____

Names	Oral/Slate				Written Part A						Written Part B				
	1. Determine how many 5s are in 35, what number times 7 equals 63, multiply 400 by 9, and so on. [Operations and Computation Goal 2]	**2. Determine whether 4,492 is divisible by 2, by 3, by 9, and so on.** [Number and Numeration Goal 3]	**3. Solve multiplication problems involving fact extensions.** [Operations and Computation Goal 2]	**4. Express remainders as whole numbers, fractions, and decimals.** [Operations and Computation Goal 3]	**1–3. Use a map scale to estimate distance.** [Operations and Computation Goal 7; Measurement and Reference Frames Goal 1]	**4, 5. Use a friendly number strategy to divide.** [Number and Numeration Goal 4; Operations and Computation Goals 2 and 3]	**6, 7, 13, 14. Use the partial-quotients algorithm.** [Operations and Computation Goals 2 and 3]	**8, 9. Make a magnitude estimate to place the decimal point.** [Operations and Computation Goal 6]	**10–12. Write and solve number sentences.** [Patterns, Functions, and Algebra Goal 2]		**15, 16. Use the partial-quotients algorithm.** [Operations and Computation Goals 2 and 3]	**17, 18. Divide decimals.** [Operations and Computation Goal 3]	**17, 18. Make reasonable magnitude estimates.** [Operations and Computation Goal 6]	**19, 20. Write number sentences that model number stories.** [Patterns, Functions, and Algebra Goal 2]	**19, 20. Interpret remainders in a division problem.** [Operations and Computation Goal 3]
1.															
2.															
3.															
4.															
5.															
6.															
7.															
8.															
9.															
10.															
11.															
12.															
13.															
14.															
15.															
16.															
17.															
18.															
19.															
20.															
21.															
22.															
23.															
24.															
25.															

Assess Progress: **A** = adequate progress   **N** = not adequate progress   **N/A** = not assessed   **Formative Assessments**

Individual Profile of Progress

Name _____   Date _____

Lesson	Recognizing Student Achievement	A.P.*	Comments
5◆1	**Find the unit fraction of a set.** [Operations and Computation Goal 7]		
5◆2	**Find the value of a region based on a defined unit fraction.** [Operations and Computation Goal 7]		
5◆3	**Explain the relationship between the numerator and denominator of a fraction.** [Number and Numeration Goal 6]		
5◆4	**Find equivalent fractions.** [Number and Numeration Goal 5]		
5◆5	**Convert between fractions and decimals.** [Number and Numeration Goal 5]		
5◆6	**Compare fractions.** [Number and Numeration Goal 6]		
5◆7	**Convert between fractions and decimals.** [Number and Numeration Goal 5]		
5◆8	**Identify percent equivalents for fractions.** [Number and Numeration Goal 5]		
5◆9	**Compare features of bar and circle graphs.** [Data and Chance Goal 1]		
5◆10	**Estimate and find the measure of circle-graph sectors.** [Measurement and Reference Frames Goal 1]		
5◆11	**Use fractions to draw circle-graph sectors.** [Data and Chance Goal 1]		
5◆12	**Estimate answers to +, −, *, and ÷ problems.** [Operations and Computation Goal 6]		

*Assess Progress: **A** = adequate progress   **N** = not adequate progress   **N/A** = not assessed

Individual Profile of Progress

Unit 5

Name _____   Date _____

Problem(s)	Progress Check 5	A.P.*	Comments
Oral/Slate Assessment			
1	**Give an equivalent decimal and percent for fractions.** [Number and Numeration Goal 5]		
2	**Compare and order sets of fractions.** [Number and Numeration Goal 6]		
3	**Write equivalent mixed numbers or whole numbers on slates.** [Number and Numeration Goal 5]		
4	**Write equivalent improper fractions on slates.** [Number and Numeration Goal 5]		
Written Assessment Part A			
1–3	**Name equivalent fractions.** [Number and Numeration Goal 5]		
4–10	**Convert between fractions and mixed numbers.** [Number and Numeration Goal 5]		
11–13	**Add fractions using fraction sticks.** [Operations and Computation Goal 4]		
14–16	**Order and compare fractions.** [Number and Numeration Goal 6]		
Written Assessment Part B			
17–19	**Order and compare fractions with unlike denominators.** [Number and Numeration Goal 6]		
20	**Convert between fractions and percents.** [Number and Numeration Goal 5]		
21–23	**Estimate and measure sectors of a circle graph.** [Measurement and Reference Frames Goal 1]		
23–26	**Read and construct circle graphs.** [Data and Chance Goals 1 and 2]		

*Assess Progress: **A** = adequate progress   **N** = not adequate progress   **N/A** = not assessed   **Formative Assessments**

Class Checklist:
Recognizing Student Achievement

Class _____

Date _____

Names	Find the unit fraction of a set. [Operations and Computation Goal 7] 5•1	Find the value of a region based on a defined unit fraction. [Operations and Computation Goal 7] 5•2	Explain the relationship between the numerator and denominator of a fraction. [Number and Numeration Goal 6] 5•3	Find equivalent fractions. [Number and Numeration Goal 5] 5•4	Convert between fractions and decimals. [Number and Numeration Goal 5] 5•5	Compare fractions. [Number and Numeration Goal 6] 5•6	Convert between fractions and decimals. [Number and Numeration Goal 5] 5•7	Identify percent equivalents for fractions. [Number and Numeration Goal 5] 5•8	Compare features of bar and circle graphs. [Data and Chance Goal 1] 5•9	Estimate and find the measure of circle-graph sectors. [Measurement and Reference Frames Goal 1] 5•10	Use fractions to draw circle-graph sectors. [Data and Chance Goal 1] 5•11	Estimate answers to +, −, *, and ÷ problems. [Operations and Computation Goal 6] 5•12
1.												
2.												
3.												
4.												
5.												
6.												
7.												
8.												
9.												
10.												
11.												
12.												
13.												
14.												
15.												
16.												
17.												
18.												
19.												
20.												
21.												
22.												
23.												
24.												
25.												

Assess Progress: **A** = adequate progress   **N** = not adequate progress   **N/A** = not assessed

Class _____

Date _____

Names	Oral/Slate				Written Part A				Written Part B			
	1. Give an equivalent decimal and percent for fractions. [Number and Numeration Goal 5]	2. Compare and order sets of fractions. [Number and Numeration Goal 6]	3. Write equivalent mixed numbers or whole numbers on slates. [Number and Numeration Goal 5]	4. Write equivalent improper fractions on slates. [Number and Numeration Goal 5]	1–3. Name equivalent fractions. [Number and Numeration Goal 5]	4–10. Convert between fractions and mixed numbers. [Number and Numeration Goal 5]	11–13. Add fractions using fraction sticks. [Operations and Computation Goal 4]	14–16. Order and compare fractions. [Number and Numeration Goal 6]	17–19. Order and compare fractions with unlike denominators. [Number and Numeration Goal 6]	20. Convert between fractions and percents. [Number and Numeration Goal 5]	21–23. Estimate and measure sectors of a circle graph. [Measurement and Reference Frames Goal 1]	23–26. Read and construct circle graphs. [Data and Chance Goals 1 and 2]
1.												
2.												
3.												
4.												
5.												
6.												
7.												
8.												
9.												
10.												
11.												
12.												
13.												
14.												
15.												
16.												
17.												
18.												
19.												
20.												
21.												
22.												
23.												
24.												
25.												

Assess Progress: **A** = adequate progress   **N** = not adequate progress   **N/A** = not assessed   **Formative Assessments**

Individual Profile of Progress

Name _____   Date _____

Lesson	Recognizing Student Achievement	A.P.*	Comments
6•1	**Display data on a line plot and identify the data landmarks.** [Data and Chance Goals 1 and 2]		
6•2	**Measure lengths to the nearest centimeter and $\frac{1}{4}$ inch.** [Measurement and Reference Frames Goal 1]		
6•3	**Explain the advantage of displaying data in stem-and-leaf plots.** [Data and Chance Goal 1]		
6•4	**Interpret data displayed in line plots.** [Data and Chance Goal 2]		
6•5	**Describe how to find the percent of a number.** [Number and Numeration Goal 2]		
6•6	**Name fraction-decimal equivalents.** [Number and Numeration Goal 5]		
6•7	**Rename fractions as decimals and percents.** [Number and Numeration Goal 5]		
6•8	**Use benchmarks to estimate sums and differences.** [Operations and Computation Goal 6]		
6•9	**Add and subtract fractions with unlike denominators.** [Operations and Computation Goal 4]		
6•10	**Find common denominators.** [Number and Numeration Goal 5]		

*Assess Progress: **A** = adequate progress   **N** = not adequate progress   **N/A** = not assessed

Individual Profile of Progress

Name _____ Date _____

Problem(s)	Progress Check 6	A.P.*	Comments
Oral/Slate Assessment			
1	**Use benchmarks to estimate fraction sums and differences.** [Operations and Computation Goal 6]		
2	**Round numbers up or down to the indicated place value.** [Number and Numeration Goal 1]		
3	**Write the decimal and percent for each given fraction.** [Number and Numeration Goal 5]		
4	**Rename given numbers as improper fractions.** [Number and Numeration Goal 5]		
Written Assessment Part A			
1–5a, 16	**Find and use data landmarks.** [Data and Chance Goal 2]		
6, 8	**Add and subtract fractions with like denominators.** [Operations and Computation Goal 4]		
7, 9–13	**Add and subtract fractions with unlike denominators.** [Operations and Computation Goal 4]		
14, 15	**Find a common denominator.** [Number and Numeration Goal 5]		
5b, 5c	**Understand how sample size affects results.** [Data and Chance Goal 2]		
Written Assessment Part B			
17, 20a	**Read and interpret stem-and-leaf plots and bar graphs.** [Data and Chance Goal 2]		
18	**Construct stem-and-leaf plots.** [Data and Chance Goal 1]		
19a	**Measure to the nearest $\frac{1}{8}$ of an inch.** [Measurement and Reference Frames Goal 1]		
19b	**Add and subtract fractions with unlike denominators.** [Operations and Computation Goal 4]		
19c	**Add and subtract fractions with common denominators.** [Operations and Computation Goal 4]		
20b–20d	**Solve problems involving percent.** [Number and Numeration Goal 2]		
20e	**Understand how sample size affects results.** [Data and Chance Goal 2]		
21	**Find a common denominator.** [Number and Numeration Goal 5]		
22	**Convert between fractions, decimals, and percents.** [Number and Numeration Goal 5]		

*Assess Progress: **A** = adequate progress   **N** = not adequate progress   **N/A** = not assessed   **Formative Assessments**

Class Checklist:
Recognizing Student Achievement

Class _____

Date _____

Names	Display data on a line plot and identify the data landmarks. [Data and Chance Goals 1 and 2] 6·1	Measure lengths to the nearest centimeter and $\frac{1}{4}$ inch. [Measurement and Reference Frames Goal 1] 6·2	Explain the advantage of displaying data in stem-and-leaf plots. [Data and Chance Goal 1] 6·3	Interpret data displayed in line plots. [Data and Chance Goal 2] 6·4	Describe how to find the percent of a number. [Number and Numeration Goal 2] 6·5	Name fraction-decimal equivalents. [Number and Numeration Goal 5] 6·6	Rename fractions as decimals and percents. [Number and Numeration Goal 5] 6·7	Use benchmarks to estimate sums and differences. [Operations and Computation Goal 6] 6·8	Add and subtract fractions with unlike denominators. [Operations and Computation Goal 4] 6·9	Find common denominators. [Number and Numeration Goal 5] 6·10
1.										
2.										
3.										
4.										
5.										
6.										
7.										
8.										
9.										
10.										
11.										
12.										
13.										
14.										
15.										
16.										
17.										
18.										
19.										
20.										
21.										
22.										
23.										
24.										
25.										

Assess Progress:  **A** = adequate progress   **N** = not adequate progress   **N/A** = not assessed

 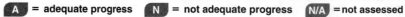

Class _____

Date _____

	Oral/Slate			Written Part A						Written Part B								
Names	1. Use benchmarks to estimate fraction sums and differences. [Operations and Computations 6]	2. Round numbers up or down to the indicated place value. [Number and Numeration Goal 1]	3. Write the decimal and percent for each given fraction. [Number and Numeration Goal 5]	4. Rename given numbers as improper fractions. [Number and Numeration Goal 5]	1–5a, 16. Find and use data landmarks. [Data and Chance Goal 2]	6, 8. Add and subtract fractions with like denominators. [Operations and Computation Goal 4]	7, 9–13. Add and subtract fractions with unlike denominators. [Operations and Computation Goal 4]	14–15. Find a common denominator. [Number and Numeration Goal 5]	5b, 5c. Understand how sample size affects results. [Data and Chance Goal 2]	17, 20a. Read and interpret stem-and-leaf plots and bar graphs. [Data and Chance Goal 2]	18. Construct stem-and-leaf plots. [Data and Chance Goal 1]	19a. Measure to the nearest $\frac{1}{8}$ of an inch. [Measurement and Reference Frames Goal 1]	19b. Add and subtract fractions with unlike denominators. [Operations and Computation Goal 4]	19c. Add and subtract fractions with common denominators. [Operations and Computation Goal 4]	20b–20d. Solve problems involving percent. [Number and Numeration Goal 2]	20e. Understand how sample size affects results. [Data and Chance Goal 2]	21. Find a common denominator. [Number and Numeration Goal 5]	22. Convert between fractions, decimals, and percents. [Number and Numeration Goal 5]
1.																		
2.																		
3.																		
4.																		
5.																		
6.																		
7.																		
8.																		
9.																		
10.																		
11.																		
12.																		
13.																		
14.																		
15.																		
16.																		
17.																		
18.																		
19.																		
20.																		
21.																		
22.																		
23.																		
24.																		
25.																		

Assess Progress: **A** = adequate progress **N** = not adequate progress **N/A** = not assessed **Formative Assessments**

Lesson	Recognizing Student Achievement	A.P.*	Comments
7◆1	**Identify and correct mistakes in writing numbers using exponential notation.** [Number and Numeration Goal 4]		
7◆2	**Use powers of 10 to write equivalent names for numbers.** [Number and Numeration Goal 1]		
7◆3	**Translate numbers from standard notation to expanded notation.** [Number and Numeration Goal 1]		
7◆4	**Write expressions containing parentheses to represent a number story.** [Patterns, Functions, and Algebra Goal 3]		
7◆5	**Compare decimals.** [Number and Numeration Goal 6]		
7◆6	**Add and subtract fractions with like and unlike denominators.** [Operations and Computation Goal 4]		
7◆7	**Use order of operations to solve problems.** [Patterns, Functions, and Algebra Goal 3]		
7◆8	**Model problems with positive and negative counters.** [Operations and Computation Goal 1]		
7◆9	**Write and compare decimals.** [Number and Numeration Goals 1 and 6]		
7◆10	**Add and compare fractions.** [Number and Numeration Goal 6 and Operations and Computation Goal 4]		
7◆11	**Convert fractions to whole numbers or mixed numbers in simplest form.** [Number and Numeration Goal 5]		

*Assess Progress: **A** = adequate progress **N** = not adequate progress **N/A** = not assessed

Individual Profile of Progress

Name _____   Date _____

Problem(s)	Progress Check 7	A.P.*	Comments
Oral/Slate Assessment			
1	Use > , < , or = to compare numbers. [Number and Numeration Goal 6]		
2	Identify power of 10 for given numbers. [Number and Numeration Goal 4]		
3	Solve addition and subtraction problems with positive and negative numbers. [Operations and Computation Goal 1]		
4	Write numbers given in scientific notation in number-and-word notation. [Number and Numeration Goal 1]		
Written Assessment Part A			
1–9	Order and compare positive and negative numbers. [Number and Numeration Goal 6]		
7–10, 18–26	Add and subtract positive and negative numbers. [Operations and Computation Goal 1]		
10	Identify number sentences and tell whether they are true or false. [Patterns, Functions, and Algebra Goal 2]		
11–17	Understand and apply order of operations and use of parentheses to evaluate expressions and solve number sentences. [Patterns, Functions, and Algebra Goal 3]		
Written Assessment Part B			
27–33	Add and subtract positive and negative numbers. [Operations and Computation Goal 1]		
34	Understand and apply scientific notation, powers of 10, and exponential notation. [Number and Numeration Goals 1 and 4]		
35	Interpret line graphs. [Data and Chance Goal 2]		
36	Create line graphs. [Data and Chance Goal 1]		

*Assess Progress: **A** = adequate progress   **N** = not adequate progress   **N/A** = not assessed   Formative Assessments

Class Checklist:
Recognizing Student Achievement

Class _____

Date _____

Names	7·1	7·2	7·3	7·4	7·5	7·6	7·7	7·8	7·9	7·10	7·11
	Identify and correct mistakes in writing numbers using exponential notation. [Number and Numeration Goal 4]	Use powers of 10 to write equivalent names for numbers. [Number and Numeration Goal 1]	Translate numbers from standard notation to expanded notation. [Number and Numeration Goal 1]	Write expressions containing parentheses to represent a number story. [Patterns, Functions, and Algebra Goal 3]	Compare decimals. [Number and Numeration Goal 6]	Add and subtract fractions with like and unlike denominators. [Operations and Computation Goal 4]	Use order of operations to solve problems. [Patterns, Functions, and Algebra Goal 3]	Model problems with positive and negative counters. [Operations and Computation Goal 1]	Write and compare decimals. [Number and Numeration Goals 1 and 6]	Add and compare fractions. [Number and Numeration Goal 6 and Operations and Computation Goal 4]	Convert fractions to whole numbers or mixed numbers in simplest form. [Number and Numeration Goal 5]
1.											
2.											
3.											
4.											
5.											
6.											
7.											
8.											
9.											
10.											
11.											
12.											
13.											
14.											
15.											
16.											
17.											
18.											
19.											
20.											
21.											
22.											
23.											
24.											
25.											

Assess Progress: **A** = adequate progress **N** = not adequate progress **N/A** = not assessed

Class Checklist:
Progress Check 7

Class _____

Date _____

Names	Oral/Slate				Written Part A					Part B			
	1. Use >, <, or = to compare numbers. [Number and Numeration Goal 6]	2. Identify power of 10 for given numbers. [Number and Numeration Goal 4]	3. Solve addition and subtraction problems with positive and negative numbers. [Operations and Computation Goal 1]	4. Write numbers given in scientific notation in number-and-word notation. [Number and Numeration Goal 1]	1–9. Order and compare positive and negative numbers. [Number and Numeration Goal 6]	7–10, 18–26. Add and subtract positive and negative numbers. [Operations and Computation Goal 1]	10. Identify number sentences and tell whether they are true or false. [Patterns, Functions, and Algebra Goal 2]	11–17. Understand and apply order of operations and use of parentheses to evaluate expressions and solve number sentences. [Patterns, Functions, and Algebra Goal 3]	27–33. Add and subtract positive and negative numbers. [Operations and Computation Goal 1]	34. Understand and apply scientific notation, powers of 10, and exponential notation. [Number and Numeration Goals 1 and 4]	35. Interpret line graphs. [Data and Chance Goal 2]	36. Create line graphs. [Data and Chance Goal 1]	
1.													
2.													
3.													
4.													
5.													
6.													
7.													
8.													
9.													
10.													
11.													
12.													
13.													
14.													
15.													
16.													
17.													
18.													
19.													
20.													
21.													
22.													
23.													
24.													
25.													

Assess Progress: **A** = adequate progress   **N** = not adequate progress   **N/A** = not assessed   **Formative Assessments**

Individual Profile of Progress

Name _____   Date _____

Lesson	Recognizing Student Achievement	A.P.*	Comments
8◆1	**Compare fractions using benchmarks.** [Number and Numeration Goal 6]		
8◆2	**Rename fractions to have common denominators and be in simplest form.** [Number and Numeration Goal 5; Operations and Computation Goal 4]		
8◆3	**Estimate sums and differences of mixed numbers using benchmarks.** [Operations and Computation Goals 4 and 6]		
8◆4	**Order fractions.** [Number and Numeration Goal 6]		
8◆5	**Use a number-line model to solve fraction multiplication problems.** [Operations and Computation Goal 5]		
8◆6	**Use an area model to solve fraction multiplication problems.** [Operations and Computation Goal 5]		
8◆7	**Convert fractions to decimals and percents.** [Number and Numeration Goal 5]		
8◆8	**Multiply mixed numbers.** [Operations and Computation Goal 5]		
8◆9	**Convert between fractions, decimals, and percents.** [Number and Numeration Goal 5]		
8◆10	**Use unit fractions and unit percents to solve problems.** [Number and Numeration Goal 2]		
8◆11	**Add fractions.** [Number and Numeration Goal 5; Operations and Computation Goal 4]		
8◆12	**Use a visual model to divide fractions.** [Operations and Computation Goal 5]		

*Assess Progress: **A** = adequate progress   **N** = not adequate progress   **N/A** = not assessed

Individual Profile of Progress

Name _____   Date _____

Problem(s)	Progress Check 8	A.P.*	Comments
Oral/Slate Assessment			
1	**Indicate if given fractions and mixed numbers are equivalent or not.** [Number and Numeration Goal 5]		
2	**Indicate if the product of multiplying fractions is correct or not.** [Operations and Computation Goal 5]		
3	**Find a common denominator for given pairs of fractions.** [Number and Numeration Goal 5]		
4	**Find the percent of given numbers.** [Number and Numeration Goal 2]		
Written Assessment Part A			
1, 2	**Convert between fractions, decimals, and percents.** [Number and Numeration Goal 5]		
3, 4, 8–11, 13, 19	**Find common denominators.** [Number and Numeration Goal 5]		
5, 6, 20	**Order and compare fractions using benchmarks.** [Number and Numeration Goal 6]		
7	**Measure to the nearest $\frac{1}{4}$ inch.** [Measurement and Reference Frames Goal 1]		
7, 9, 10, 12, 14	**Use an algorithm to subtract fractions and mixed numbers.** [Operations and Computation Goal 4]		
8, 11, 13	**Use an algorithm to add fractions and mixed numbers.** [Operations and Computation Goal 4]		
15–18	**Convert between fractions and whole or mixed numbers.** [Number and Numeration Goal 5]		
Written Assessment Part B			
22, 23	**Use an algorithm to subtract mixed numbers.** [Operations and Computation Goal 4]		
25	**Find a percent of a number.** [Number and Numeration Goal 2]		
21, 24, 26, 27	**Multiply fractions and mixed numbers.** [Operations and Computation Goal 5]		
28, 29	**Divide fractions.** [Operations and Computation Goal 5]		

*Assess Progress: **A** = adequate progress   **N** = not adequate progress   **N/A** = not assessed   **Formative Assessments**

Go to *www.everydaymathonline.com* for digital checklists.   Individual Profile of Progress   **275**

Class Checklist:
Recognizing Student Achievement

Class _____

Date _____

Names	8·1 Compare fractions using benchmarks. [Number and Numeration Goal 6]	8·2 Rename fractions to have common denominators and be in simplest form. [Number and Numeration Goal 5; Operations and Computation Goal 4]	8·3 Estimate sums and differences of mixed numbers using benchmarks. [Operations and Computation Goals 4 and 6]	8·4 Order fractions. [Number and Numeration Goal 6]	8·5 Use a number-line model to solve fraction multiplication problems. [Operations and Computation Goal 5]	8·6 Use an area model to solve fraction multiplication problems. [Operations and Computation Goal 5]	8·7 Convert fractions to decimals and percents. [Number and Numeration Goal 5]	8·8 Multiply mixed numbers. [Operations and Computation Goal 5]	8·9 Convert between fractions, decimals, and percents. [Number and Numeration Goal 5]	8·10 Use unit fractions and unit percents to solve problems. [Number and Numeration Goal 2]	8·11 Add fractions. [Number and Numeration Goal 5; Operations and Computation Goal 4]	8·12 Use a visual model to divide fractions. [Operations and Computation Goal 5]
1.												
2.												
3.												
4.												
5.												
6.												
7.												
8.												
9.												
10.												
11.												
12.												
13.												
14.												
15.												
16.												
17.												
18.												
19.												
20.												
21.												
22.												
23.												
24.												
25.												

Assess Progress: 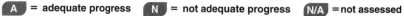 **A** = adequate progress   **N** = not adequate progress   **N/A** = not assessed

Class Checklist:
Progress Check 8

Class _____

Date _____

Names	Oral/Slate				Written — Part A								Written — Part B			
	1. Indicate if given fractions and mixed numbers are equivalent or not. [Number and Numeration Goal 5]	**2.** Indicate if the product of multiplying fractions is correct or not. [Operations and Computation Goal 5]	**3.** Find a common denominator for given pairs of fractions. [Number and Numeration Goal 5]	**4.** Find the percent of given numbers. [Number and Numeration Goal 2]	**1, 2.** Convert between fractions, decimals, and percents. [Number and Numeration Goal 5]	**3, 4, 8–11, 13, 19.** Find common denominators. [Number and Numeration Goal 5]	**5, 6, 20.** Order and compare fractions using benchmarks. [Number and Numeration Goal 6]	**7, 9, 10, 12, 14.** Use an algorithm to subtract fractions and mixed numbers. [Operations and Computation Goal 4]	**7.** Measure to the nearest $\frac{1}{4}$ inch. [Measurement and Reference Frames Goal 1]	**8, 11, 13.** Use an algorithm to add fractions and mixed numbers. [Operations and Computation Goal 4]	**15–18.** Convert between fractions and whole or mixed numbers. [Number and Numeration Goal 5]	**22, 23.** Use an algorithm to subtract mixed numbers. [Operations and Computation Goal 4]	**25.** Find a percent of a number. [Number and Numeration Goal 2]	**21, 24, 26, 27.** Multiply fractions and mixed numbers. [Operations and Computation Goal 5]	**28, 29.** Divide fractions. [Operations and Computation Goal 5]
1.															
2.															
3.															
4.															
5.															
6.															
7.															
8.															
9.															
10.															
11.															
12.															
13.															
14.															
15.															
16.															
17.															
18.															
19.															
20.															
21.															
22.															
23.															
24.															
25.															

Assess Progress:  **A** = adequate progress **N** = not adequate progress **N/A** = not assessed **Formative Assessments**

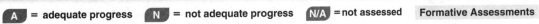

Individual Profile of Progress

Name _____ Date _____

Lesson	Recognizing Student Achievement	A.P.*	Comments
9◆1	Translate numbers written in scientific notation to standard notation and number-and-word notation. [Number and Numeration Goal 1]		
9◆2	Plot ordered number pairs and identify decimals on a number line. [Number and Numeration Goal 1; Measurement and Reference Frames Goal 4]		
9◆3	Plot points on a coordinate grid. [Measurement and Reference Frames Goal 4]		
9◆4	Calculate area. [Measurement and Reference Frames Goal 2]		
9◆5	Draw line segments and explain that congruent line segments have the same length. [Geometry Goal 2]		
9◆6	Write formulas for finding the area of triangles and parallelograms. [Measurement and Reference Frames Goal 2]		
9◆7	Solve fraction of problems. [Number and Numeration Goal 2]		
9◆8	Find common denominators and write fractions in simplest form. [Number and Numeration Goal 5]		
9◆9	Match polygons with their properties. [Geometry Goal 2]		
9◆10	Distinguish between volume and capacity. [Measurement and Reference Frames Goal 3]		

*Assess Progress: 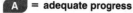 **A** = adequate progress **N** = not adequate progress **N/A** = not assessed

Individual Profile of Progress

Name_____   Date_____

Problem(s)	Progress Check 9	A.P.*	Comments
Oral/Slate Assessment			
1	**Indicate if statements about area and volume are true or false.** [Measurement and Reference Frames Goal 2]		
2	**Indicate if a situation involves finding volume or area.** [Measurement and Reference Frames Goal 2]		
3	**Calculate the areas of rectangles with the given dimensions.** [Measurement and Reference Frames Goal 2]		
4	**Calculate the volumes of rectangular prisms with the given dimensions.** [Measurement and Reference Frames Goal 2]		
Written Assessment Part A			
1–4, 12, 13	**Identify and plot ordered pairs on a one- and four-quadrant coordinate grid.** [Measurement and Reference Frames Goal 4]		
5, 11	**Understand the concept of area of a figure.** [Measurement and Reference Frames Goal 2]		
6–9	**Use a formula to find the areas of triangles and parallelograms.** [Measurement and Reference Frames Goal 2]		
10	**Identify the base and height of triangles and parallelograms.** [Geometry Goal 2]		
14, 15	**Understand the concept of volume of a figure.** [Measurement and Reference Frames Goal 2]		
16, 17	**Use a formula to find the volume of prisms.** [Measurement and Reference Frames Goal 2]		
Written Assessment Part B			
18–21	**Use a formula to find the volume of prisms.** [Measurement and Reference Frames Goal 2]		
22	**Understand the concept of volume of a figure.** [Measurement and Reference Frames Goal 2]		

*Assess Progress: **A** = adequate progress   **N** = not adequate progress   **N/A** = not assessed   Formative Assessments

Go to *www.everydaymathonline.com* for digital checklists.

Class Checklist:
Recognizing Student Achievement

Class _____

Date _____

Names	Translate numbers written in scientific notation to standard notation and number-and-word notation. [Number and Numeration Goal 1] 9•1	Plot ordered number pairs and identify decimals on a number line. [Number and Numeration Goal 1; Measurement and Reference Frames Goal 4] 9•2	Plot points on a coordinate grid. [Measurement and Reference Frames Goal 4] 9•3	Calculate area. [Measurement and Reference Frames Goal 2] 9•4	Draw line segments and explain that congruent line segments have the same length. [Geometry Goal 2] 9•5	Write formulas for finding the area of triangles and parallelograms. [Measurement and Reference Frames Goal 2] 9•6	Solve fraction of problems. [Number and Numeration Goal 2] 9•7	Find common denominators and write fractions in simplest form. [Number and Numeration Goal 5] 9•8	Match polygons with their properties. [Geometry Goal 2] 9•9	Distinguish between volume and capacity. [Measurement and Reference Frames Goal 3] 9•10
1.										
2.										
3.										
4.										
5.										
6.										
7.										
8.										
9.										
10.										
11.										
12.										
13.										
14.										
15.										
16.										
17.										
18.										
19.										
20.										
21.										
22.										
23.										
24.										
25.										

Assess Progress: **A** = adequate progress   **N** = not adequate progress   **N/A** = not assessed

Go to *www.everydaymathonline.com* for digital checklists.

Class _____

Date _____

Names	Oral/Slate				Written — Part A							Part B	
	1. Indicate if statements about area and volume are true or false. [Measurement and Reference Frames Goal 2]	2. Indicate if a situation involves finding volume or area. [Measurement and Reference Frames Goal 2]	3. Calculate the areas of rectangles with the given dimensions. [Measurement and Reference Frames Goal 2]	4. Calculate the volumes of rectangular prisms with the given dimensions. [Measurement and Reference Frames Goal 2]	1–4, 12, 13. Identify and plot ordered pairs on a one- and four-quadrant coordinate grid. [Measurement and Reference Frames Goal 4]	5, 11. Understand the concept of area of a figure. [Measurement and Reference Frames Goal 2]	6–9. Use a formula to find the areas of triangles and parallelograms. [Measurement and Reference Frames Goal 2]	10. Identify the base and height of triangles and parallelograms. [Geometry Goal 2]	14, 15. Understand the concept of volume of a figure. [Measurement and Reference Frames Goal 2]	16, 17. Use a formula to find the volume of prisms. [Measurement and Reference Frames Goal 2]	18–21. Use a formula to find the volume of prisms. [Measurement and Reference Frames Goal 2]	22. Understand the concept of volume of a figure. [Measurement and Reference Frames Goal 2]
1.													
2.													
3.													
4.													
5.													
6.													
7.													
8.													
9.													
10.													
11.													
12.													
13.													
14.													
15.													
16.													
17.													
18.													
19.													
20.													
21.													
22.													
23.													
24.													
25.													

Assess Progress: **A** = adequate progress   **N** = not adequate progress   **N/A** = not assessed   **Formative Assessments**

Name _____   Date _____

Lesson	Recognizing Student Achievement	A.P.*	Comments
10◆1	**Apply a formula to find the volume of a rectangular prism.** [Measurement and Reference Frames Goal 2]		
10◆2	**Solve equations using a pan-balance model.** [Patterns, Functions, and Algebra Goal 2]		
10◆3	**Write algebraic expressions that model situations.** [Patterns, Functions, and Algebra Goal 2]		
10◆4	**Use table data to plot points on a graph.** [Data and Chance Goal 1]		
10◆5	**Solve addition and subtraction open sentences containing negative and positive numbers.** [Patterns, Functions, and Algebra Goal 2]		
10◆6	**Read and interpret graphs.** [Data and Chance Goal 2]		
10◆7	**Interpret line graphs.** [Data and Chance Goal 2]		
10◆8	**Describe area and perimeter.** [Measurement and Reference Frames Goal 2]		
10◆9	**Replace variables in number sentences and solve problems.** [Patterns, Functions, and Algebra Goal 2]		

*Assess Progress: 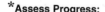 **A** = adequate progress    **N** = not adequate progress   **N/A** = not assessed

Individual Profile of Progress

Name _____   Date _____

Problem(s)	Progress Check 10	A.P.*	Comments
Oral/Slate Assessment			
1	Indicate if circumference would be used to solve given problems. [Measurement and Reference Frames Goal 2]		
2	Indicate if given statements about circles are true or false. [Measurement and Reference Frames Goal 2]		
3	Write an algebraic expression to complete each given statement. [Patterns, Functions, and Algebra Goal 2]		
4	Write a number sentence to represent each story. [Patterns, Functions, and Algebra Goal 2]		
Written Assessment Part A			
1–3, 7	Write algebraic expressions to represent situations. [Patterns, Functions, and Algebra Goal 2]		
4–6	Solve one-step pan-balance problems. [Patterns, Functions, and Algebra Goal 2]		
8	Interpret mystery line plots and graphs. [Data and Chance Goal 2]		
9–11	Distinguish between circumference and area of a circle. [Measurement and Reference Frames Goal 2]		
Written Assessment Part B			
12, 13	Measure length to the nearest centimeter. [Measurement and Reference Frames Goal 1]		
14, 15	Use formulas to find the area and circumference of a circle. [Measurement and Reference Frames Goal 2]		
16	Solve two-step pan-balance problems. [Patterns, Functions, and Algebra Goal 2]		
17, 18	Represent rate problems using a table, graph, and formula. [Patterns, Functions, and Algebra Goal 1]		

*Assess Progress: **A** = adequate progress   **N** = not adequate progress   **N/A** = not assessed   **Formative Assessments**

Class _____

Date _____

Names	10·1 Apply a formula to find the volume of a rectangular prism. [Measurement and Reference Frames Goal 2]	10·2 Solve equations using a pan-balance model. [Patterns, Functions, and Algebra Goal 2]	10·3 Write algebraic expressions that model situations. [Patterns, Functions, and Algebra Goal 2]	10·4 Use table data to plot points on a graph. [Data and Chance Goal 1]	10·5 Solve addition and subtraction open sentences containing negative and positive numbers. [Patterns, Functions, and Algebra Goal 2]	10·6 Read and interpret graphs. [Data and Chance Goal 2]	10·7 Interpret line graphs. [Data and Chance Goal 2]	10·8 Describe area and perimeter. [Measurement and Reference Frames Goal 2]	10·9 Replace variables in number sentences and solve problems. [Patterns, Functions, and Algebra Goal 2]
1.									
2.									
3.									
4.									
5.									
6.									
7.									
8.									
9.									
10.									
11.									
12.									
13.									
14.									
15.									
16.									
17.									
18.									
19.									
20.									
21.									
22.									
23.									
24.									
25.									

Assess Progress:  **A** = adequate progress   **N** = not adequate progress   **N/A** = not assessed

Names	Oral/Slate				Written Part A				Part B			
	1. Indicate if circumference would be used to solve given problems. [Measurement and Reference Frames Goal 2]	2. Indicate if given statements about circles are true or false. [Measurement and Reference Frames Goal 2]	3. Write an algebraic expression to complete each given statement. [Patterns, Functions, and Algebra Goal 2]	4. Write a number sentence to represent each story. [Patterns, Functions, and Algebra Goal 2]	1–3, 7. Write algebraic expressions to represent situations. [Patterns, Functions, and Algebra Goal 2]	4–6. Solve one-step pan-balance problems. [Patterns, Functions, and Algebra Goal 2]	8. Interpret mystery line plots and graphs. [Data and Chance Goal 2]	9–11. Distinguish between circumference and area of a circle. [Measurement and Reference Frames Goal 2]	12, 13. Measure length to the nearest centimeter. [Measurement and Reference Frames Goal 1]	14, 15. Use formulas to find the area and circumference of a circle. [Measurement and Reference Frames Goal 2]	16. Solve two-step pan-balance problems. [Patterns, Functions, and Algebra Goal 2]	17, 18. Represent rate problems using a table, graph, and formula. [Patterns, Functions, and Algebra Goal 1]
1.												
2.												
3.												
4.												
5.												
6.												
7.												
8.												
9.												
10.												
11.												
12.												
13.												
14.												
15.												
16.												
17.												
18.												
19.												
20.												
21.												
22.												
23.												
24.												
25.												

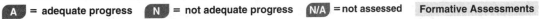

Assess Progress: **A** = adequate progress   **N** = not adequate progress   **N/A** = not assessed   **Formative Assessments**

Go to *www.everydaymathonline.com* for digital checklists.

Class Checklist   **285**

Individual Profile of Progress

Unit 11

Name _____ Date _____

Lesson	Recognizing Student Achievement	A.P.*	Comments
11◆1	**Identify the properties of geometric solids.** [Geometry Goal 2]		
11◆2	**Compare prisms, pyramids, cylinders, and cones.** [Geometry Goal 2]		
11◆3	**Explain what is similar and what is different between finding the volume of cylinders and finding the volume of prisms.** [Measurement and Reference Frames Goal 2]		
11◆4	**Calculate a fraction of a whole.** [Number and Numeration Goal 2]		
11◆5	**Compare fractions.** [Number and Numeration Goal 6]		
11◆6	**Write number sentences using the order of operations.** [Number and Numeration Goal 4; Patterns, Functions, and Algebra Goal 3]		
11◆7	**Measure to the nearest $\frac{1}{4}$ inch and centimeter and find the area of circles, triangles, and rectangles.** [Measurement and Reference Frames Goals 1 and 2]		

Assess Progress:  = adequate progress    = not adequate progress   = not assessed

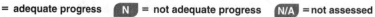

Name _____ Date _____

Problem(s)	Progress Check 11	A.P.*	Comments
Oral/Slate Assessment			
1	**Indicate if statements about shapes are true or false.** [Geometry Goal 2]		
2	**Indicate if problems would be solved by finding the capacity or by another method.** [Measurement and Reference Frames Goal 2]		
3	**Find the areas of figures.** [Measurement and Reference Frames Goal 2]		
4	**Find the volumes of geometric figures and the heights of prisms.** [Measurement and Reference Frames Goal 2]		
Written Assessment Part A			
1–4, 7–9, 13	**Know the properties of geometric figures.** [Geometry Goal 2]		
5, 6, 11–16	**Use formulas to find the volume of prisms and cylinders.** [Measurement and Reference Frames Goal 2]		
7–10, 12	**Use formulas to find the area of polygons and circles.** [Measurement and Reference Frames Goal 2]		
16	**Write number sentences to represent finding volume.** [Patterns, Functions, and Algebra Goal 2]		
Written Assessment Part B			
17	**Find the surface area of prisms.** [Measurement and Reference Frames Goal 2]		
18	**Understand how to find the surface area of cylinders.** [Measurement and Reference Frames Goal 2]		
19, 20	**Understand and write number sentences to represent the relationship between the volume of pyramids and prisms and the volume of cones and cylinders.** [Measurement and Reference Frames Goal 2; Patterns, Functions, and Algebra Goal 2]		
21, 22	**Understand the concept of capacity and how to calculate it.** [Measurement and Reference Frames Goal 3]		

*Assess Progress: **A** = adequate progress   **N** = not adequate progress   **N/A** = not assessed   **Formative Assessments**

Class Checklist:
Recognizing Student Achievement

Class _____

Date _____

Names	11·1	11·2	11·3	11·4	11·5	11·6	11·7
	Identify the properties of geometric solids. [Geometry Goal 2]	Compare prisms, pyramids, cylinders, and cones. [Geometry Goal 2]	Explain what is similar and what is different between finding the volume of cylinders and finding the volume of prisms. [Measurement and Reference Frames Goal 2]	Calculate a fraction of a whole. [Number and Numeration Goal 2]	Compare fractions. [Number and Numeration Goal 6]	Write number sentences using the order of operations. [Number and Numeration Goal 4; Patterns, Functions, and Algebra Goal 3]	Measure to the nearest $\frac{1}{4}$ inch and centimeter and find the area of circles, triangles, and rectangles. [Measurement and Reference Frames Goals 1 and 2]
1.							
2.							
3.							
4.							
5.							
6.							
7.							
8.							
9.							
10.							
11.							
12.							
13.							
14.							
15.							
16.							
17.							
18.							
19.							
20.							
21.							
22.							
23.							
24.							
25.							

Assess Progress: 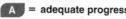 **A** = adequate progress **N** = not adequate progress 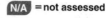 **N/A** = not assessed

Go to *www.everydaymathonline.com* for digital checklists.

Class Checklist:
Progress Check 11

Class _____

Date _____

Names	Oral/Slate				Written Part A				Part B			
	1. Indicate if statements about shapes are true or false. [Geometry Goal 2]	2. Indicate if problems would be solved by finding the capacity or by another method. [Measurement and Reference Frames Goal 2]	3. Find the areas of figures. [Measurement and Reference Frames Goal 2]	4. Find the volumes of geometric figures and the heights of prisms. [Measurement and Reference Frames Goal 2]	1–4, 7–9, 13. Know the properties of geometric figures. [Geometry Goal 2]	5, 6, 11–16. Use formulas to find the volume of prisms and cylinders. [Measurement and Reference Frames Goal 2]	7–10, 12. Use formulas to find the area of polygons and circles. [Measurement and Reference Frames Goal 2]	16. Write number sentences to represent finding volume. [Patterns, Functions, and Algebra Goal 2]	17. Find the surface area of prisms. [Measurement and Reference Frames Goal 2]	18. Understand how to find the surface area of cylinders. [Measurement and Reference Frames Goal 2]	19, 20. Understand and write number sentences to represent the relationship between the volume of pyramids and prisms and the volume of cones and cylinders. [Measurement and Reference Frames Goal 2; Patterns, Functions, and Algebra Goal 2]	21, 22. Understand the concept of capacity and how to calculate it. [Measurement and Reference Frames Goal 3]
1.												
2.												
3.												
4.												
5.												
6.												
7.												
8.												
9.												
10.												
11.												
12.												
13.												
14.												
15.												
16.												
17.												
18.												
19.												
20.												
21.												
22.												
23.												
24.												
25.												

Assess Progress: 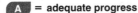 **A** = adequate progress   **N** = not adequate progress   **N/A** = not assessed   **Formative Assessments**

Name _____   Date _____

Lesson	Recognizing Student Achievement	A.P.*	Comments
12◆1	**Factor numbers and identify the prime factorizations.** [Number and Numeration Goal 3]		
12◆2	**Express probability using fractions and basic probability terms.** [Data and Chance Goal 4]		
12◆3	**Solve fraction division problems.** [Operations and Computation Goal 5]		
12◆4	**Solve ratio problems.** [Operations and Computation Goal 7]		
12◆5	**Estimate and solve multidigit multiplication problems.** [Operations and Computation Goal 6]		
12◆6	**Identify equivalent expressions.** [Number and Numeration Goal 4]		
12◆7	**Round numbers.** [Number and Numeration Goal 1]		
12◆8	**Plot points in all four quadrants of a coordinate grid.** [Measurement and Reference Frames Goal 4]		

*Assess Progress:  **A** = adequate progress    **N** = not adequate progress   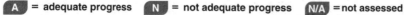 **N/A** = not assessed

Individual Profile of Progress

Name _____ Date _____

Problem(s)	Progress Check 12	A.P.*	Comments
Oral/Slate Assessment			
1	Indicate if the first number given is a factor of the second or not. [Number and Numeration Goal 3]		
2	Identify all possible outcomes for a situation. [Data and Chance Goal 4]		
3	Name all the factors of each number: 12, 16, 36, 47. [Number and Numeration Goal 3]		
4	Make a tree diagram to show the possible choices. [Data and Chance Goal 4]		
Written Assessment Part A			
1, 2	Find the factors of numbers. [Number and Numeration Goal 3]		
1–3	Find the prime factorization of numbers. [Number and Numeration Goal 3]		
4	Find the greatest common factor of two numbers. [Number and Numeration Goal 3]		
5–9	Find the least common multiple of two numbers. [Number and Numeration Goal 3]		
6–8	Use least common multiples to find common denominators. [Number and Numeration Goal 5]		
10–13	Solve ratio and rate number stories. [Operations and Computation Goal 7]		
14	Solve a fraction multiplication problem. [Operations and Computation Goal 5]		
15	Solve a fraction division problem. [Operations and Computation Goal 5]		
Written Assessment Part B			
16	Understand and use tree diagrams. [Data and Chance Goal 4]		
17	Compute the probability of outcomes. [Data and Chance Goal 4]		
18–22	Solve ratio and rate number stories. [Operations and Computation Goal 7]		

*Assess Progress: **A** = adequate progress   **N** = not adequate progress   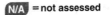 **N/A** = not assessed   **Formative Assessments**

Class _____

Date _____

Names	12·1	12·2	12·3	12·4	12·5	12·6	12·7	12·8
	Factor numbers and identify the prime factorizations. [Number and Numeration Goal 3]	Express probability using fractions and basic probability terms. [Data and Chance Goal 4]	Solve fraction division problems. [Operations and Computation Goal 5]	Solve ratio problems. [Operations and Computation Goal 7]	Estimate and solve multidigit multiplication problems. [Operations and Computation Goal 6]	Identify equivalent expressions. [Number and Numeration Goal 4]	Round numbers. [Number and Numeration Goal 1]	Plot points in all four quadrants of a coordinate grid. [Measurement and Reference Frames Goal 4]
1.								
2.								
3.								
4.								
5.								
6.								
7.								
8.								
9.								
10.								
11.								
12.								
13.								
14.								
15.								
16.								
17.								
18.								
19.								
20.								
21.								
22.								
23.								
24.								
25.								

Assess Progress: **A** = adequate progress   **N** = not adequate progress   **N/A** = not assessed

Class _____

Date _____

	Oral/Slate			Written											
				Part A									Part B		
Names	1. Indicate if the first number given is a factor of the second or not. [Number and Numeration Goal 3]	2. Identify all possible outcomes for a situation. [Data and Chance Goal 4]	3. Name all the factors of each number: 12, 16, 36, 47. [Number and Numeration Goal 3]	4. Make a tree diagram to show the possible choices. [Data and Chance Goal 4]	1, 2. Find the factors of numbers. [Number and Numeration Goal 3]	1–3. Find the prime factorization of numbers. [Number and Numeration Goal 3]	4. Find the greatest common factor of two numbers. [Number and Numeration Goal 3]	5–9. Find the least common multiple of two numbers. [Number and Numeration Goal 3]	6–8. Use least common multiples to find common denominators. [Number and Numeration Goal 5]	10–13. Solve ratio and rate number stories. [Operations and Computation Goal 7]	14. Solve a fraction multiplication problem. [Operations and Computation Goal 5]	15. Solve a fraction division problem. [Operations and Computation Goal 5]	16. Understand and use tree diagrams. [Data and Chance Goal 4]	17. Compute the probability of outcomes. [Data and Chance Goal 4]	18–22. Solve ratio and rate number stories. [Operations and Computation Goal 7]
1.															
2.															
3.															
4.															
5.															
6.															
7.															
8.															
9.															
10.															
11.															
12.															
13.															
14.															
15.															
16.															
17.															
18.															
19.															
20.															
21.															
22.															
23.															
24.															
25.															

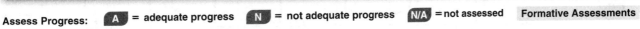

Assess Progress: **A** = adequate progress   **N** = not adequate progress   **N/A** = not assessed   **Formative Assessments**

Names	Goal																						
		Number and Numeration													**Operations and Computation**									
	Goal	1	3	3	1	3	4	3	6	5	6	1	6	6	7	2	2	1	1	1	6	3	2
	Lesson	1·1	1·3	1·4	1·5	1·6	1·7	1·9	2·5	2·6	2·10	3·1	3·6	3·10	1·2	1·8	2·1	2·2	2·3	2·7	2·8	2·9	3·2	3·5
	Date																						
1.																							
2.																							
3.																							
4.																							
5.																							
6.																							
7.																							
8.																							
9.																							
10.																							
11.																							
12.																							
13.																							
14.																							
15.																							
16.																							
17.																							
18.																							
19.																							
20.																							
21.																							
22.																							

Quarterly Checklist: Quarter 1

Names	Data and Chance			Measurement and Reference Frames			Geometry						Patterns, Functions, and Algebra		
Goal				1	1		2	2	1		2		2		
Lesson				3•3	3•4		3•7	3•8	3•9		2•4				
Date															
1.															
2.															
3.															
4.															
5.															
6.															
7.															
8.															
9.															
10.															
11.															
12.															
13.															
14.															
15.															
16.															
17.															
18.															
19.															
20.															
21.															
22.															

Quarterly Checklist: Quarter 2

	Goal																			
		Number and Numeration										**Operations and Computation**								
	Goal	1	6	5	5	6	5	5	2	5	5	5	3	3	3	3	6	3	7	7	6	6	4
	Lesson	4·3	5·3	5·4	5·5	5·6	5·7	5·8	6·5	6·6	6·7	6·10	4·1	4·2	4·4	4·5	4·6	5·1	5·2	5·12	6·8	6·9
Names	Date																					
1.																						
2.																						
3.																						
4.																						
5.																						
6.																						
7.																						
8.																						
9.																						
10.																						
11.																						
12.																						
13.																						
14.																						
15.																						
16.																						
17.																						
18.																						
19.																						
20.																						
21.																						
22.																						

Quarterly Checklist: Quarter 2

Names	Goal	1	1	1	1	2	1	1	2				
		Data and Chance					**Measurement and Reference Frames**		**Geometry**			**Patterns, Functions, and Algebra**	
	Lesson	5·9	5·11	6·1	6·3	6·4	5·10	6·2	4·7				
	Date												
1.													
2.													
3.													
4.													
5.													
6.													
7.													
8.													
9.													
10.													
11.													
12.													
13.													
14.													
15.													
16.													
17.													
18.													
19.													
20.													
21.													
22.													

Names	Goal	4	1	1	6	6	6	5	6	6	5	5	5	2	5	2	4	4	4	4	5	5	5	4	5
	Number and Numeration → (left) / **Operations and Computation** → (right)																								
	Lesson	7·1	7·2	7·3	7·5	7·9	7·10	7·11	8·1	8·4	8·7	8·9	8·10	9·1	9·7	9·8	7·6	7·8	7·10	8·2	8·3	8·5	8·6	8·8	8·11	8·12
	Date																								
1.																									
2.																									
3.																									
4.																									
5.																									
6.																									
7.																									
8.																									
9.																									
10.																									
11.																									
12.																									
13.																									
14.																									
15.																									
16.																									
17.																									
18.																									
19.																									
20.																									
21.																									
22.																									

Goal row (by column): 4, 1, 1, 6, 6, 6, 5, 6, 6, 5, 5, 5, 2, 5, 2, 4, 4, 4, 4, 5, 5, 5, 4, 5

Quarterly Checklist: Quarter 3

Names	Data and Chance			Measurement and Reference Frames				Geometry			Patterns, Functions, and Algebra		
Goal				4	4	2	2	3	2	2	3	3	
Lesson				9•2	9•3	9•4	9•6	9•10	9•5	9•9	7•4	7•7	
Date													
1.													
2.													
3.													
4.													
5.													
6.													
7.													
8.													
9.													
10.													
11.													
12.													
13.													
14.													
15.													
16.													
17.													
18.													
19.													
20.													
21.													
22.													

Quarterly Checklist: Quarter 4

Names	Number and Numeration								Operations and Computation				Data and Chance			
Goal	2	6	4	3	5	5	1		5	7	6		1	2	2	4
Lesson	11·4	11·5	11·6	12·1	12·3	12·6	12·7		12·3	12·4	12·5		10·4	10·6	10·7	12·2
Date																
1.																
2.																
3.																
4.																
5.																
6.																
7.																
8.																
9.																
10.																
11.																
12.																
13.																
14.																
15.																
16.																
17.																
18.																
19.																
20.																
21.																
22.																

Quarterly Checklist: Quarter 4

Names	Measurement and Reference Frames						Geometry			Patterns, Functions, and Algebra				
Goal	2	2	2	1	2	2	2	2	2	2	2	2	3
Lesson	10·1	10·8	11·3	11·7	11·7	12·8	11·1	11·2	10·2	10·3	10·5	10·9	11·6
Date													
1.													
2.													
3.													
4.													
5.													
6.													
7.													
8.													
9.													
10.													
11.													
12.													
13.													
14.													
15.													
16.													
17.													
18.													
19.													
20.													
21.													
22.													

Individual Profile of Progress

Name _____ Date _____

Lesson	Recognizing Student Achievement	A.P.*	Comments

*Assess Progress:  A = adequate progress N = not adequate progress N/A = not assessed

Class Checklist:
Recognizing Student Achievement

Class _____

Date _____

Names								
1.								
2.								
3.								
4.								
5.								
6.								
7.								
8.								
9.								
10.								
11.								
12.								
13.								
14.								
15.								
16.								
17.								
18.								
19.								
20.								
21.								
22.								
23.								
24.								
25.								

Assess Progress: **A** = adequate progress **N** = not adequate progress **N/A** = not assessed

Evaluating My Math Class

Interest Inventory

Dislike a Lot 1	Dislike 2	Neither Like nor Dislike 3	Like 4	Like a Lot 5

Use the scale above to describe how you feel about:

1. your math class.   _____

2. working with a partner or in a group.   _____

3. working by yourself.   _____

4. solving problems.   _____

5. making up problems for others to solve.   _____

6. finding new ways to solve problems.   _____

7. challenges in math class.   _____

8. playing mathematical games.   _____

9. working on Study Links.   _____

10. working on projects that take
    more than a day to complete.   _____

11. Which math lesson has been your favorite so far? Why?

_____

_____

_____

_____

_____

_____

_____

My Math Class

Interest Inventory

1. In math class, I am good at _____

   _____

   _____

   _____

2. One thing I like about math is _____

   _____

   _____

   _____

3. One thing I find difficult in mathematics class is _____

   _____

   _____

   _____

4. The most interesting thing I have learned in math so far this year is ____

   _____

   _____

   _____

5. Outside school, I used mathematics when I _____

   _____

   _____

   _____

6. I would like to know more about _____

   _____

   _____

   _____

Weekly Math Log

1. What did you study in math this week?

_____

_____

_____

_____

_____

_____

_____

2. Many ideas in math are related to other ideas within math. Think about how the topic(s) you studied in class this week relate to other topics you learned before.

Your reflection can include what you learned in previous years.

_____

_____

_____

_____

_____

_____

_____

_____

_____

_____

_____

_____

Name _____ Date _____

Math Log

_____

_____

_____

_____

_____

_____

_____

_____

_____

_____

_____

Number-Story Math Log

1. Write an easy number story that uses mathematical ideas that you have studied recently. Solve the problem.

Number Story _____

_____

_____

_____

_____

Solution _____

_____

_____

_____

_____

2. Write a difficult number story that uses mathematical ideas that you have studied recently. If you can, solve the number story. If you are not able to solve it, explain what you need to know to solve it.

Number Story _____

_____

_____

_____

_____

Solution _____

_____

_____

_____

Sample Math Work

Attach a sample of your work to this form.

1. This work is an example of:

_____

_____

_____

_____

_____

_____

_____

2. This work shows that I can:

_____

_____

_____

_____

_____

_____

_____

OPTIONAL

3. This work shows that I still need to improve:

_____

_____

_____

_____

_____

_____

_____

Discussion of My Math Work

Attach a sample of your work to this page. Tell what you think is important about your sample.

_____

_____

_____

_____

_____

_____

_____

_____

_____

_____

_____

_____

_____

_____

_____

_____

_____

_____

_____

_____

_____

_____

_____

_____

_____

_____

_____

Exit Slip

✂ -

Name   Date   Time

Exit Slip

Parent Reflections

Use some of the following questions (or your own) and tell us how you see your child progressing in mathematics.

Do you see evidence of your child using mathematics at home?

What do you think are your child's strengths and challenges in mathematics?

Does your child demonstrate responsibility for completing Study Links?

What thoughts do you have about your child's progress in mathematics?

_____

_____

_____

_____

_____

_____

_____

_____

_____

_____

_____

_____

_____

_____

_____

_____

_____

_____

_____

Glossary

Assessment Management Spreadsheets
Digital versions of the Class Checklists and
Individual Profiles of Progress that help teachers
track student and class progress toward Grade-
Level Goals and Common Core State Standards.

Class Checklists Recording tools that can
be used to keep track of a class's progress on
specific Grade-Level Goals.

Content for Assessment Material that is
important for students to learn and is the focus
of assessment. *Everyday Mathematics* highlights
this content through Grade-Level Goals.

Contexts for Assessment Ongoing,
periodic, and external assessments based on
products or observations.

Enrichment Activities Optional activities
that apply or deepen students' understanding.

Evidence from Assessment Information
about student knowledge, skills, and dispositions
collected from observations or products.

External Assessments Assessments that
are independent of the curriculum, for example,
standardized tests.

Formative Assessments Assessments that
provide information about students' current
knowledge and abilities so that teachers can
plan future instruction more effectively and so
that students can identify their own areas of
weakness or strength.

Grade-Level Goals Mathematical goals
organized by content strand and articulated
across grade levels from Pre-Kindergarten
through Grade 6.

Individual Profile of Progress A recording
tool that can be used to keep track of student
progress on specific Grade-Level Goals.

Informing Instruction These notes in the
Teacher's Lesson Guide suggest how to use
observations of students' work to adapt
instruction by describing common errors and
misconceptions in students' thinking and alerting
the teacher to multiple solution strategies or
unique insights students might offer.

Making Adequate Progress On a
trajectory to meet a Grade-Level Goal.

Math Boxes Collections of problems designed
to provide distributed practice. Math Boxes
revisit content from prior units to build and
maintain important concepts and skills. One
or two problems on each page preview content
from the next unit.

Mental Math and Reflexes Exercises at
three levels of difficulty that prepare students for
the lesson, build mental-arithmetic skills, and
help teachers quickly assess individual strengths
and weaknesses.

Observational Assessments Assessments
based on observing students during daily
activities or periodic assessments.

Ongoing Assessments Assessments based on
students' everyday work during regular
classroom instruction.

Open Response An extended response
assessment included in the Progress Check
lesson of each unit.

Periodic Assessments Formal assessments
that are built into a curriculum such as the
end-of-unit Progress Checks.

Portfolios Collections of student products and observations that provide opportunities for students to reflect on their mathematical growth and for teachers to understand and document that growth.

Product Assessments Assessments based on student work from daily activities or from periodic assessments.

Program Evaluation Assessment intended to reveal how well a program of instruction is working. A school district, for example, might carry out program evaluation to identify schools with strong mathematics programs so that their success can be replicated.

Program Goals The fifteen cross-grade goals in *Everyday Mathematics* that weave the program together across grade levels. They form an organizing framework that supports both curriculum and assessment. Every Grade-Level Goal is linked to a Program Goal.

Progress Check The last lesson in every unit. Progress Check lessons include a student Self Assessment, an Oral and Slate Assessment, a Written Assessment, and an Open Response task.

Purposes of Assessment The reasons for assessment, which include providing information that can be used to plan future instruction, identifying what students have achieved during a period of time, and evaluating the quality of the mathematics program.

Readiness Activities Optional activities in many lessons that preview lesson content or provide alternative routes of access for learning concepts and skills.

Recognizing Student Achievement A feature in many lessons that highlights specific tasks used to monitor students' progress toward Grade-Level Goals. The notes identify the expectations for a student who is making adequate progress and point to skills or strategies that some students might be able to demonstrate.

Rubrics A set of suggested guidelines for scoring assessment activities.

Student Self Assessment The individual reflection included in the Progress Check lesson of each unit.

Summative Assessments Assessments that aim to measure student growth and achievement, for example, an assessment to determine whether students have learned certain material by the end of a fixed period of study such as a semester or a course.

Writing/Reasoning Prompt A question linked to a specific Math Boxes problem. Writing/Reasoning Prompts provide students with opportunities to respond to questions that extend and deepen their mathematical thinking.

Written Progress Check The Written Assessment included in the Progress Check lesson of each unit.

Index

Adequate progress. *See* Making adequate progress
Assessment. *See* Balanced Assessment; Content Assessed; Contexts for Assessment; External Assessment; Formative Assessment; Ongoing Assessment; Periodic Assessment; Purposes of Assessment; and Sources of Evidence for Assessment; Summative Assessment
Assessment Management Spreadsheets, 28–29
Assessment masters, 153–215, 227A–241. *See* Open Response tasks, assessment masters; Self Assessment masters; Written Assessments, masters.
Assessment Overviews, 51–149

Balanced Assessment, 2–8, 16, 18, 21, 23, 29
    creating a plan, 4, 7
Beginning-of-Year Assessment Answers, 242
Beginning-of-Year Assessment Goals, 51A
Beginning-of-Year Assessment masters, 227A–227D
Beginning-of-Year written assessment, 4, 18, 23, 28

Checklists. *See* Class Checklists; Individual Profiles of Progress
    using checklists, 25–27
Class Checklists, 25–27
    general master, 303
    masters, Unit 1: 248–249, Unit 2: 252–253,
        Unit 3: 256–257, Unit 4: 260–261,
        Unit 5: 264–265, Unit 6: 268–269,
        Unit 7: 272–273, Unit 8: 276–277,
        Unit 9: 280–281, Unit 10: 284–285,
        Unit 11: 288–289, Unit 12: 292–293
    quarterly checklists, 26, 294–301
Content Assessed, 5–6
Contexts for Assessment, 3–4

End-of-Year Assessment Answers, 245–245A
End-of-Year Assessment Goals, 150–152
End-of-Year Assessment masters, 234–241
End-of-Year written assessment, 4, 18, 23, 28
Enrichment activities, 12–14
Exit Slips, 4, 8, 10–11, 15
    master, 311
External Assessment, 3–4, 8, 18, 24

Formative Assessment, 2, 7, 19–20
Frequently Asked Questions, 31–35

Game record sheets, 4, 8, 10, 12
General Masters, 302–312
    Class Checklist, 303
    Discussion of My Math Work, 16, 310
    Evaluating My Math Class, 17, 304
    Exit Slip, 311
    Individual Profile of Progress, 302
    Math Log, 307
    My Math Class, 17, 305
    Number-Story Math Log, 17, 308
    Parent Reflections, 312
    Sample Math Work, 16, 309
    Weekly Math Log, 17, 306
Grade-Level Goals, 6–7, 10–14, 19–22, 25, 27–34, 37–50
    adequate progress toward, 7, 10–14, 19, 25, 27–29,
        32–34
    definition of, 6, 32
    exposure to versus mastery of, 6, 31–32, 34–35
    table, 37–50
Grading, 28, 34

Informing Instruction notes, 4, 8, 9, 20
Individual Profiles of Progress, 25–26
    general master, 302
    masters, Unit 1: 246–247, Unit 2: 250–251,
        Unit 3: 254–255, Unit 4: 258–259,
        Unit 5: 262–263, Unit 6: 266–267,
        Unit 7: 270–271, Unit 8: 274–275,
        Unit 9: 278–279, Unit 10: 282–283,
        Unit 11: 286–287, Unit 12: 290–291

Journal pages, 4, 8, 10

Kid Watching, 4, 8

Making adequate progress
  based on a rubric, 27
  definition of, 27, 32–33
  in Recognizing Student Achievement notes, 10–14, 27, 32–33
  in Written Assessments, 19
Math Boxes, 4, 8, 10–12, 15, 24, 33
Math Logs, 15, 17, 306–308
Mental Math and Reflexes, 4, 8, 10–11, 20
Mid-Year Assessment Answers, 243–244
Mid-Year Assessment Goals, 100–101
Mid-Year Assessment masters, 228–233B
Mid-Year written assessment, 4, 18, 23, 28

Observations, 4, 8, 18, 26, 28
Ongoing Assessment, 3–4, 8–17, 25–26, 28
  by unit, Unit 1: 52–53, Unit 2: 60–61, Unit 3: 68–69,
    Unit 4: 76–77, Unit 5: 84–85, Unit 6: 92–93,
    Unit 7: 102–103, Unit 8: 110–111,
    Unit 9: 118–119, Unit 10: 126–127,
    Unit 11: 134–135, Unit 12: 142–143
Open Response tasks, 4, 18, 21–22, 24, 28
  assessment masters, 157, 163, 169, 174, 179, 184,
    189, 193, 198, 204, 209, 215
  by unit, Unit 1: 55–59, Unit 2: 63–67, Unit 3: 71–75,
    Unit 4: 79–83, Unit 5: 87–91, Unit 6: 95–99,
    Unit 7: 105–109, Unit 8: 113–117,
    Unit 9: 121–125, Unit 10: 129–133,
    Unit 11: 137–141, Unit 12: 145–149
Oral and Slate Assessments, 20
Outside tests, 24

Parent Reflections, 17, 312
Performance-based assessments, 24, 32–33
Periodic Assessment, 3–4, 18–23, 25–26
  by unit, Unit 1: 54–59, Unit 2: 62–67, Unit 3: 70–75,
    Unit 4: 78–83, Unit 5: 86–91, Unit 6: 94–99,
    Unit 7: 104–109, Unit 8: 112–117,
    Unit 9: 120–125, Unit 10: 128–133,
    Unit 11: 136–141, Unit 12: 144–149
Planning tips, 7
Portfolios, 4, 8, 15, 16–17, 26
Product Assessment, 16–17, 26
Products 4, 8, 18
Program Goals, 5–6, 28, 32, 37–50
  definition of, 5–6
  table list, 37–50
    Data and Chance, 5, 44–45
    Geometry, 5, 48
    Measurement and Reference Frames, 5, 46–47
    Number and Numeration, 5, 37–39
    Operations and Computation, 5, 40–43
    Patterns, Functions, and Algebra, 5, 49–50
  track progress toward, 32
Program Evaluation, 2
Progress Check Oral/Slate Assessments, 4, 18, 20, 28
Progress Check Written Assessments, 4, 18, 19, 20, 28,
  154–215, 216–227
Purposes of Assessment, 2

Readiness activities, 12–14, 21
Recognizing Student Achievement notes, 4, 8, 10–14,
  25–28, 32–34
Record Keeping, 25–29, 34
  Assessment Management Spreadsheets, 28–29
  options for recording data on checklists, 27
Rubrics, 22–23, 27, 29

Self Assessment masters, 21, 154, 158, 164, 170, 175, 180,
  185, 190, 194, 199, 205, 210
Student Self Assessment, 4, 21
Sources of Evidence for Assessment, 4
Summative Assessment, 2, 7, 19–20

Written Assessments, 4, 8, 19–20
  masters, Unit 1: 155–156, Unit 2: 159–162,
    Unit 3: 165–168, Unit 4: 171–173
    Unit 5: 176–178, Unit 6: 181–183,
    Unit 7: 186–188, Unit 8: 191–192,
    Unit 9: 195–197, Unit 10: 200–203,
    Unit 11: 206–208, Unit 12: 211–214
Writing/Reasoning Prompts for Math Boxes, 4, 8, 15